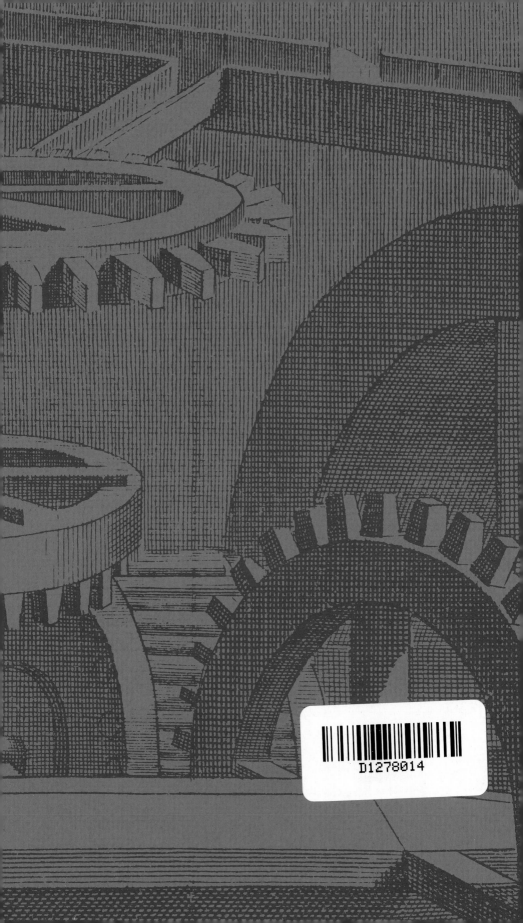

D1278014

HOW THINGS WORK

HOW THINGS WORK

III

ILLUSTRATIONS RESEARCHED BY
ROGER JEAN SÉGALAT

13 047 03 R3

CONTENTS

HOW THINGS WORK

AEROSOLS

An aerosol is a colloidal system consisting of very finely divided liquid or solid particles dispersed in and surrounded by a gas. In recent years aerosols have become familiar as products discharged from spray dispensers, and the term "aerosol" has, in popular speech, also come to mean the dispenser itself—i.e., a pressurized container made of metal or glass and provided with a discharge valve, which may be a spray valve or a foam valve. It is filled with the product to be sprayed and the propellant gas under pressure (Fig. 4).

The product that is to be dispersed as an aerosol may have the liquefied propellant mixed with it in the form of a solution (Fig. 1). Alternatively, the propellant may be present as a separate gaseous phase in the dispenser, in which case it does not mingle with the product (two-phase system: Fig. 2).

An example of the first type is afforded by hair spray. The spray (or lacquer), usually dissolved in alcohol, is completely miscible with the liquefied propellant. When the valve button on the dispenser is pressed, the propellant vaporizes immediately, and its pressure forces the liquid out of the nozzle. The liquid (i.e., the lacquer solution) is discharged as a fine mist. The most commonly employed propellants are chlorinated hydrocarbons, butane, propane, isobutane, vinyl chloride and nitrogen. Nitrogen is used particularly for products that must on no account be contaminated in flavor or smell: e.g., toothpaste packaged in aerosol dispensers.

Aerosol toothpaste is an example of the second category of aerosol systems—namely, the two-phase system—in which the propellant gas forms a separate layer over the product to be discharged. The dispenser is usually about half filled with nitrogen (or some other suitable gas) and half with the product. The pressure in the dispenser is about 6 to 8 atm. (90 to 120 lb./in.^{2}). Nitrogen is also used as the propellant for foods packaged in aerosol form—e.g., cheese spreads, malt extracts, vitamin preparations, syrups, pudding sauces, whipped cream.

Filling an aerosol dispenser at the factory is a simple operation (Fig. 3: stages 1 to 5). First, the product is introduced into the dispenser (1). This is done by a pneumatic filling machine. Then the aerosol valve is placed on the dispenser (2). In the next stage the valve is force-fitted under high pressure (about $\frac{3}{4}$ ton) into the neck of the dispenser, so that a strong gastight seal is formed between the latter and the valve unit (3). The propellant gas is now forced into the dispenser (4). Finally, the dispenser is immersed in water to test it for possible leakage, which is manifested by escaping bubbles of gas (5).

Aerosols are coming into increasingly widespread use in industry, too. For instance, they are used for the disinfection of milk tanks. For this purpose a spraying device is used which draws the disinfectant solution by suction from a container and disperses it as an aerosol by means of two atomizing discs. These discs rotate, and their centrifugal action sets up a suction which draws the disinfectant forward through the hollow shaft of the motor. To make the aerosol mist flow in the desired direction, a second air stream is needed. A turbine installed behind the motor sucks in air, which flows along the motor and emerges from the annular aperture around the atomizing discs. This stream of air carries along the aerosol particles of disinfectant (Fig. 5).

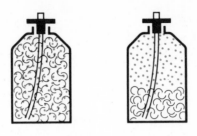

FIG. 1   FIG. 2

PRINCIPLE OF AEROSOL PRESSURIZED PACKAGING

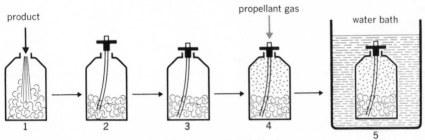

FIG. 3   STAGES IN FILLING AN AEROSOL DISPENSER

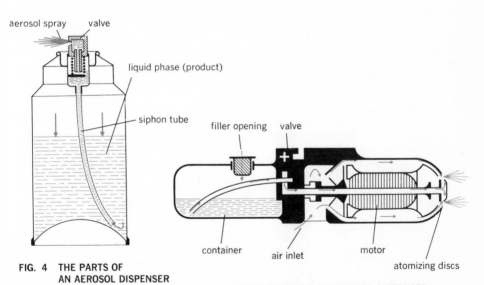

FIG. 4   THE PARTS OF
AN AEROSOL DISPENSER

FIG. 5   SECTION THROUGH AN AEROSOL DISPENSER

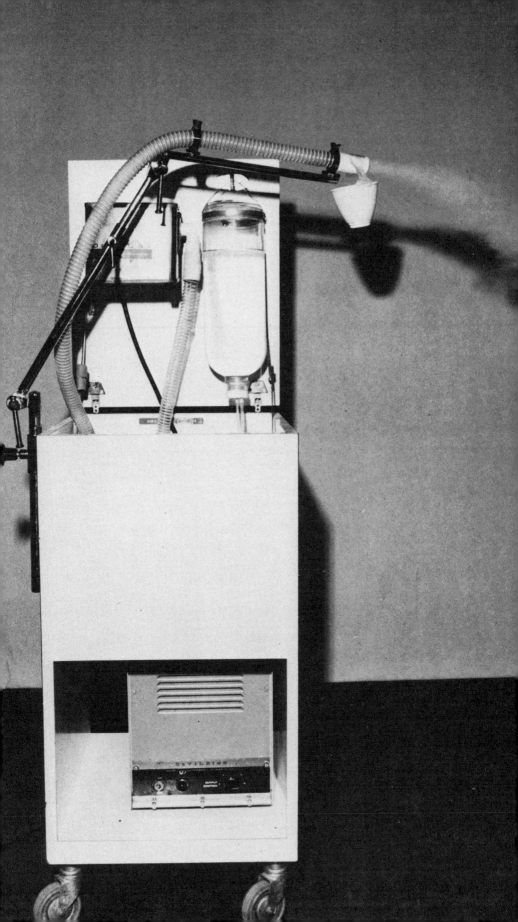

NUCLEAR FUSION

Energy that is released as a result of fission of heavy atom nuclei (e.g., uranium) in atomic reactors has been utilized already for a good many years. Another possible method of nuclear-energy production is by the fusion of the nuclei of the lightest chemical elements. Fusion of this kind—called nuclear (or thermonuclear) fusion—may occur, for example, when in a mixture of the two gases deuterium and tritium (which are heavy hydrogen isotopes indicated by the symbols ^{2}H and ^{3}H respectively) the atom nuclei collide with one another with sufficiently high energy (i.e., with sufficiently high relative velocity). In such circumstances the electrostatic repulsion operating between the nuclei (which are positively charged) can be overcome (see Fig. 1), so that the colliding nuclei "fuse" together. This phenomenon is accompanied by the release of individual nuclear components with high kinetic energy.

The principal processes that may occur in a mixture of deuterium and tritium are:

$$D + D \rightarrow \, ^3He + n + 3.25 \text{ MeV} \qquad ^3He + D \rightarrow \, ^4He + p + 18.3 \text{ MeV}$$
$$D + D \rightarrow T + p + 4 \text{ MeV} \qquad\qquad T + D \rightarrow \, ^4He + n + 17.6 \text{ MeV}$$

D denotes a deuterium nucleus (deuteron), T a tritium nucleus (triton), p a proton and n a neutron, while ^{3}He and ^{4}He denote helium nuclei with mass numbers equal to 3 and 4, respectively. The energy that is released is expressed in mega-electron-volts (1 MeV $= 4.45 \times 10^{-20}$ kWh).

There are many other possible ways of achieving the fusion of light atom nuclei. In the sun and other stars there occur, besides the fusion of hydrogen nuclei, complex fusion processes involving the participation of heavy nuclei. It is these processes that produce the vast amounts of energy that are constantly radiated into space by the stars. The devastating effect of a hydrogen-bomb explosion is also due to the energy released by fusion processes of this type: with an atomic bomb as a detonator, an explosive—or uncontrolled—chain reaction of nuclear fusion processes is initiated. "Taming the hydrogen bomb" in the sense of bringing these reactions under control in a so-called fusion reactor would place a tremendous new source of energy at man's disposal. Using pure deuterium as "fuel," it would be possible to produce about 10^{25} kWh of energy from the quantity of heavy water (deuterium oxide) estimated to be present in the natural waters of the earth.

As already stated, fusion processes take place only when nuclei of atoms collide at high velocities. To achieve these, the gas serving as fuel must be heated to such extremely high temperatures T that the average energy kT of the particles (k denotes the Boltzmann constant) is of the order of magnitude of the potential wall U_0. Since the potential wall is to a certain extent "permeable" to the particles whose energy is less than U_0 (quantum-mechanical tunnel effect), nuclear reactions already take place at kinetic-energy values of 10 to 100 keV. Hence, sufficiently large numbers of nuclei can react with one another in "thermal collisions," if kT $\approx$ 100 keV—i.e., T $\approx$ 100 million degrees centigrade. Nuclear reactions caused by thermal collisions are generally called *thermonuclear reactions*.

Since each fusion results in the release of several MeV of energy, it is possible in principle to achieve a positive energy balance even when only a small proportion of the nuclei react with one another. If the energy that is released can be kept together for some length of time, spontaneous heating of the gas may be initiated. At these extremely high temperatures the gas employed is completely ionized: i.e., all the atoms have been split up into freely moving electrons and "naked" nuclei. The gas has thus become a completely ionized plasma. Because of this, it can be compressed into a relatively small space and be contained there by the action of a sufficiently strong magnetic field (approx. 100 kilogauss); see Fig. 3. (It is, of course, not possible to contain the plasma in any sort of material receptacle, as this would be vaporized at these high temperatures.) The escape of neutrons and radiation (more particularly the so-called "bremsstrahlung," shown in Fig. 4) inevitably causes losses of energy. A positive energy balance and therefore a continuation of the fusion processes can

(more)

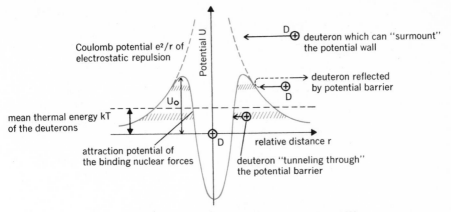

Coulomb potential e²/r of electrostatic repulsion

mean thermal energy kT of the deuterons

attraction potential of the binding nuclear forces

deuteron which can "surmount" the potential wall

deuteron reflected by potential barrier

relative distance r

deuteron "tunneling through" the potential barrier

FIG. 1 POTENTIAL DISTRIBUTION FOR THE INTERACTION OF CHARGED NUCLEI (DEUTERONS)

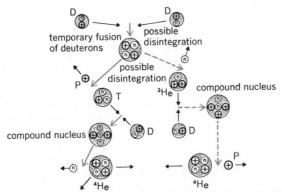

temporary fusion of deuterons

possible disintegration

possible disintegration

compound nucleus

³He

compound nucleus

⁴He

⁴He

FIG. 2 SCHEMATIC REPRESENTATION OF THE PRINCIPAL NUCLEAR-FUSION PROCESSES IN A DEUTERIUM-TRITIUM MIXTURE

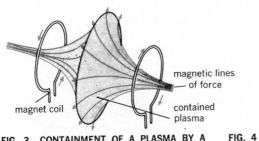

magnetic lines of force

magnet coil

contained plasma

FIG. 3 CONTAINMENT OF A PLASMA BY A MAGNETIC FIELD; THE CURRENTS IN THE COILS PRODUCING THE FIELD FLOW IN OPPOSITE DIRECTIONS

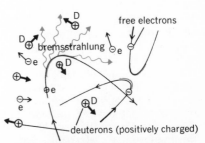

free electrons

bremsstrahlung

deuterons (positively charged)

FIG. 4 FULLY IONIZED DEUTERIUM PLASMA; AN ELECTRON EMITS "BREMSSTRAHLUNG" RADIATION AS SOON AS ITS PATH CEASES TO BE LINEAR, IN CONSEQUENCE OF INTERACTION WITH OTHER PARTICLES

be achieved only if the energy of the electrically charged reaction products that are formed is able to make up for these losses. This is the case with a mixture comprising 50% deuterium and 50% tritium at temperatures of more than 50 million degrees centigrade (for pure deuterium it would require a temperature of 400 million degrees).

One of the best-known pieces of apparatus used in nuclear-fusion research and in efforts to utilize this phenomenon for purposes of practical energy production is *Zeta* (Fig. 5). It operates on the principle of the transformer. The primary winding is of the usual type; a condenser bank is discharged through it. The secondary winding is formed by plasma which is produced in an annular tube (torus). Before the condensers are discharged, the gas in the torus (e.g., deuterium) at a pressure of 10^{-4} mm is slightly ionized—that is, made electrically conductive—by the action of high-frequency electromagnetic waves. As soon as the discharge through the primary winding commences, a powerful current (up to 200,000 amps.) is induced in this plasma. The charge carriers move in circular paths parallel to the wall of the torus. These "current filaments," like all electric currents flowing in parallel paths, attract one another: The ring of plasma, which initially fills the entire space within the torus, contracts and becomes detached from the wall. This phenomenon is called "pinch effect." The resulting compression of the plasma is attended with a considerable rise in temperature. At the same time, the degree of ionization increases so greatly that the plasma becomes completely ionized. In this way the conditions in which nuclear-fusion processes can occur are established.

With the aid of Zeta it has proved possible to keep the compressed plasma tube, the so-called "pinch," stable for periods of a few milliseconds and to reach temperatures of 5 million degrees centigrade. It has not yet, however, proved possible to make the fusion process self-sustaining.

Another type of apparatus is the *Stellarator*. In this device the containment and the heating of the plasma take place independently of each other. In a torus of double-loop shape (a figure 8), a magnetic field is produced by an electric current flowing through a winding (Fig. 6). The magnetic-field strength increases with the distance from the axis to the wall of the torus. The plasma is thereby kept away from the wall. Heating is effected on the transformer principle, just as in Zeta (electrical resistance produces heat in the plasma functioning as the secondary winding). However, this phenomenon generates a temperature of only about 1 million degrees centigrade, because at elevated temperatures the electrical conductivity of the plasma increases and the resistance therefore decreases.

Yet another method of raising the temperature to very high values is based on periodic variation of a magnetic field by means of a booster coil (see Fig. 6). An alternating current flowing through this coil produces periodic increases and decreases in the density of the magnetic lines of force in the torus (this effect is called "magnetic pumping"). By choosing an appropriate frequency it is thus possible to supply energy more particularly to the nuclei (as distinct from the electrons), so that the bremsstrahlung losses due to the electrons are kept low.

In a third type of apparatus, the containment of the plasma is achieved by a magnetic field which is stronger at the (externally open) ends than in the middle (Fig. 7). The regions of higher field strength act as "magnetic mirrors": They are able to reflect plasma particles. This type of configuration for the containment of a plasma in controlled-thermonuclear-reaction experiments is referred to as a "magnetic bottle." The initially cold plasma is compressed and heated by rapid intensification of the magnetic field. Temperatures exceeding 10 million degrees centigrade are thus attained in very small regions of the plasma.

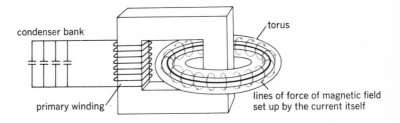

condenser bank

torus

primary winding

lines of force of magnetic field
set up by the current itself

FIG. 5 ZETA (SCHEMATIC)

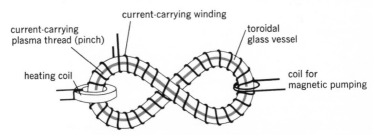

current-carrying winding

current-carrying
plasma thread (pinch)

toroidal
glass vessel

heating coil

coil for
magnetic pumping

**FIG. 6 DOUBLE-LOOP STELLARATOR TORUS; THE GUIDING
MAGNETIC FIELD IS PRODUCED BY MAGNET COILS
(HERE REPRESENTED SCHEMATICALLY BY THE
WINDING); STABILIZATION OF THE PINCH IS
ACHIEVED BY MEANS OF ADDITIONAL WINDINGS**

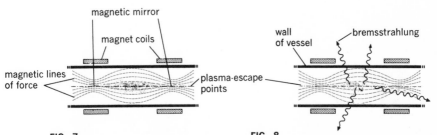

magnetic mirror

magnet coils

magnetic lines
of force

plasma-escape
points

wall
of vessel

bremsstrahlung

**FIG. 7
PRINCIPLE OF A MAGNETIC BOTTLE
WITH CONTAINED PLASMA**

**FIG. 8
THE PLASMA IS COMPRESSED BY INCREASING
THE STRENGTH OF THE CURRENT FLOWING
THROUGH THE COIL; FUSIONS TAKE PLACE
WHICH CAUSE EMISSION OF NEUTRONS AND
"BREMSSTRAHLUNG" RADIATION**

NUCLEAR REACTORS

Pressurized-water reactor: This is the simplest form of thermal reactor, in which water serves as the coolant and also as the moderator (i.e., the substance that is used to reduce the velocity of the fast neutrons produced by nuclear fission). The pressure in the primary circuit is so high, and the boiling point of the water consequently so raised, that no steam can form in the reactor core. The pressure, and therefore the attainable temperature, is limited by the technically practicable dimensions of the reactor vessel. Ordinary water (H_2O) as well as "heavy" water (deuterium oxide, D_2O) may be used as the coolant. The water in the primary circuit is kept in circulation by pumping. The heat absorbed in the core is transferred by means of a heat exchanger to the secondary circuit, where it is utilized to raise steam which drives turbines, which in turn drive the generators for producing electricity.

An example of this reactor type is the KWO pressurized water reactor built at Obrigheim on the River Neckar, in Germany, which has a thermal output of 907.5 MW and an electric power output of 283 MW (Fig. 1). The reactor core is accommodated in a pressure vessel with an internal diameter of 3.27 m (10 ft. 9 in.), which is provided with cooling-water inlet and outlet pipe connections. The inflowing water first passes through an annular gap in the bottom chamber of the pressure vessel and flows through the core in the upward direction. The coolant has a temperature of 283° C on entering the reactor and is heated to an exit temperature of 310° C. In the steam-raising unit, saturated steam of 50 atm. (735 lb./in.^{2}) at 263° C is generated.

The reactor fuel consists of slightly enriched uranium dioxide (average 3% U 235), which is enclosed in gastight sealed zircaloy (a zirconium alloy) tubes. One hundred eighty such fuel rods are combined into one fuel element. There are 121 fuel elements in the reactor core.

For short-term control operations, there are 27 control rods uniformly distributed over the core, which are inserted into it from above. To compensate for the initial reactivity necessary for high consumption rates or for slow control operations, the boron concentration in the coolant can be altered.

Pressure-tube reactor: A very interesting and promising form of construction of the pressurized-water reactor is the pressure-tube type. Instead of the pressure vessel there is now a set of parallel pressure tubes through which the coolant flows. The fuel elements are inside these tubes. Externally the latter are surrounded by the moderator. Since the coolant and the moderator are separate from each other, the moderator can be at a much lower pressure and lower temperature than the coolant. Almost any type of coolant can be employed, and the temperatures thereof can be freely chosen. Thus, the AKB project for a heavy-water pressure-tube reactor (100 MW electric-power output) developed by the German engineering firm of Siemens uses carbon dioxide as the coolant. The exit temperature of this substance is so high that the live steam is generated at 530° C and a pressure of 105 atm. (1545 lb./in.^{2}). This makes possible the use of modern steam turbogenerators. The moderator is heavy water, which surrounds the pressure tubes and is constantly circulated (by pumping) and cooled (Fig. 2). In contrast with the Canadian and French reactors of the same general type, in this German reactor the cooling tubes, of which there are 351, are vertical. In the fission zone they consist of zircaloy and have a wall thickness of 2.7 mm (0.106 in.). Above and below this zone the cooling tubes are of steel. Each tube contains a fuel element comprising 19 fuel rods. These rods consist of uranium dioxide pellets, made with very slightly enriched uranium, enclosed in thin-walled steel tubes. The pressure-tube reactor is controlled by raising and lowering the level of the moderator. For this purpose the heavy water is kept under a low-pressure helium atmosphere.

(more)

18

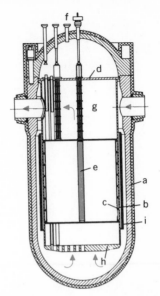

a pressure vessel
b core-supporting
   framework
c core cage
d top supporting
   plate
e bundle of fuel
   elements
f control-rod drive
g control rod
h bottom supporting
   plate
i thermal shield

FIG. 1 SECTION THROUGH THE KWO
        PRESSURIZED-WATER REACTOR
        AT OBRIGHEIM, GERMANY

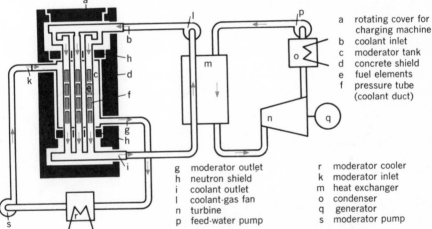

a rotating cover for
   charging machine
b coolant inlet
c moderator tank
d concrete shield
e fuel elements
f pressure tube
   (coolant duct)

g moderator outlet   r moderator cooler
h neutron shield   k moderator inlet
i coolant outlet   m heat exchanger
l coolant-gas fan   o condenser
n turbine   q generator
p feed-water pump   s moderator pump

FIG. 2 CIRCUIT DIAGRAM OF A PRESSURE-TUBE REACTOR
        WITH SCHEMATIC SECTION THROUGH THE REACTOR
        (AKB PROJECT FOR NIEDERAICHBACH, GERMANY)

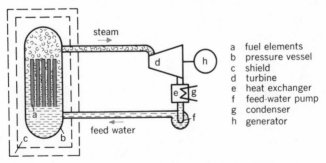

a fuel elements
b pressure vessel
c shield
d turbine
e heat exchanger
f feed-water pump
g condenser
h generator

FIG. 3 DIRECT CIRCUIT OF A BOILING-WATER REACTOR

Nuclear reactor at Marcoule, France
Photo Cartier-Bresson, Magnum

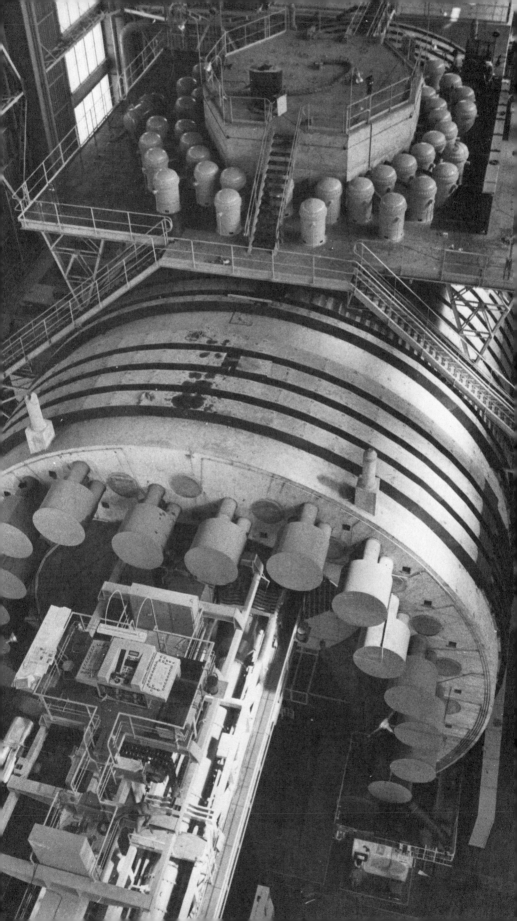

Nuclear Reactors (continued)

Boiling-water reactor: In this type of reactor the coolant also serves as the moderator. Its general construction closely resembles that of the pressurized-water reactor (see page 18), and the fuel elements are also very similar. As a rule, the reactor vessel comprises a steam chamber above the water level. The object of this steam chamber, which is provided with various internal fittings, is to promote the separation of the phases and to prevent carry-over of large quantities of water from the liquid to the vapor phase, besides compensating for minor variations in pressure. Ordinary water (H_2O) is used as the coolant and moderator; it is, however, also possible in principle to use heavy water (D_2O). The reactor normally generates saturated steam, which is either passed direct to the turbine or used to generate secondary steam in a steam converter. Depending on whether or not there is a main heat exchanger for the transfer of the whole of the energy between the reactor and the turbine, the terms "direct circuit" and "indirect circuit" are applicable. Fig. 3 (p. 27) shows an installation operating on the former principle: inside the reactor core, the water or the steam-and-water mixture flows upwards. After separation of the two phases above the core, the saturated steam flows direct to the turbine, while the liquid phase (the water) flows downwards in an externally disposed annular space, where feed water, to make up for the quantity of saturated steam that has been produced, is added.

The dynamic properties can be improved by using the so-called two-circuit system (Fig. 1). From the pressure vessel a mixture of steam and water is passed into the water separator. The steam flows onward through a valve to the turbine. The water, which has been separated from the steam, is returned to the reactor vessel by means of a pump and through the heat exchanger. On the secondary side of the heat exchanger low-pressure steam is formed, which is likewise passed through a valve to the turbine. The KRB nuclear power station at Gundremmingen, Germany, operates on this principle. This reactor has a thermal output of 801 MW and an electric-power output of 237 MW (Fig. 2).

Superheated-steam reactor: The saturated steam produced in the boiling-water reactor can be superheated by nuclear action, the steam being returned for this purpose to the reactor core, where it can absorb more thermal energy. The superheated-steam reactor, functioning on this principle, can generate steam at the temperatures and pressures normally employed in conventional steam-powered electricity-generating stations.

In the boiling-water reactor the bundles of fuel elements are composed of individual rods, but in the superheated-steam reactor the fuel elements are tubular. For example, in the nuclear power station at Grosswelzheim, Germany, the fuel-element assembly comprising 8×8 tubes is accommodated in a container, just as in the boiling-water reactor. These tubes are cooled externally by boiling water, so that saturated steam is produced. The saturated steam, which collects in the space above the water surface, is returned to the fuel elements for superheating. The saturated steam flows downwards through the interior of the tubular fuel elements in its first pass through the core of the reactor; in the course of this journey it cools the elements internally and becomes superheated. Below the core, the direction of flow of the steam is reversed: it now flows upwards in its second pass through other fuel elements and so becomes further superheated. This cycle is shown schematically in Fig. 3, while Fig. 4 is a vertical section through this reactor. The latter is of relatively low capacity, and for this reason the steam actually makes four passes through the core. With large superheated steam reactors, however, a double pass will suffice to attain the desired superheated-steam temperature.

(more)

22

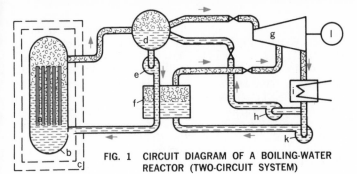

FIG. 1 CIRCUIT DIAGRAM OF A BOILING-WATER REACTOR (TWO-CIRCUIT SYSTEM)

a fuel elements
b pressure vessel
c shield
d water separator
e pump
f heat exchanger
g turbine
h pump
i condenser
k pump
l generator

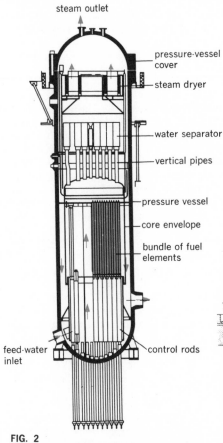

steam outlet

pressure-vessel cover

steam dryer

water separator

vertical pipes

pressure vessel

core envelope

bundle of fuel elements

feed-water inlet

control rods

FIG. 2
SECTION THROUGH KRB BOILING-WATER REACTOR AT GRUNDREMMINGEN

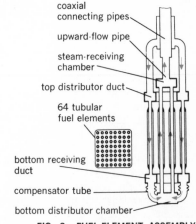

coaxial connecting pipes

upward-flow pipe

steam-receiving chamber

top distributor duct

64 tubular fuel elements

bottom receiving duct

compensator tube

bottom distributor chamber

FIG. 3 FUEL-ELEMENT ASSEMBLY OF A SUPERHEATED-STEAM REACTOR (SCHEMATIC)

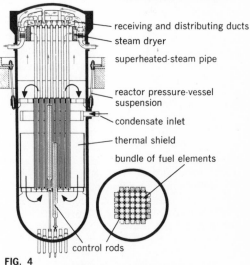

receiving and distributing ducts

steam dryer

superheated-steam pipe

reactor pressure-vessel suspension

condensate inlet

thermal shield

bundle of fuel elements

control rods

FIG. 4
SECTION THROUGH THE SUPERHEATED-STEAM REACTOR AT GROSSWELZHEIM, GERMANY

→ saturated steam 285° C
---→ superheated steam 400° C and superheated steam 500° C
→ water circulation

23

Gas-cooled reactor (Calder Hall type): Along with the pressurized water reactor, the gas-cooled reactor of the type installed at Calder Hall power station in Great Britain is one of the well-tried types of nuclear reactor. This reactor is operated with natural uranium. The moderator is graphite and the coolant is carbon dioxide gas (CO_2). The circuit is shown schematically in Fig. 1. A large cylindrical block of graphite pierced by channels forms the reactor core. The rod-shaped fuel elements are so disposed in these channels that a gap remains between each element and the wall of its channel. Carbon dioxide (the coolant) flows through this gap. The heat that the gas absorbs in the core is transferred to the secondary water-and-steam circuit in a heat exchanger installed under the reactor pressure vessel. In this heat exchanger saturated steam is formed, which drives a turbine (see Fig. 2).

The gas-cooled reactor has the advantage over the liquid-cooled reactor that there are no corrosion problems. A disadvantage, however, is the high power consumption of the fans for circulating the gaseous coolant. This can be reduced by increasing the pressure of the gas, but the construction of the pressure vessel imposes limits in this respect.

The Calder Hall reactor has a thermal output of 180 MW and an electric-power output of 34.5 MW. The pressure vessel has an internal diameter of 11.3 m (37 ft.) and is 28 m (70 ft.) high, with a wall thickness of about 50 mm (2 in.). It encloses the core, which consists of 58,000 blocks of graphite stacked on a grid structure. The core contains 1696 vertical channels for the fuel elements. The latter consist of natural uranium clad ("canned") in magnesium sheaths provided with spiral fins. The gaseous coolant flows upwards along the elements in the channels. Each uranium rod is about 30 mm (1.18 in.) in diameter and 1 m (3 ft. $3\frac{1}{2}$ in.) long. Control of the reactor is effected by means of 160 rods which are inserted into the core from above. The carbon dioxide coolant is used at a pressure of 6.8 atm. (100 lb./in.^{2}). On entering the reactor the gas has a temperature of 140° C; its exit temperature is 345° C. After Calder Hall, ten more nuclear power stations operating on the same principle have been built in Britain. The gas pressure employed has progressively been increased to 28 atm. (about 400 lb./in.^{2}) and the gas exit temperature to 414° C. At the two latest power stations (Oldbury and Wylfa) the pressure vessels are of pre-stressed concrete, not steel, which was previously employed.

Advanced gas-cooled reactor: Derived from the Calder Hall type, this reactor represents the next stage of British nuclear-reactor development. A characteristic feature is that the coolant temperature has been raised from 414° C to over 600° C. It is thus possible to attain steam conditions and efficiencies comparable to those of conventional thermal power stations. The attainment of these high temperatures is made possible by the use of sintered UO_2 as the fuel and of corrosion-resisting steel as the cladding material. The Dungeness nuclear power station has an electrical output of 1200 MW, supplied by two reactors and two turbogenerating sets (Fig. 1, p. 27). Each reactor, with its core, cooling gas fan and heat exchanger, is enclosed in a cylindrical pressure vessel of prestressed concrete (Fig. 2). The core is similar in construction to that of the Calder Hall reactor. It is enclosed within a steel dome which is installed coaxially in the pressure vessel. This dome subdivides the interior of the vessel into a "cold gas" and a "hot gas" space. In the annular space between the dome and the cylindrical concrete shell of the pressure vessel are four steam-raising units and their respective coolant fans. The graphite moderator assembly is supported by a steel structure which is anchored into the concrete bottom of the pressure vessel.

(more)

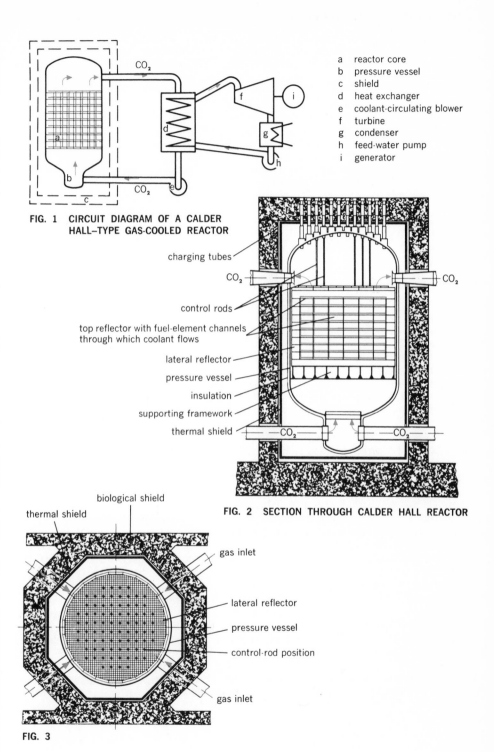

a	reactor core
b	pressure vessel
c	shield
d	heat exchanger
e	coolant-circulating blower
f	turbine
g	condenser
h	feed-water pump
i	generator

CO_2

CO_2

FIG. 1   CIRCUIT DIAGRAM OF A CALDER
HALL–TYPE GAS-COOLED REACTOR

charging tubes

CO_2 — — CO_2

control rods

top reflector with fuel-element channels
through which coolant flows

lateral reflector

pressure vessel

insulation

supporting framework

thermal shield — CO_2 — — CO_2

FIG. 2   SECTION THROUGH CALDER HALL REACTOR

biological shield

thermal shield

gas inlet

lateral reflector

pressure vessel

control-rod position

gas inlet

FIG. 3

25

Here again the coolant is carbon dioxide gas. The cold gas is drawn from the steam-raising units by the four fans and is forced into the annular duct at the base of the dome. From this duct it flows through openings in the wall of the dome into the annular space between the dome and the reactor core, where it flows upwards. Then it flows downwards to cool the moderator. From the space under the reactor the gas passes through the supporting grid and upwards along the fuel elements. The temperature of the gas on entering the cooling channels is 318° C; its outlet temperature is 675° C. Cooling is effected in four steam-raising units, through which the gas flows downwards. The maximum gas pressure is 34.3 atm. (500 lb./in.²).

The fissionable material (i.e., the fuel) is ceramic uranium oxide whose content of U 235 has been enriched to 1.47–1.76%. The cladding material is stainless steel. Thirty-six fuel rods enclosed within a graphite sheath constitute a fuel element. While the reactor is in service, the fuel elements can be removed and replaced by means of a charging machine. Access to each element is possible through standpipes passing through the roof of the pressure vessel. Control is effected by means of 53 control rods which are inserted from above into the core.

High-temperature reactor: The graphite-moderated gas-cooled high-temperature reactor is essentially a further development of the British graphite-moderated reactors. A characteristic feature of the latter is the use of carbon dioxide gas as the coolant and the use of metal-clad fuel elements. Their power density is in the region of 1 MW/m³. In the high-temperature reactor the fuel elements are not clad in metal, the coolant is helium, and the power density attainable is as much as 10 MW/m³. The coolant temperature in this type of reactor is above 700° C, thus permitting the use of modern turbogenerators.

Metal as the material for "canning" the fuel elements is ruled out by the high operating temperatures. The main consequences of this are twofold. In the first place, the neutron losses in the reactor core are very low, so that more neutrons are left for producing fresh fissionable material. Because of these good conversion properties of the high-temperature reactor, the fuel elements can attain long service lives and thus ensure efficient fuel utilization. On the other hand—as the second consequence—with unclad fuel elements the liberation of fission products presents a special problem. In order to obviate inadmissibly intense liberation of fission products and thus prevent excessive contamination of the primary circuit, the individual fuel particles are enveloped in an impermeable material. The fuel consists of a uranium-thorium mixture in carbide form, while the enveloping material is pyrolytically precipitated carbon. The carbide particles are 200 microns in diameter; the enveloping layer on each particle is 100 microns thick. These particles are pressure-molded with graphite powder to form suitably shaped fuel elements. The high-temperature gas-cooled reactor built at Peach Bottom, Pennsylvania (U.S.A.), has rod-shaped fuel elements (Fig. 1, p. 29).

Externally, a fuel element looks like a solid cylinder of graphite, about 3.7 m (12 ft.) long and 9 cm ($3\frac{1}{2}$ in.) in diameter, with a graphite mushroom head which a gripping device can seize for extracting and replacing the element. Inside the graphite cylinder, in the active part, are rings of fuel material loosely threaded on a solid rod of graphite. The reactor core is made of 804 such rods, which are enclosed within a 60 cm (2 ft.) thick radial graphite reflector. The arrangement of the fuel elements in the pressure vessel is seen in Fig. 2. The pressure vessel is about 9 m (30 ft.) high and about 4 m (13 ft.) in diameter. The 36 control rods and 19 emergency shutdown rods are inserted into the core from below.

(more)

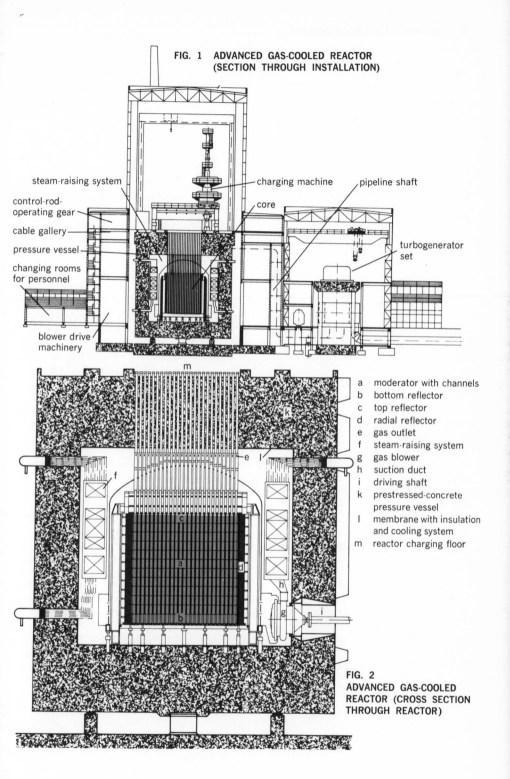

FIG. 1 ADVANCED GAS-COOLED REACTOR
(SECTION THROUGH INSTALLATION)

steam-raising system

control-rod-
operating gear

cable gallery

pressure vessel

changing rooms
for personnel

blower drive
machinery

charging machine

core

pipeline shaft

turbogenerator
set

a moderator with channels
b bottom reflector
c top reflector
d radial reflector
e gas outlet
f steam-raising system
g gas blower
h suction duct
i driving shaft
k prestressed-concrete
   pressure vessel
l membrane with insulation
   and cooling system
m reactor charging floor

FIG. 2
ADVANCED GAS-COOLED
REACTOR (CROSS SECTION
THROUGH REACTOR)

The inlet and outlet pipes for the coolant (helium) are concentric pipes. The inner pipe conveys the hot gas to the heat exchanger, and the cold gas delivered by the fan is returned to the reactor through the outer pipe. The cold gas passes downwards along the wall of the reactor vessel and flows upwards through the core; during this journey it is heated from 350° C to 720° C at a pressure of 24 atm. (350 lb./in.^{2}). Steam at 538° C and 100 atm. (1470 lb./in.^{2}) is generated in two steam-raising units installed outside the reactor pressure vessel. For a thermal output of 115 MW from the reactor, the power-generating plant has a net electrical output of 40 MW. The cover of the pressure vessel is provided with a number of ports for the removal and replacement of fuel elements. These operations are performed by a special manipulating machine, which is introduced into the vessel through the central port while the reactor is switched off. This machine is able to reach and manipulate every fuel element and to replace it by a fresh element, which is inserted through one of the lateral ports.

The AVR nuclear reactor built at Jülich, Germany (Fig. 4), utilizes spherical fuel elements, which enable the fuel to be inserted and removed while the reactor is in service. Thus the reactor can be fed continuously with fuel; significant operational advantages are thus gained, and the conversion properties of the high-temperature reactor are further improved.

The fuel element of the AVR reactor (Fig. 3) consists of a hollow graphite sphere with a diameter of 6 cm ($2\frac{3}{8}$ in.) and a shell thickness of 1 cm (0.4 in.), closed with a screw plug. It is filled with a so-called matrix containing highly enriched uranium in the form of coated uranium–thorium carbide particles mixed with graphite powder.

The reactor core consists of about 100,000 of these spherical elements and is enclosed in a 50 cm (20 in.) thick graphite reflector. The spheres are fed pneumatically into the core from above through five tubes and are removed through a bottom discharge tube. The space occupied by the charge in the core is 3 m (9 ft. 10 in.) in diameter and 3 m high. From the graphite reflector four projections extend radially into the core over the entire height. Each of these projections contains a channel for the emergency rods, which are inserted into the core from below. For reasons of thermal insulation and radiation shielding, the graphite reflector is surrounded by a carbon-block blanket and a thermal shield. The reactor is of the single-vessel type: i.e., all the components of the primary circuit are accommodated in one vessel. The core is in the bottom part of the pressure vessel, above which, in the top part, is the steam-raising unit. The gaseous coolant is circulated by two fans which are installed in the so-called fan dome. The gas flows through the supporting grid on which the reactor is seated and into the mass of spherical fuel elements through channels in the bottom reflector. After passing through the spaces between the fuel elements, the gas flows through slots in the carbon bridge into the steam-raising unit. On leaving the latter, it flows along the wall of the pressure vessel to the fan inlet. The gas used as the coolant is helium at a pressure of 10 atm. (147 lb./in.^{2}). In the reactor core the temperature of the gas is raised from 175° C to 850° C. In the steam-raising unit, superheated steam at 505° C and 75 atm. (1100 lb./in.^{2}) is produced. The thermal output of the reactor is 46 MW and the electrical output is 15 MW.

(more)

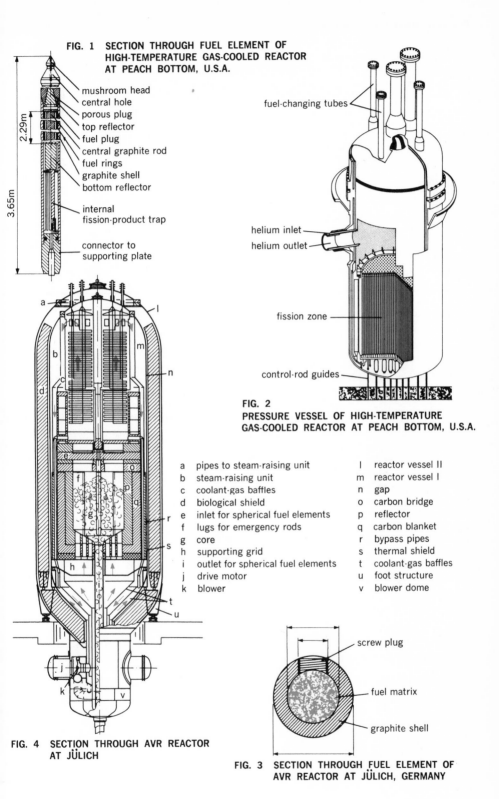

FIG. 1 SECTION THROUGH FUEL ELEMENT OF HIGH-TEMPERATURE GAS-COOLED REACTOR AT PEACH BOTTOM, U.S.A.

mushroom head
central hole
porous plug
top reflector
fuel plug
central graphite rod
fuel rings
graphite shell
bottom reflector

internal fission-product trap

connector to supporting plate

2.29m

3.65m

fuel-changing tubes

helium inlet
helium outlet

fission zone

control-rod guides

FIG. 2 PRESSURE VESSEL OF HIGH-TEMPERATURE GAS-COOLED REACTOR AT PEACH BOTTOM, U.S.A.

a   pipes to steam-raising unit
b   steam-raising unit
c   coolant-gas baffles
d   biological shield
e   inlet for spherical fuel elements
f   lugs for emergency rods
g   core
h   supporting grid
i   outlet for spherical fuel elements
j   drive motor
k   blower

l   reactor vessel II
m   reactor vessel I
n   gap
o   carbon bridge
p   reflector
q   carbon blanket
r   bypass pipes
s   thermal shield
t   coolant-gas baffles
u   foot structure
v   blower dome

screw plug

fuel matrix

graphite shell

FIG. 4 SECTION THROUGH AVR REACTOR AT JÜLICH

FIG. 3 SECTION THROUGH FUEL ELEMENT OF AVR REACTOR AT JÜLICH, GERMANY

29

Sodium reactor: To enable a nuclear reactor to give off its heat at the highest possible temperature and yet avoid the need for a thick-walled pressure vessel, a substance with a low melting point and a high boiling point can efficiently be used as the heat-transfer medium. A suitable substance for the purpose is the metal sodium. There are, however, some unavoidable drawbacks associated with its use. Bombardment with neutrons makes sodium highly radioactive within the reactor. For this reason, with a sodium-cooled reactor the heat exchanger cannot be directly connected to the primary circuit; a secondary circuit must be interposed. This prevents radioactive material from coming into close proximity to the water that is to be converted to steam. Sodium is usually employed as the coolant for the secondary circuit also (Fig. 1). Another problem associated with the use of sodium is its reactivity with water and with atmospheric oxygen. Besides, the presence of even small amounts of sodium dioxide in the heat-transfer medium (coolant) causes a significant increase in corrosive attack of the stainless steel used as the construction material for those parts which come into contact with the sodium. In comparison with moderator materials, sodium has a relatively large initial cross section for neutrons; for this reason it is necessary to take special precautions to prevent an escape of the sodium from the reactor core and thus avoid a sudden intensification of the chain reaction.

The moderator chiefly used for the sodium reactors developed in the United States is graphite. Liquid sodium is, however, liable to penetrate into graphite, thereby causing a marked increase in the harmful absorption of neutrons in the moderator. For this reason the graphite elements of the moderator are clad with zirconium. Alternatively, this cladding can be dispensed with if zirconium hydride is used as the moderator (as is envisaged for the so-called KNK reactor developed by the Interatom undertaking).

The core of the KNK reactor (Fig. 2) is enclosed in a steel vessel 1.9 m (6 ft. 3 in.) in diameter. The coolant flows upwards through the 66 fuel elements of the core. Each fuel element consists of two rows of fuel rods in an annular arrangement. The cylindrical central cavity as well as the annular intermediate cavity is filled with zirconium hydride elements, which form the moderator and remain in the reactor when the fuel elements are changed. The control rods occupy fuel element positions. The reflector is a 13 cm (5 in.) thick stainless steel casing. Each of the two sodium-heated steam-raising units has a thermal output of 29 MW and supplies superheated steam at $510°$ C and 85 atm. (1250 lb./in.^{2}).

(more)

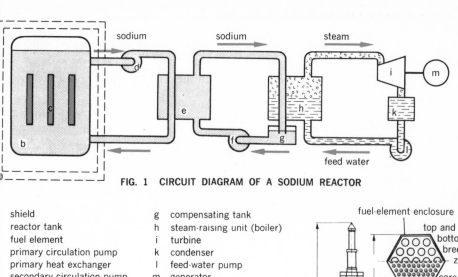

FIG. 1   CIRCUIT DIAGRAM OF A SODIUM REACTOR

a   shield
b   reactor tank
c   fuel element
d   primary circulation pump
e   primary heat exchanger
f   secondary circulation pump

g   compensating tank
h   steam-raising unit (boiler)
i   turbine
k   condenser
l   feed-water pump
m   generator

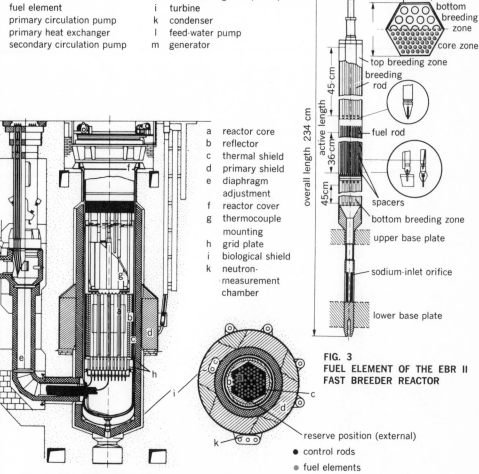

a   reactor core
b   reflector
c   thermal shield
d   primary shield
e   diaphragm
    adjustment
f   reactor cover
g   thermocouple
    mounting
h   grid plate
i   biological shield
k   neutron-
    measurement
    chamber

FIG. 3
FUEL ELEMENT OF THE EBR II
FAST BREEDER REACTOR

fuel-element enclosure
top and
bottom breeding zone
core zone
top breeding zone
breeding rod
overall length 234 cm
active length
45 cm
36 cm
45 cm
fuel rod
spacers
bottom breeding zone
upper base plate
sodium-inlet orifice
lower base plate

reserve position (external)
● control rods
● fuel elements

FIG. 2   KNK REACTOR (LONGITUDINAL SECTION
AND CROSS SECTION)

31

Breeder reactors: In nuclear fission each neutron that causes fission releases more than one new neutron. It is this fact that not only enables a chain reaction to be sustained but also, under certain conditions, makes possible the "breeding" of fissionable material—i.e.. the procedure whereby the chain reaction is made to produce more fissionable material than is consumed in generating energy. The isotopes uranium 238 and thorium 232 are suitable for this process. The breeding process based on uranium extends from the fission of U 235 to the transmutation of U 238 into fissionable plutonium 239 (U-Pu cycle). In this cycle the use of fast neutrons is advantageous, as the neutron yield for plutonium 239 in the fast energy range is higher than at thermal energy levels.

In the so-called *fast breeder reactor*, the moderator needed for slowing down the neutrons is dispensed with. This in turn results in a more compact core, which now contains only the requisite fuel elements and the coolant. In contrast with the U-Pu cycle, the thorium-uranium cycle (Th-U cycle) operates more favorably in the thermal energy range. In this process the fission of U 235 likewise results in the transmutation of Th 232 into fissionable U 233. In comparison with the fast breeder reactor, the so-called *thermal breeder reactor* is characterized by a lower breeding gain, a lower fissionable-material requirement, and the absence of special safety problems. A significant feature is that with the breeder reactor, as compared with the ordinary nuclear reactor, it is possible to attain fifty times better utilization of the available uranium resources when the U-Pu cycle is employed, and that with the Th-U cycle the large natural deposits of thorium can be exploited. Whereas the thermal breeder reactors were progressively evolved from existing types (pressurized- or boiling-water reactor with D_2O coolant; high-temperature reactor), the fast breeder reactors represent what is very largely an entirely new technical development. The first experimental reactors of this kind were built in the United States, Great Britain and the U.S.S.R. All use fuel elements in the form of rods and sodium as the coolant. A typical fuel element is illustrated in Fig. 3, p. 31. The core zone consists of a number of sheathing tubes containing the fuel (U 235), usually in metallic form. Above and below this zone are breeding zones in which the neutrons escaping from the reactor are trapped. These zones likewise comprise a number of sheathing tubes, here containing U 238 as the fertile material. The whole assembly is accommodated in a fuel-element container made of stainless steel.

Fig. 4 is a cutaway drawing of the EBR II, an American fast breeder reactor. The core has an approximately hexagonal cross section, with a height of about 36 cm (14 in.) and a volume of 73 dm^3 (4500 in.^{3}). The coolant is fed into the reactor at the bottom and flows upwards through the core and the surrounding "blanket." At full output, the inlet and outlet temperatures of the sodium are 371° and 473° C respectively. The reactor is enclosed in a tank into which the control rods are inserted from above. The whole assembly is surrounded laterally by a shield of boronated graphite.

The first large power reactor of this type is the Enrico Fermi reactor, which has a thermal output of 300 MW and an electrical output of 100 MW. Fig. 5 is a cutaway drawing of this American reactor. The core, surrounded by a blanket of uranium, is 77 cm (30 in.) in height and has a volume of 380 dm^3 (23,000 in.^{3}). The reactor inlet and outlet temperatures of the sodium are 288° C and 427° C respectively. The coolant flows upwards through the rod-shaped fuel elements. Above the reactor are arranged the control-rod drive equipment and the fuel-charging devices. The whole installation is surrounded by primary shield tanks, and the reactor itself is accommodated in a reactor vessel.

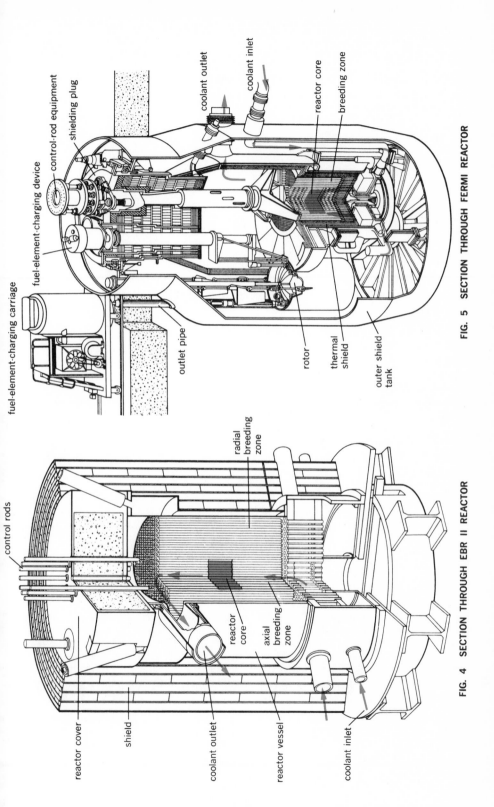

fuel-element-charging carriage

control-rod equipment

shielding plug

fuel-element-charging device

coolant outlet

coolant inlet

reactor core

breeding zone

fuel-element-charging carriage

outlet pipe

rotor

thermal shield

outer shield tank

FIG. 5   SECTION THROUGH FERMI REACTOR

control rods

radial breeding zone

reactor cover

shield

coolant outlet

reactor core

axial breeding zone

reactor vessel

coolant inlet

FIG. 4   SECTION THROUGH EBR II REACTOR

SYNTHETIC AMMONIA PROCESS

Ammonia (NH_3) is a colorless gas which can readily be liquefied by compression. The liquid is colorless and highly refractive and has a boiling point of $-33°$ C. Because of its high heat of vaporization, ammonia is widely used in refrigeration.

Most ammonia is produced by the Haber, or Haber-Bosch, process—first applied technically on a large scale by the BASF chemical works in Germany in 1913. In this process, hydrogen and nitrogen are combined at a temperature of $500°$ C and a pressure of 200 atm. (approx. 3000 lb./in.^{2}) according to the reaction $3 H_2 + N_2 \rightarrow 2 NH_3$, which takes place in contact with a catalyst consisting of iron stabilized with aluminum oxide and potassium oxide. The initial materials are obtained from air and water, the oxygen being removed by means of carbon (in the form of coke) as a reducing agent. At elevated temperature, air is converted in a gas producer (1) according to the following reaction:

$$4 N_2 + O_2 + 2 C \rightarrow 4 N_2 + 2 CO$$

whereby so-called producer gas is formed. As a result of this reaction, in which air is blown through the gas producer, the coke charge in the latter is heated to incandescence. Then water vapor (steam) is passed through the incandescent coke and is decomposed into so-called water gas, a mixture of hydrogen and carbon monoxide, as follows:

$$C + H_2O \rightarrow H_2 + CO$$

As a result of passing steam through the coke, the temperature in the gas producer is lowered. The cycle can then be repeated by blowing air again, to yield producer gas and heat up the coke, and so on.

Hydrogen sulphide, which is present in the coke, is liable to contaminate the catalyst and therefore has to be removed. This is done in the gas washer (2) by means of the alkazide method. The gas mixture, consisting of nitrogen, hydrogen and carbon monoxide (i.e., the combination of producer gas and water gas alternately supplied by the gas producer), is drawn from the gas storage tank (3) by the fan (4) and subjected to what is referred to as a conversion process (5) in order to get rid of the carbon monoxide, as this gas too is harmful to the catalyst used in the synthetic ammonia process. Conversion is effected with steam and catalytic contact with iron oxide and chromium oxide at $500°$ C: $CO + H_2O \rightarrow CO_2 + H_2$.

The cooled converted gas (N_2, H_2, CO_2 and traces of CO) is compressed to 25 atm. (370 lb./in.^{2}) by compressors (6) and passed to the carbon dioxide washer (7), where about 99% of the carbon dioxide is removed by means of water under pressure. Remaining traces of carbon monoxide and dioxide are removed with ammoniacal copper (I) chloride solution. The gas mixture, compressed to 100 atm. (1470 lb./in.^{2}), is passed through the washing tower (8, 9). With correct adjustment of the mix proportions of producer gas and water gas, the right gas mixture for the synthetic ammonia process can be obtained, consisting of three parts of nitrogen to one part of hydrogen. This nitrogen-hydrogen mixture is passed through the contact reactor (10), which contains a system of heat-exchanger tubes and contact tubes in which the synthesis reaction takes place. On entering the reactor, the gas is preheated by absorbing the heat of reaction evolved from the gas mixture that has already reacted. Once the reaction has been started with the aid of an electric heating device, no heat from an outside source is needed to sustain it: it produces its own heat. Eleven percent of the gas introduced into the synthetic process is transformed into ammonia. The resulting gas mixture (NH_3 and unreacted N_2 and H_2) is cooled with water in a tubular cooler (11) and then further cooled in a low-temperature cooler (12) to between $-20°$ and $-30°$ C. As a result of this refrigeration, liquid ammonia is formed. The low temperature in the last-mentioned cooler is obtained by evaporation of liquid ammonia diverted for this purpose from the production process. The recycle gas is returned to the contact reactor by a circulation pump (13), with additional fresh nitrogen-hydrogen mixture to compensate for the ammonia removed from the system.

36

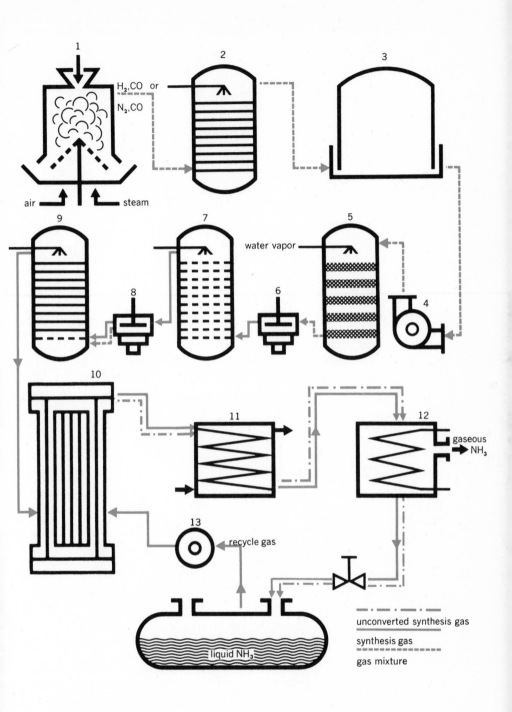

1

H₂,CO or
N₂,CO

2

3

air steam

9

7

water vapor

5

8

6

4

10

11

12

gaseous
NH₃

13

recycle gas

liquid NH₃

— · — · — unconverted synthesis gas
———— synthesis gas
= = = = = gas mixture

Liquid ammonia tank. Lonza, Viège, Switzerland
Photo Roland Schneider, Len Sirman Press

SYNTHESIS GAS AND METHANOL SYNTHESIS

Various gas mixtures that are used for the manufacture of chemical compounds —mixtures of ammonia, methanol, ethylene, or hydrocarbons generally—are sometimes referred to as synthesis gases. The term "synthesis gas" is, however, more specifically applicable to a mixture of nitrogen (N_2) and hydrogen (H_2) which is employed in the synthetic production of ammonia $(N_2 + 3 H_2 \rightarrow 2 NH_3)$. In the early 1960s over 80% of this mixture was still being produced from solid fuels (cf. synthetic ammonia process, p. 36). At the present time, however, processes for making synthesis gas from natural gas and hydrocarbons are gaining ground. Of increasing importance, too, are gas mixtures that are used for the manufacture of hydrocarbons and alcohols:

$$n\ CO + 2\ n\ H_2 \rightarrow (CH_2)_n + n\ H_2O \qquad \text{(n = number of}$$
$$\text{molecules or}$$
$$CO + 2\ H_2 \rightarrow CH_3OH \qquad\qquad \text{molecule groups)}$$

The accompanying diagrams illustrate the possibilities for the production of synthesis gases. As contrasted with the processing of solid fuels in the synthetic ammonia process, these diagrams show the processing of liquid and gaseous hydrocarbons. Crude oil, light gasoline (petrol), liquid gas (butane), refinery gas or natural gas is converted to synthesis gas either with the aid of platinum-nickel catalysts (no combustion being employed) or by partial combustion. The preheated hydrocarbons and preheated oxygen enter the reactor. Synthesis gas for the ammonia process requires additional air. The hot decomposition gases are passed through a waste-heat boiler. The steam formed in the boiler may be supplied to the reactor. Soot sludge is removed in a pressure-washing installation. The synthesis gas is cooled in a spray cooler and then undergoes cleaning or aftertreatment. More particularly, the products obtained by gasification of solid fuels contain tar, dust and organic compounds (such as naphthalene, phenol and sulphur compounds) which are objectionable in further processing and must therefore be removed. The liquid or gaseous fuels employed usually have a very low sulphur content or are desulphurized before the reaction takes place.

Another type of aftertreatment is re-forming: the transformation of methane with water vapor into carbon monoxide and hydrogen. If the ratio of carbon monoxide to hydrogen is not suited for the synthesis to be performed, a conversion process is applied (cf. town-gas detoxication, p. 44).

Methanol synthesis: The synthesis gas in the correct proportions reacts in contact with chromium oxide and zinc oxide catalysts at a pressure of 300 atm. (4400 lb. in.^{2}) and a temperature of $330°$–$370°$ C. The gas containing methanol (methyl alcohol) flows through a heat exchanger in which it is cooled by so-called recycle gas—i.e., unreacted synthesis gas which is returned to the process. Then follows further cooling with water, causing methanol to condense. In a separator the methanol is separated from the residual gas, the latter being returned to the reactor (recycle gas). The crude methanol is distilled (methanol boils at $64.5°$ C) in order to free it of the small amounts of water and by-products that it still contains.

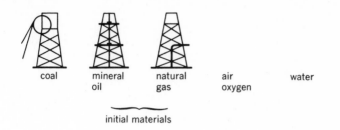

coal   mineral   natural   air   water
oil   gas   oxygen

initial materials

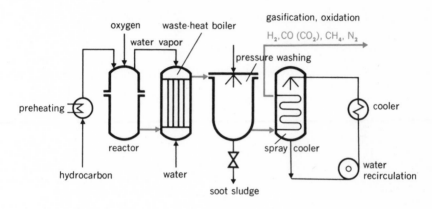

gasification, oxidation
H_2, CO (CO_2), CH_4, N_2

oxygen   waste-heat boiler

water vapor

pressure washing

preheating

cooler

reactor

spray cooler

hydrocarbon   water

water recirculation

soot sludge

cleaning

re-forming
$CH_4 + H_2O$ $CO + 3H_2$

converting
$CO + H_2O$ $CO_2 + H_2$

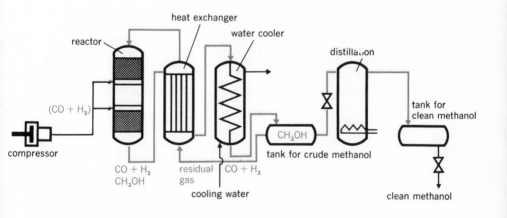

heat exchanger

water cooler

reactor

distillation

tank for clean methanol

$(CO + H_2)$

CH_3OH

compressor

tank for crude methanol

$CO + H_2$
CH_3OH

residual gas

$CO + H_2$

cooling water

clean methanol

41

Pipeline in the desert near Dhahran, Saudi Arabia
Photo Fred Peer, Camera Press, Len Sirman Press

TOWN-GAS DETOXICATION (Conversion of Carbon Monoxide)

"Town gas" is the name given to the gas with which many Americans cook. Town gas that is produced by the gasification of solid fuels contains—after removal of tar, ammonia and benzene—about 50% hydrogen, 20 to 30% methane and 6 to 17% carbon monoxide (percentages by volume). In addition, the gas contains some carbon dioxide, nitrogen and other impurities. Detoxication consists in removing the carbon monoxide, a highly poisonous colorless and odorless gas. It does not sustain combustion, but burns with a characteristic blue flame.

In order to obtain a nontoxic gas, it is necessary to reduce the carbon monoxide content to between 1 and 1.5%. This can be fairly easily achieved by conversion of carbon monoxide by means of water vapor (steam):

$$CO + H_2O \rightarrow CO_2 + H_2$$

In this process, steam and carbon monoxide, at a temperature of 400°–480° C and atmospheric pressure, are passed over a catalyst (chromium oxide and iron oxide). The town gas flows upwards through a spray tower in which hot water is admitted at the top. As a result, the gas becomes saturated with water vapor. In a heat exchanger the gas mixture acquires the requisite temperature, the heat contained in the hot gas leaving the contact reactor (in which the above-mentioned reaction takes place in contact with the catalyst) being utilized to heat the incoming gas on its way to the reactor. To obtain better control over the reaction, the reactor comprises two chambers with different temperatures; or alternatively, two separate reactors may be employed, operating at 400° C and 480° C respectively. At the higher temperature the reaction proceeds more rapidly, but at the lower temperature the reaction equilibrium is more favorable: i.e., more CO is converted into CO_2 than at the higher temperature. In the two-stage process envisaged here, the greater part of the CO is rapidly converted at the higher temperature, and the reaction is then "finalized" at the lower temperature. The hot gases are first cooled in the heat exchanger (as already mentioned) and then further cooled in an injection condenser. The conversion process is associated with a final cleaning treatment: virtually all ammonia, hydrocyanic acid and nitric oxide are removed as well. To the detoxicated town gas obtained in this way certain odorous components may then be added in order to give it a characteristic smell, so that a leakage or escape of gas can be detected speedily. Conversion is also applied in the synthetic ammonia process (cf. p. 36) to get rid of the carbon monoxide, which would otherwise adversely affect the process. The carbon dioxide formed is removed in a washing plant.

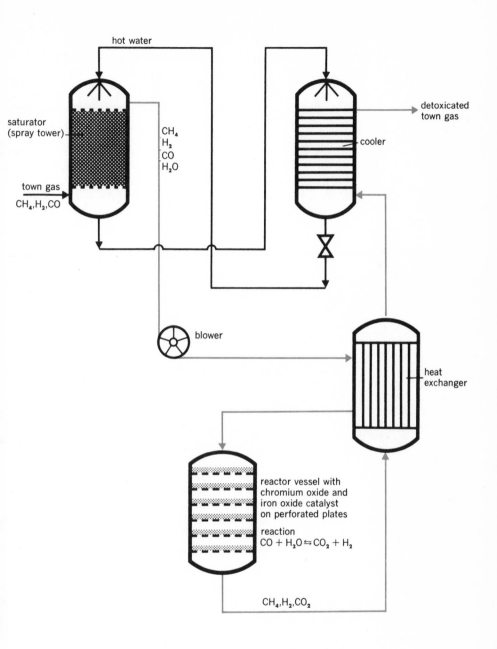

hot water

saturator
(spray tower)

town gas
CH_4, H_2, CO

CH_4
H_2
CO
H_2O

detoxicated
town gas

cooler

blower

heat
exchanger

reactor vessel with
chromium oxide and
iron oxide catalyst
on perforated plates

reaction
$CO + H_2O \leftrightharpoons CO_2 + H_2$

CH_4, H_2, CO_2

PHOSPHORUS

Phosphorus occurs in nature only in the form of the salts of phosphoric acid. From these it is obtained by reduction. There are three so-called allotropic forms of elementary phosphorus: white, red and black. Of these, black phosphorus is the form that is most stable at room temperature; it is obtained from the white form by the application of high pressures.

Black phosphorus is mainly of scientific interest, whereas the other two allotropic forms are technically important. White phosphorus melts at 44.1° C and, when finely divided, reacts with atmospheric oxygen even at room temperature. Red phosphorus is obtained from white phosphorus by heating the latter in a closed container (exclusion of air).

Phosphorus is prepared by heating calcium phosphate with carbon and silica (SiO_2) in an electric furnace. The reaction is represented by the following equation:

$$2 \ Ca_3(PO_4)_2 + 6 \ SiO_2 + 10 \ C \rightarrow 6 \ CaSiO_3 + P_4 + 10 \ CO$$

The phosphate is fed to the furnace in lump form. To make them suitable for processing in this way, finely granular phosphates first have to be agglomerated by pelletizing. Agents used for binding the particles together into pellets are soda water glass (sodium silicate), Cottrell dust (from electrostatic precipitation processes) and other admixtures, which are intimately mixed with the phosphate grains in a screw mixer and then pelletized in a revolving pan. The pellets are transformed to firm, hard balls (nodules) by sintering at high temperatures in rotary kilns or on special sintering grates. The nodules, mixed with coke and silica pebbles, are fed to the furnace.

The three-phase electric furnace consists of a steel tank of which the bottom part is lined with hard-burned carbon blocks and the top part with fireclay bricks. At the bottom are two tapholes for tapping the ferrophosphorus and the slag respectively. The furnace cover is provided with openings for the three electrodes, the feed pipe and the gas outlet. The electrodes are made of carbon and are fed from above at a rate sufficient to compensate for loss by burning. The gas discharged from the furnace, consisting of phosphorus and CO, is passed through Cottrell-type electrostatic dust precipitators (dust filters) in which the dust in the gas is trapped and collected. These precipitators are heated to prevent condensation of phosphorus inside them. The dust is returned to the sintering plant. The exit gases, which have a temperature of 250°–350° C, are passed to Ströder washers in which the phosphorus is condensed. The white phosphorus obtained in this process is stored under water to prevent the spontaneous combustion that results from contact with air. The CO gas that is discharged from the washers is utilized for heating the sintering plant and steam boilers or is burned at the top of high flare stacks.

Phosphorus is used in the manufacture of detergents. The plastics industry uses phosphorus-based plasticizers. Red phosphorus is employed in the friction striking surfaces on matchboxes.

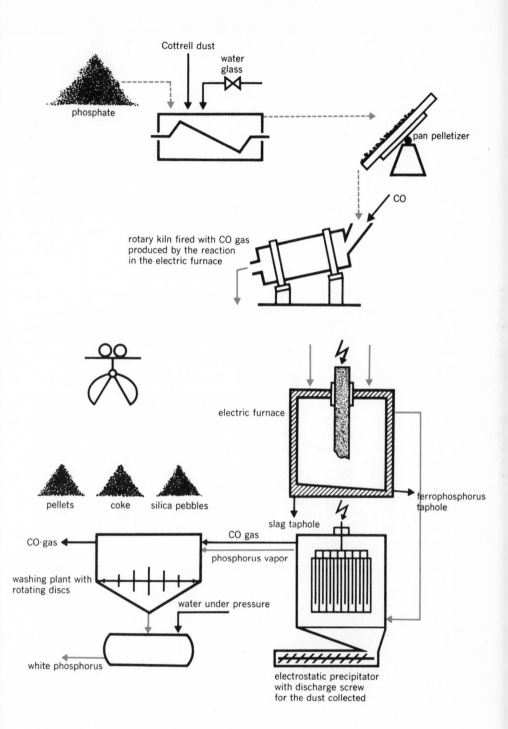

Cottrell dust

water glass

phosphate

pan pelletizer

CO

rotary kiln fired with CO gas
produced by the reaction
in the electric furnace

electric furnace

pellets   coke   silica pebbles

ferrophosphorus
taphole

slag taphole

CO gas

CO-gas

phosphorus vapor

washing plant with
rotating discs

water under pressure

white phosphorus

electrostatic precipitator
with discharge screw
for the dust collected

SULPHURIC ACID

In the pure state, sulphuric acid is a clear, colorless, oily liquid. One-hundred-percent H_2SO_4 has its melting point at $10°$ C; when heated, it gives off SO_3 until the concentration of the acid has fallen to 98.5%, and it then boils at a constant temperature of $338°$ C. Considerable evolution of heat occurs when concentrated sulphuric acid is diluted with water. Substantial amounts of SO_3 can dissolve in the acid. The resulting solution is known commercially as fuming sulphuric acid (oleum).

Sulphuric acid does not occur as a free acid in nature. It is found only in the form of its salts (sulphates): gypsum ($CaSO_4 \cdot 2H_2O$), Epsom salts ($MgSO_4 \cdot 7H_2O$), barite ($BaSO_4$) and Glauber's salt ($Na_2SO_4 \cdot 10H_2O$). Up to about the eighteenth century, sulphuric acid was made by heating alum (aluminum potassium sulphate) or iron vitriol (hydrous ferrous sulphate). This method was superseded by the burning of natural sulphur with saltpeter, which eventually evolved into the so-called lead-chamber process, first introduced in the early part of the nineteenth century and still used. At the present time, however, most sulphuric acid is produced by the contact process, which has the advantage that the acid can be obtained in any desired concentration, whereas the highest attainable concentration with the lead-chamber process is 78%.

The contact process is as follows. Sulphur dioxide (SO_2) is obtained by roasting iron pyrites (FeS_2) in a rotary kiln, shelved roasting kiln or fluidized bed kiln. Which of these kiln types is employed depends on the particle size and nature of the pyrites to be processed. When the gases from the roasting process have cooled— in gas ducts, by radiation of heat—from $1000°$ C to about $400°$–$500°$ C, the dust they contain is removed in electrostatic precipitators ("electric filters").

Next, the SO_2 gas is passed through a washing tower, where constituents that are present in vapor form (mainly compounds of arsenic, selenium and chlorine) are removed with sulphuric acid serving as the washing liquid. Remaining traces of impurities present as very fine suspended droplets ("fog") are removed in an irrigated electrostatic precipitator ("wet" precipitator). Then the gas is dried by being brought into contact with concentrated ($98°_0$) sulphuric acid.

A blower draws in the cold dried SO_2 gas and delivers it into the converter, which is a tank or tower in which a suitable catalyst—e.g., vanadium pentoxide (V_2O_5)—is placed in layers on shelves or arranged in some other appropriate manner to ensure thorough contact with the gas. The reaction whereby SO_2 is converted to SO_3 by oxidation ($2SO_2 + O_2 \rightarrow 2\ SO_3$) takes place at $430°$ to $550°$ C. A heat exchanger installed before the converter serves to cool the gas discharged from the converter and at the same time preheats the incoming gas flowing to the converter.

The hot SO_3 gas that comes out of the converter is cooled with air to around $120°$–$150°$ C in tubular coolers and is then passed to absorbers, which are steel towers lined with ceramic materials and containing specially shaped packing bodies called Raschig rings. These towers are rather similar to the washing towers. The SO_3 is absorbed by concentrated (98%) sulphuric acid. Water is then added to obtain the desired concentration. The heat evolved by the dilution is dissipated by spray coolers.

Sulphuric acid is the most important of all acids. It is used in the manufacture of superphosphate and ammonium sulphate fertilizers, petroleum refining, the manufacture of explosives and synthetic fibers, and a host of other industrial processes.

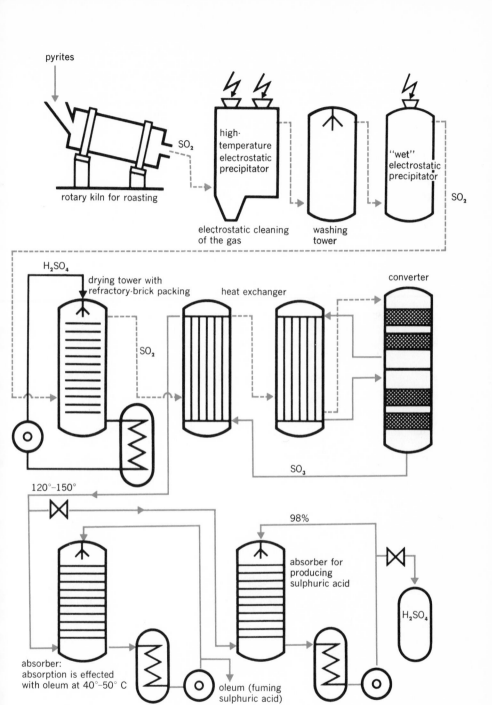

pyrites

rotary kiln for roasting

SO₂

high-temperature electrostatic precipitator

electrostatic cleaning of the gas

washing tower

"wet" electrostatic precipitator

SO₂

H₂SO₄

drying tower with refractory-brick packing

SO₂

heat exchanger

converter

SO₃

120°–150°

98%

absorber for producing sulphuric acid

H₂SO₄

absorber: absorption is effected with oleum at 40°–50° C

oleum (fuming sulphuric acid)

NITRIC ACID

For a long time all nitric acid (HNO_3) used to be produced from nitrates occurring in nature. For example, nitric acid can be obtained by adding sulphuric acid to saltpeter (potassium nitrate), whereby the latter undergoes decomposition.

In the pure state the acid is a colorless liquid which boils at $87°$ C. The boiling point rises with increasing dilution. As pure nitric acid will always undergo some decomposition when left to stand, especially when exposed to the action of light, acid with a concentration exceeding 90% almost invariably contains some dissolved NO_2. This decomposition process can be stopped by diluting the acid with water.

The various processes for the commercial manufacture of nitric acid are based on any of three principles: the decomposition of nitrates (more particularly Chile saltpeter) with sulphuric acid (this method is now virtually obsolete); the direct synthesis of NO from nitrogen and oxygen in an electric arc, followed by the last two reactions of the ammonia process (described in further detail below); or the catalytic oxidation of ammonia.

The last-mentioned method (ammonia process) is now most widely employed, more particularly with platinum as the catalyst. (In certain variants of the process the catalyst may, however, be Fe_2O_3, Mn_2O_3 or Bi_2O_3). In this process liquid ammonia is vaporized in an evaporator and is mixed with air. The gas mixture (10% ammonia and 90% air) makes its way through a filter and a preheater to the contact reactor, in which it passes over platinum gauze (the catalyst) heated initially to about $900°$ C. Heat liberated in the reaction maintains the temperature of the catalyst. In the reactor about 90% of the ammonia is oxidized to nitric oxide:

$$4 NH_3 + 5 O_2 \rightarrow 4 NO + 6 H_2O$$

Directly after the platinum gauze are filtering agents which trap the unstable platinum compounds present in the gas discharged from the reactor: the platinum precipitated in this way is recovered. This gas, of which $97\frac{1}{2}$% is NO, is cooled in the gas cooler. On leaving the cooler, it is passed through absorption towers, filled with rings made of ceramic material, in which two reactions take place. In the first tower the nitric oxide is oxidized to nitrogen dioxide: $2 NO + O_2 \rightarrow 2 NO_2$. In the following towers (four in all) the dioxide reacts with water to form nitric acid: $3 NO_2 + H_2O \rightarrow 2 HNO_3$. The requisite water is added in the last tower. In the preceding towers the NO_2 is brought into contact not with water, but with nitric acid solution, which is circulated by pumps and passed through cooling apparatus to remove the heat evolved in the reaction, as low temperatures are favorable to the absorption reactions. In a degasifying tower air is blown through the acid to remove such amounts of NO gas as are still present in it. The exhaust gas from the final absorption tower contains 0.3 to 0.4% NO.

The installation described here produces nitric acid in a concentration of between 40 and 60%. A higher concentration (up to 99.5%) is obtainable by distillation with concentrated sulphuric acid.

Nitric acid is used in the manufacture of fertilizers, explosives, lacquers, dyes, plastics and synthetic fibers.

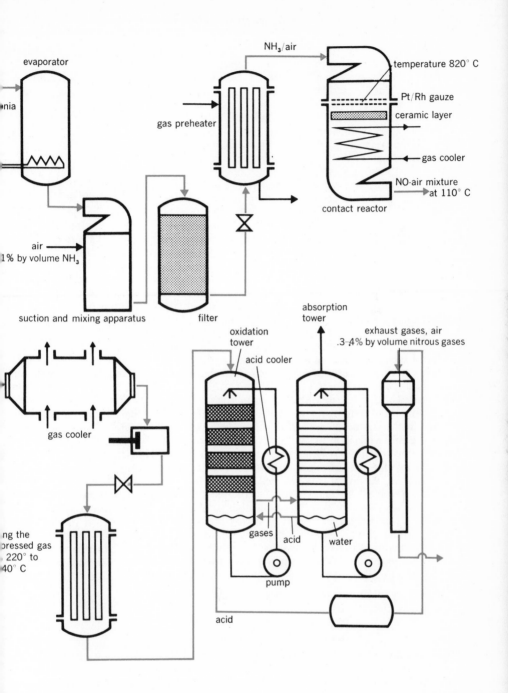

evaporator

nia

NH₃/air

temperature 820° C

gas preheater

Pt/Rh gauze

ceramic layer

gas cooler

NO-air mixture
at 110° C

contact reactor

air
1% by volume NH₃

suction and mixing apparatus

filter

absorption
tower

oxidation
tower

exhaust gases, air
.3–.4% by volume nitrous gases

acid cooler

gas cooler

ng the
ressed gas
220° to
40° C

gases   acid   water

pump

acid

FOAM PLASTICS

A characteristic feature of foam-type materials is the structural configuration of the cells. Absorbent cotton (cotton wool), felt and glass wool, for example, do not belong to this category of materials; sponges and cork, on the other hand, do. A distinction can be made between true and false foams. In a true foam the individual cells are not mere relatively thick-walled cavities or pores, but are separated only by thin partitions and are interdependent for their stability (Fig. 1). The mechanical strength is highest in the case of foams with closed (nonintercommunicating) cells. Since no convection is possible in such materials, they possess good thermal insulating capacity. With open (intercommunicating) cells the mechanical strength and thermal insulation are lower; on the other hand, these materials have a high sound-absorbing capacity and are therefore good acoustic insulators.

Artificial foam materials, including more particularly foam plastics, can be manufactured by three different methods: by churning (Fig. 2), by expansion with chemical agents (Fig. 4) and by physical methods (Fig. 3). The initial materials that can suitably be processed into foams include polyvinyl chloride (PVC), polystyrene, urea and formaldehyde condensation products, and natural and synthetic rubber. In the churning process of producing foam rubber, latex to which fillers, vulcanization accelerators and foaming agents (surface-active substances) have been added is stirred with air to form a foam, which sets and is then vulcanized with hot air (Dunlop process). Urea-formaldehyde foams are made by foaming a soap solution with an incompletely condensed water-soluble resin solution and air in an impeller-type high-speed mixer. Further condensation is brought about by the addition of acid. In the process based on physical methods, the foaming (expanding) action is produced by gases such as nitrogen, carbon dioxide or pentane. Gas dissolved in the material under pressure is liberated from the solution and thus forms bubbles in the material when the pressure is reduced; this is the foaming action. For example, PVC pastes are processed with carbon dioxide at a pressure of about 20 atm. (300 lb./in.^{2}) and a temperature between $-5°$ and $0°$ C. The fluid mass is passed into the heating zone of the installation. Here the dissolved CO_2 escapes and thus foams the material. The foam sets at a temperature of $150°$ C and is solidified by cooling. Polystyrene is foamed with pentane, which is added at the polymerization stage (e.g., in the manufacture of Styropor). Chemical foaming methods are based on the fact that certain substances will, on being heated, decompose and liberate gas, which forms small bubbles (foam cells). Azo compounds, N-nitroso compounds and azides are employed as foaming agents. What all these compounds have in common is that they liberate nitrogen when they decompose. For the manufacture of polyurethane foam plastics (e.g., the German product named Moltopren), compounds containing hydroxyl groups of high molecular weight are mixed with di-isocyanates and water. The foam plastic is formed according to the equation

$$HO \cdot R_1 \cdot OH + OCN \cdot R_2 \cdot NCO \rightarrow \ldots CO_2 \cdot R_1 CO_2 \cdot NH \cdot R_2 NH \cdot CO_2 \cdot R_1 \cdot CO_2 \ldots$$

Surplus isocyanate groups react with the added water 'and CO_2 is evolved, which acts as a foaming agent:

$$R\text{--}NCO + H_2O \rightarrow R\text{--}NH_2 + CO_2$$

isocyanate   amine

The reaction mixture is cast in molds in which both the foaming and the hardening process take place. Blocks of foam are cut up into slabs or sheets by cutting machines.

In the building industry foam plastics have achieved importance as heat and sound insulating materials. They are also used for a number of other purposes—e.g., as paddings, packing materials, materials for the manufacture of sponges, and bath mats.

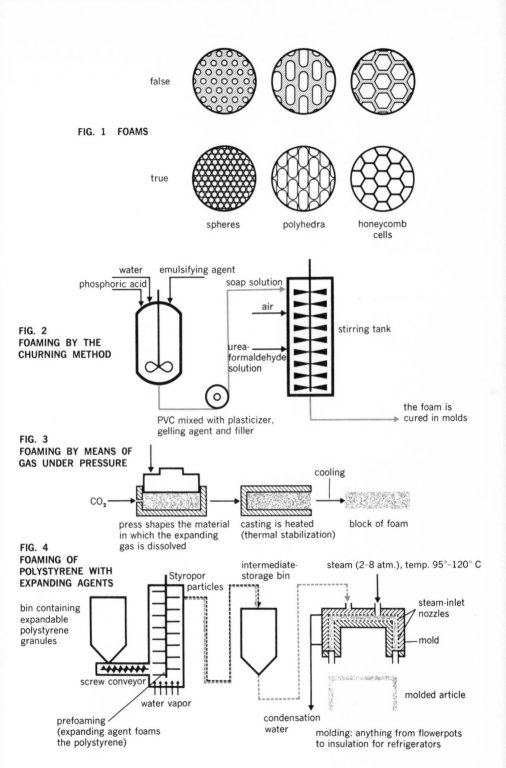

false

FIG. 1 FOAMS

true

spheres   polyhedra   honeycomb
                              cells

FIG. 2
FOAMING BY THE
CHURNING METHOD

water   emulsifying agent
phosphoric acid   soap solution
                       air   stirring tank
                       urea-
                       formaldehyde
                       solution
                                      the foam is
                                      cured in molds
PVC mixed with plasticizer,
gelling agent and filler

FIG. 3
FOAMING BY MEANS OF
GAS UNDER PRESSURE

cooling

CO_2

press shapes the material   casting is heated   block of foam
in which the expanding   (thermal stabilization)
gas is dissolved

FIG. 4
FOAMING OF
POLYSTYRENE WITH
EXPANDING AGENTS

Styropor
particles

intermediate-
storage bin

steam (2–8 atm.), temp. 95°–120° C

bin containing
expandable
polystyrene
granules

steam-inlet
nozzles

mold

screw conveyor

water vapor

condensation
water

molded article

prefoaming
(expanding agent foams
the polystyrene)

molding: anything from flowerpots
to insulation for refrigerators

53

Chemical plant in North Carolina, USA for the production of "Dacron" polyester fibre. DuPont de Nemours & Co.

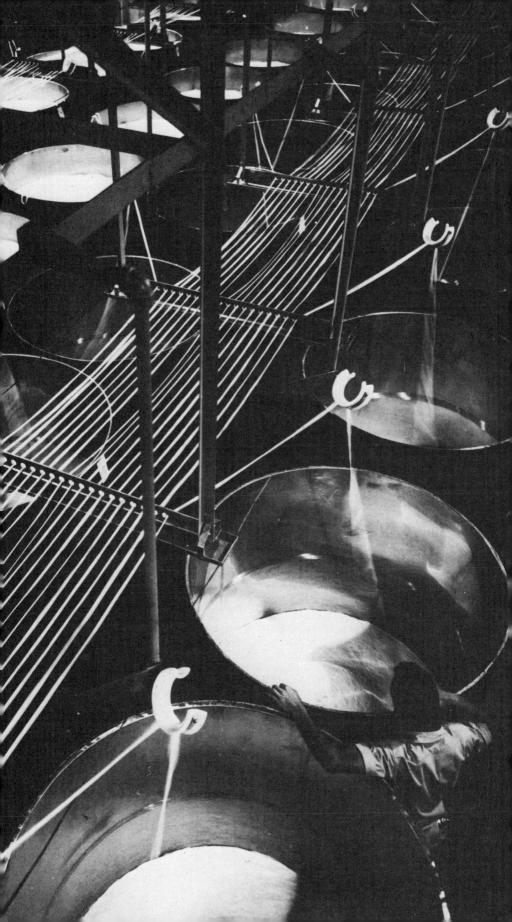

TANK TRUCKS

Tank trucks (road tank vehicles) are used for supplying gasoline (petrol) and diesel fuel to roadside filling stations and fuel oil to schools, hospitals, office buildings and residential buildings. Fig. 1 shows three types of tank vehicles most frequently found on the roads: (a) truck (lorry) with removable tank, capacity approx. 2.5–6 m³ (90–210 ft.³); (b) tank vehicle, capacity approx. 6–22 m³ (210–780 ft.³), sometimes with tank trailer; (c) articulated tank vehicle, capacity approx. 22–35 m³ (780–1240 ft.³). Removable tanks are usually not subdivided, but larger tanks comprise a number of compartments (up to six) for reasons of stability. Each compartment has its own bottom valve and is connected by pipes to the equipment and instrument cubicle. The latter can be dispensed with if the entire contents of the tank are delivered to one customer. The tank, or the individual chambers, are sealed, and the driver is issued a certificate showing the quantity of fuel put into his vehicle at the filling point. Fig. 2 shows the arrangement of pipelines and fittings, the volume-metering equipment (operating on the oval-gear or the oscillating-piston principle) and the hose drum in the equipment cubicle of a two-compartment tank vehicle. The various possible connection combinations are listed in a table. Since the contents of the tank are a commercial commodity, the metering equipment has to conform to certain standards of accuracy and reliability laid down by the public authorities. An important requirement is that the liquid must be free of bubbles on discharge from the tank. Since a volume meter will measure gaseous as well as liquid volumes, it is necessary to install a gas separator or, in some cases, an arresting device to prevent gas from being carried along into the meter. The gas separator is connected to the tank or compartment by a pipe through which flows a certain proportion of the liquid together with the separated gas. The liquid being metered has to be kept under constant observation through a sight glass. If bubbles appear, the flow must be throttled down or cut off. On the other hand, the gas-arresting device functions automatically (Fig. 3).

Before metering commences, the metering apparatus must be filled with the liquid and the air in it must be removed by actuation of the air-release valve. The metering apparatus is full of liquid when the latter has reached the level (1). The float lever and the control-valve push rod are now not in contact: the connection between supply pipe and return-flow pipe is cut off. The pointers on the meter dial may be set to zero, if necessary, and then the three-way valve can be opened. When the pump lever is moved to and fro, oil is delivered from the pump casing through valves 1 and 2 into the supply pipe and to the control piston of the three-way valve until the oil pressure compels the latter to open. Valve 1 remains closed, valve 2 open; metering commences. The gas that flows into the arresting device during metering—and more particularly on changing over from one tank compartment to another—slowly forces the liquid level down, so that the float likewise descends. When the liquid reaches the level (3), the lever attached to the float comes into contact with the push rod of the control valve, and the latter is pushed up and thus opened when the liquid level falls still lower. At the level (4) the control valve is fully open, and the oil under pressure can now flow into the return-flow pipe, in which there is no previously existing pressure. The control valve is relieved, and the spring-loaded three-way valve closes. The metering operation is thus interrupted. Valve 2 is now also closed. If metering has to be stopped earlier, this can be effected by moving the pump lever briefly backwards. The pump piston thus ascends, opens valve 3 and equalizes the pressure. To resume the metering operation, the initial procedure described above must be repeated. The metering apparatus on a tank vehicle may also be provided with a printing mechanism which issues a printed delivery note, stating the metered quantity delivered to the customer.

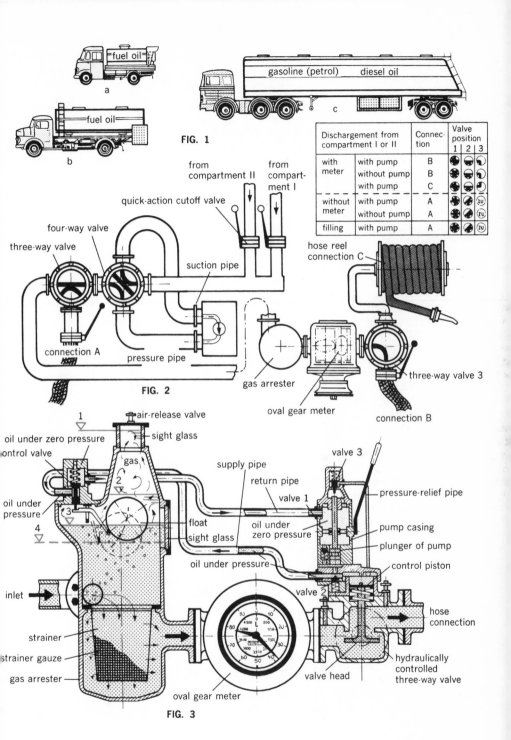

fuel oil

a

fuel oil

b

gasoline (petrol)   diesel oil

c

FIG. 1

Dischargement from compartment I or II		Connec-tion	Valve position		
			1	2	3
with meter	with pump	B			
	without pump	B			
	with pump	C			
without meter	with pump	A			
	without pump	A			
filling	with pump	A			

from compartment II

from compart-ment I

quick-action cutoff valve

four-way valve

three-way valve

suction pipe

hose reel connection C

connection A

pressure pipe

gas arrester

oval gear meter

three-way valve 3

connection B

FIG. 2

air-release valve

1

sight glass

oil under zero pressure control valve

gas

2

supply pipe

return pipe

valve 3

valve 1

pressure-relief pipe

oil under pressure

3

float

sight glass

oil under zero pressure

pump casing

plunger of pump

4

oil under pressure

control piston

inlet

valve 2

hose connection

strainer

strainer gauze

gas arrester

hydraulically controlled three-way valve

valve head

oval gear meter

FIG. 3

57

PLASTICS PROCESSING

The properties of plastics and the many different requirements applied to the finished products made from them have led to the development of a number of methods for shaping and molding these materials. From the manufacturers who synthetically produce plastics for industrial use the fabricating industry obtains the specified initial materials, i.e., the appropriate polymers with or without the requisite additives. In the latter case the user will have to add auxiliary materials such as plasticizers, stabilizers, pigments and fillers. Batch mixing of the powdered ingredients is performed in agitators or mixing drums. Alternatively, kneaders or mixing rolls (Fig. 1) are used for plastifiable materials. The last-mentioned device comprises a pair of rollers which revolve in opposite directions and which can be heated or cooled as required. The material entering the gap between the rollers is squeezed and mixed. On completion of this treatment the so-called rough sheet is stripped from the rollers (Fig. 1) and passed to a further stage of processing. Continuous mixing is performed in extruders, which offer the additional advantage of filtering the plastics before they undergo further processing (Fig. 4).

The shaping of plastic articles and components without the application of pressure is effected by casting. The simplest method of shaping in conjunction with pressure is by molding (Fig. 2), which is suitable for both thermosetting and thermoplastic compositions. (Thermoplastics can be softened by the application of heat; thermosetting plastics undergo chemical change under the action of heat and are thereby converted to infusible masses which cannot be softened by subsequent heating.) The material is fed into the mold in the form of powder or pellets. For the process known as compression molding the mold is heated; for impact molding the material itself is preheated. Paper or textile fabrics for making laminated plastics (laminates) are impregnated with thermosetting compositions; this is done on multiplaten presses. Such presses are also used for the manufacture of fiberboard (phenolic plastic with wood chips as filler). Another method of producing molded articles is by injection molding (Fig. 5), which has the advantage over ordinary (pressure) molding that preheating, plasticizing and shaping are done by the same machine. The only materials suitable for injection molding are thermoplastics of high fluidity. The granules are introduced through a hopper into the cylinder, in which they are heated—by means of a heating jacket—to above their softening point. A moving piston plasticizes the material and forces it through a nozzle into the mold. The plasticizing action can be enhanced by the use of a screw instead of a piston (Fig. 6).

Articles or components can also be shaped by the machining of semifinished products—films, sheets, rods or tubes. Machining is more particularly employed in cases where the articles are of complex shape or where only a small number are required. Whereas thermosetting plastics can be shaped only by machining (milling, turning, cutting, drilling) once they have hardened, semifinished thermoplastic materials can be shaped by heating and joined by welding. Hot shaping of thick sheets can be effected by bending or drawing (Fig. 3). In the drawing process the material to be shaped is gripped, heated and deformed to the desired shape. If the wall thickness must remain constant, the sheet must be resiliently gripped; with so-called stretch forming a reduction in wall thickness occurs.

In recent years shaping by the vacuum process has gained importance. In the female-mold (or negative-mold) method, the heated plastic sheet is laid on a concave mold and subjected to further heating. Air is extracted through holes in the mold, so that the sheet is drawn (by suction) into the mold. For the molding of complex components the plate is prestretched before the actual "negative"-molding operation begins. Alternatively, a convex master model may be used, in which case the

(more)

feeding   mixing   stripping

FIG. 1 MIXING ROLLERS

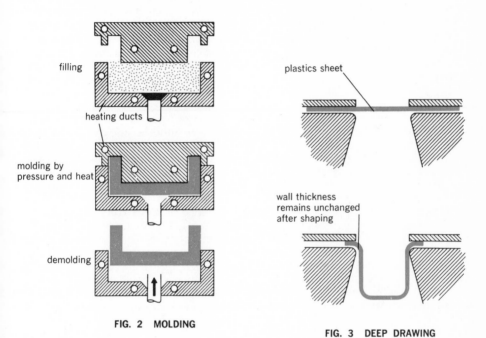

filling

heating ducts

molding by
pressure and heat

demolding

FIG. 2   MOLDING

plastics sheet

wall thickness
remains unchanged
after shaping

FIG. 3   DEEP DRAWING

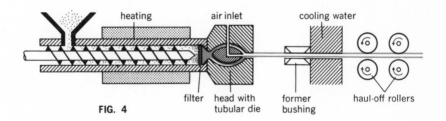

heating   air inlet   cooling water

filter   head with   former   haul-off rollers
          tubular die   bushing

FIG. 4

process is known as the male-mold (or positive-mold) method. The preheated sheet is placed over the master model and preformed. When the air is evacuated, the desired shape is obtained. These molding techniques are schematically illustrated in Figs. 8 and 9.

"Endless" products such as sections, sheet, strip and film are produced by extruders (Figs. 4 and 6). Extrusion consists in forcing a plastic material through a suitably shaped die to produce the desired cross-section shape. The extruding force may be exerted by a piston or ram (ram extrusion) or by a rotating screw (screw extrusion) which operates within a cylinder in which the material is heated and plasticized and from which it is then extruded through the die in a continuous flow. Different kinds of die are used to produce different products—e.g., blown film (formed by blow head for blown extrusions), sheet and strip (slot dies) and hollow and solid sections (circular dies). Wires and cables can be sheathed with plastics extruded from oblique heads. The extruded material is cooled and is taken off by means of suitable devices which are so designed as to prevent any subsequent deformation.

For the manufacture of large quantities of film or thin sheet, the so-called sheeting calender is employed (Fig. 7). The rough sheet from the two-roll mill is fed into the gap of the calender, a machine comprising a number of heatable parallel cylindrical rollers which rotate in opposite directions and spread out the plastics and stretch the material to the required thickness. The last roller smoothes the sheet or film thus produced. If the sheet is required to have a textured surface (e.g., to resemble wood graining), the final roller is provided with an appropriate embossing pattern; alternatively, the sheet may be reheated and then passed through an embossing calender. The calender is followed by one or more cooling drums. Finally, the finished sheet or film is reeled up.

Another field of application consists in coating a supporting material—e.g., textile fabrics, paper, cardboard, metals, various building materials—with plastics for the purpose of electrical insulation, protection against corrosion, protection against the action of moisture or chemicals, providing impermeability to gases and liquids, or increasing the mechanical strength. Coatings are applied to textiles, foil and other sheet materials by continuously operating spread-coating machines (Fig. 10). A coating knife, also known as a "doctor knife," ensures uniform spreading of the coating materials (in the form of solutions, emulsions or dispersions in water or an organic medium) on the supporting material, which is moved along by rollers. The coating is then dried. Alternatively, the coating applied to the supporting material may take the form of a film of plastic, in which case the process is called laminating.

Metal articles of complex shape can be coated with plastics by means of the whirl sintering process. The articles, heated to above the melting point of the plastics, are introduced into a fluidized bed of powdered plastics (a rising stream of air in which the powder particles are held in suspension), whereby a firmly adhering coating is deposited on the metal by sintering.

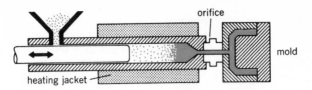

FIG. 5   INJECTION MOLDING WITH RAM EXTRUSION

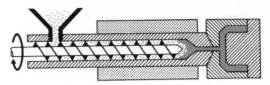

FIG. 6   INJECTION MOLDING WITH SCREW EXTRUSION

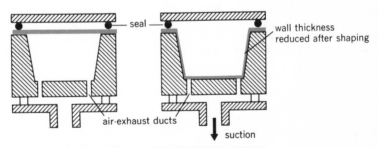

FIG. 7   SHEETING CALENDER

FIG. 10

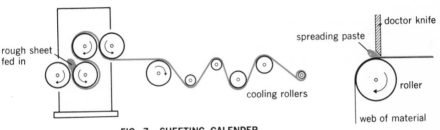

FIG. 8   VACUUM PROCESS: NEGATIVE-MOLD METHOD

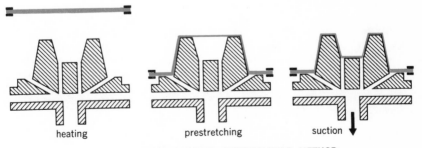

FIG. 9   VACUUM PROCESS: POSITIVE-MOLD METHOD

PROSPECTING FOR MINERALS

The increasing need for mineral raw materials of all kinds has led to the development of methods for the detection of deposits concealed underground or for ascertaining the extent of known deposits. For thousands of years man had to rely on features visible at the surface of the ground as indications of what might be hidden underneath: e.g., outcrops of mineral-bearing veins or strata, or the presence of oil or salt springs. In addition, he had recourse to the services of diviners. Indeed, the divining rod is sometimes still used in the search for underground water or other minerals.

Systematic geological mapping and a better understanding of how mineral deposits are formed (genesis) and of the history of the earth's crust (paleogeography, sedimentary rocks and the fossils they contain, the life conditions of the fossil organisms, differentiation of strata by means of "key fossils," etc.) have provided valuable clues in the quest for mineral wealth. By the beginning of the present century, applied geophysics had placed underground exploration on a scientific basis. Various physical principles are utilized in geophysical exploration: gravity, magnetism, electric equipotential, and the propagation of shock waves.

In gravimetric surveying, the deviations from the theoretical gravitational field (as predictable from the geographical latitude) of a locality is measured, the "milligal" being the unit of measurement of the gradient of gravity. This gradient corresponds to a change in gravitational acceleration by an amount equal to 0.001 cm/sec.^{2} Gravimetric surveyors use equipment comprising a pendulum or a weight suspended from a helical spring or quartz filament (Fig. 1). The magnetometric method makes use of a device called a local variometer for the detection of magnetic rock strata. In conjunction with photogeology and aerotopography, this method can be used for the exploration of inaccessible territories from aircraft carrying the necessary equipment. The most widely used geophysical method, however, is seismic exploration, which is employed especially in prospecting for oil or natural gas. High-explosive charges are electrically detonated in shallow boreholes located at grid points set out in the terrain. The "earthquake" shock waves generated by the explosions are reflected back from pronounced strata boundaries underground and reach the earth's surface after varying intervals of time, depending on the distance traveled by the waves. Here they are recorded by instruments called pickups. The electrical impulses from these are amplified and recorded on a moving film strip (provided with a millisecond time base) by means of oscillographs (Fig. 2). The curves obtained in this way are evaluated with reference to empirically known data as to depth, inclination, faults and uplifts of the strata. Information on strata at depths of up to about 4000 m (13,000 ft.) can be obtained in this way. Electrical exploration methods utilize the natural potential of mineral compounds. In this connection the differences in oxygen and metal ion concentration in the pore water contained in the relevant strata, which are associated with an oxidation and a reduction zone, are especially important. In consequence of the difference in concentration, galvanic contact potential differences are set up between separate points on the surface of the mineral deposit. A metallic ore deposit acts as an electric cell in which the ore constitutes the electrode material, while the pore water is the electrolyte whose concentration is subject to local variations (Fig. 3).

Quite often several of the above-mentioned methods are successively used on the same prospecting survey. It is important always to ascertain the "strike" and the "dip" of the deposit (Fig. 4). Before any mining operations are started, a deposit is usually further investigated by means of exploratory boreholes located at closely spaced grid points. The cores (specimens of rock or soil) obtained from the holes are subjected to petrographic examination.

62

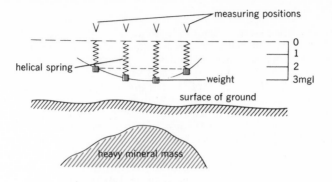

FIG. 1   GRAVIMETRIC EXPLORATION

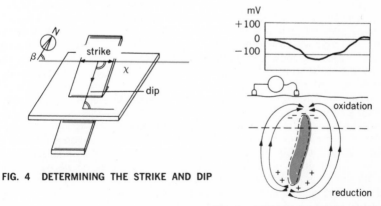

FIG. 2   SEISMIC EXPLORATION

FIG. 4   DETERMINING THE STRIKE AND DIP

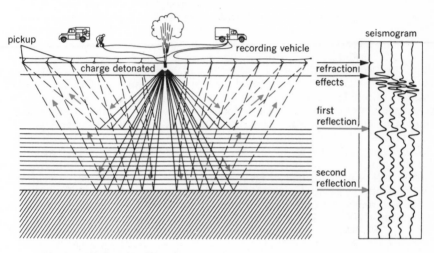

FIG. 3   NATURAL-POTENTIAL EXPLORATION

DEEP-DRILLING ENGINEERING

Deep drill holes (or boreholes) are employed in prospecting for minerals and —where these are gaseous or liquid in character—for bringing them to the surface. The high demands placed upon this branch of engineering (attainment of great depths in conjunction with rapid drilling progress) have caused the traditional percussion drilling techniques, with their various drawbacks, to be superseded by continuous rotary drilling. Depths of more than 8000 m (26,000 ft.) have been reached by this technique. The drill rod is suspended from a pulley block within a lattice steel tower (drilling derrick) which may be as much as 60 m (200 ft.) high and designed for loads of up to 600 tons. (For drilling operations on a more limited scale, a jackknife-type collapsible mast on a mobile chassis may more conveniently be used.) A square rod, which engages with a socket in a power-driven turntable, transmits the rotary motion to the drill rod and thus to the drill bit attached (by means of a screw thread) to the rod (Fig. 1). For drilling in hard rock a so-called roller bit is employed (Fig. 2), which comprises three toothed conical steel elements with welded-on hard-metal (tungsten carbide) tips. The drill rod is hollow; during drilling, a flushing liquid is pumped down through the rod and then rises to the surface through the annular space between the rod and the wall of the drill hole. This liquid, which consists of water to which certain substances (which are held in suspension) have been added to increase its specific gravity (1.2 to 1.6) and is referred to as "drilling mud," is kept in circulation by pumping. It serves to cool the drill bit and to keep the drill hole clean and free of obstructing matter; it washes away the debris produced by the drill and carries it to the surface. On emerging at the surface, the liquid is passed through vibrating screens to remove the debris. Additives to the liquid serve to consolidate the wall of the drill hole, preventing its collapse. Another function of the liquid is to counteract, by its high specific gravity, any gas or oil pressure that may build up in the hole.

With rotary drilling it is possible to obtain rock specimens (cores) for examination. For this purpose a core barrel provided with an annular bit (likewise tipped with hard metal) is used instead of an ordinary bit. A cylindrical specimen of rock is thus cut from the bottom of the hole and can be brought to the surface.

The drill rod is assembled from units up to 32 m (105 ft.) in length. On the working platform in the tower is the control panel for operating the machinery. Below and beside the platform are the electric motors (up to 2500 hp) for driving the winch, turntable, pumps, etc.

Another form of rotary drilling is carried out with the turbodrill. In this type of equipment the drill bit is rotated by an axial turbine power unit near the bottom of the hole, so that the long transmission distance for the rotary motion from the turntable through the drill rod is eliminated and a very considerable saving in power is effected. The turbodrill is driven by the circulating liquid with which the drill hole is flushed and which is pumped at pressures of up to 150 atm. (2200 lb./in.^{2}). Such drills rotate at speeds ranging from 400 to 900 rpm, and drilling progress rates of 10 to 20 m/hour (about 33 to 66 ft./hour) are attained, depending on the hardness of the rock encountered by the drill.

The exploration and exploitation of mineral deposits, especially those of petroleum and natural gas, in the relatively shallow coastal seas (continental shelf) have led to the extensive use of offshore drilling. The installations employed are designed for drilling to depths of about 6000 m (20,000 ft.). The essential thing is to provide a steady base for the drilling tower. There are various systems, illustrated in Figs. 3 and 4. Thus the drilling platform may be a floating barge, or be supported by a sinkable barge or pontoon resting on the seabed, or it may take the form of a spud-leg pontoon which is provided with vertical columns ("spuds") which are lowered to the seabed and serve as the legs of a huge table. So far, the maximum working depth of water for such installations has been 42 m (140 ft.).

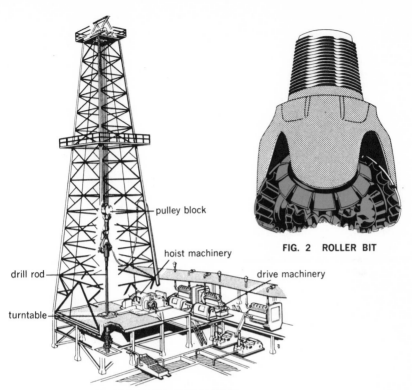

pulley block

hoist machinery

drive machinery

drill rod

turntable

FIG. 1   ROTARY-DRILLING INSTALLATION

FIG. 2   ROLLER BIT

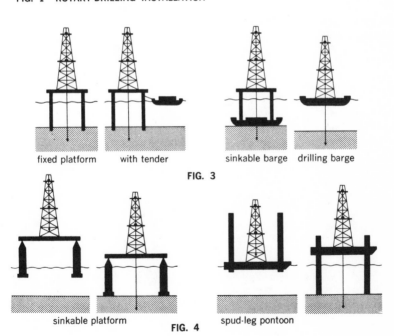

fixed platform   with tender   sinkable barge   drilling barge

FIG. 3

sinkable platform   spud-leg pontoon

FIG. 4

65

MINES AND MINING

The exploitation of mineral wealth dates from prehistoric times. For thousands of years the mining operations consisted mainly in the excavation of outcropping material or tunneling more or less horizontally into mountainsides rather than descending vertically into the ground. Mining from deep shafts became possible only when better control of rock pressure was achieved (reliable supports for tunnels, etc.), along with drainage, ventilation and the use of mechanical appliances. This progress has been closely bound up with the discovery of steam and electric power and the use of compressed air for driving tools and machinery.

Before a mining operation is undertaken, elaborate calculations are made, which relate not only to geological and technical aspects of working the mineral deposit, but also to commercial and many other matters: financing, prospects for marketing the newly mined mineral, location of the mine with regard to accessibility and transport facilities, electric-power supply, local population (availability of man-power), etc.

Although methods for the mining of mineral deposits may differ considerably from one another because of differences in geological conditions and location, all mines have certain features in common. Access to the deposit is gained either by means of a horizontal tunnel driven into a mountainside or by means of a vertical shaft. The deposit is divided into sections of suitable size and shape for mining. Only after this extensive preparatory work has been done does the actual mining commence. The various horizontal tunnels (called "levels" or "roads") extending from the shaft may be situated at vertical intervals of as much as 300 ft. and more in deposits extending to great depths (coal, potash); on the other hand, in the working of lodes or veins the levels may be at intervals of only about 100 ft. (ores, fluorite). Individual levels or sublevels are interconnected by blind shafts.

Every underground deposit is characterized by its "dip" (inclination of the strata in relation to the horizontal: the angle of dip is measured in the direction of maximum slope) and its "strike" (the horizontal direction at right angles to the dip). These two directions very largely determine the extent of the preliminary and preparatory operations (access shafts, subdivision into sections, working levels) and thus establishing the overall features of the mine.

The supports and lining to be installed in the shafts and tunnels will depend not only on the condition of the rock but also on the anticipated service life of the parts of the mine concerned. Thus, main haulage roads, which may have to last as long as the mine itself, are from the outset provided with stronger and more durable supports than, for example, headings which have to perform their function for only a relatively short time.

For every mineral deposit a systematically planned mining program must be prepared and adhered to. Although this may entail a certain amount of tunneling through unproductive rock (i.e., other than the actual mineral), the advantage of working according to a strictly applied system is that long straight haulage roads are obtained, which are advantageous with regard to mechanical handling and ventilation and are thus conducive to efficiency and safety in the mine. Especially with modern fast-moving or continuous means of conveyance (loco-hauled trains, belt conveyors), it is essential to eliminate curves as much as possible.

There are various methods of underground or deep mining for mineral deposits. The following may be used for metal ores, rock salt, etc. (methods more particularly applied in coal mining are dealt with on the next page):

(a) Stoping: levels are driven at fairly frequent intervals, and rooms ("stopes") are excavated to remove as much of the ore as possible; pillars of ore are left standing as supports; sometimes the rooms are filled up with stone waste, so that the pillars can then be mined.

(b) Caving: small sections of the ore are successively mined, and the overlying rock

(more)

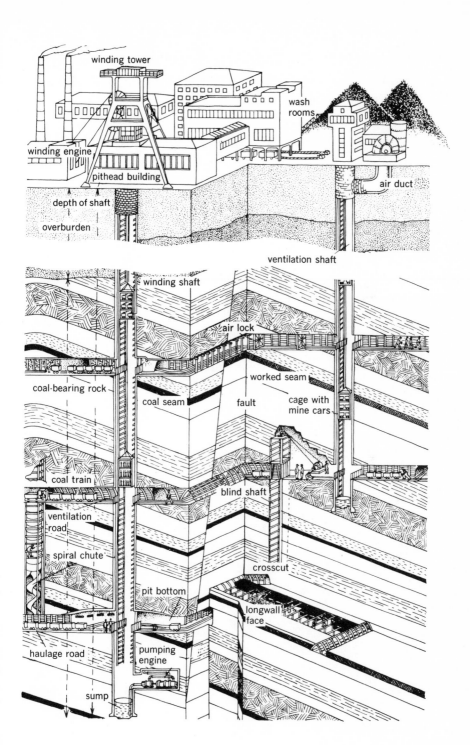

winding tower

winding engine

pithead building

depth of shaft

overburden

wash rooms

air duct

ventilation shaft

winding shaft

air lock

coal-bearing rock

worked seam

coal seam

fault

cage with mine cars

coal train

blind shaft

ventilation road

spiral chute

crosscut

pit bottom

longwall face

haulage road

pumping engine

sump

An open-cast copper mine near Bingham, Utah, USA
Photo USIS

is allowed to cave (i.e., collapse) each time; alternatively, portions of the ore may be undermined and allowed to cave.

(c) Pillaring: levels are driven in a rectangular pattern throughout the ore body, so that pillars are left standing.

Viewed as a whole, the working of a modern mine comprises a large number of interlinked operations which require careful advance planning, with adequate allowance for compensation and latitude at critical points in the system. Even the disposal of the large quantities of gangue (valueless minerals encountered in a lode or vein) presents a separate and often difficult problem, not least because of the manpower and cost it involves. In mining, wages account for something like 40 to 70% of the total prime cost of the mineral. It is therefore essential to utilize labor as carefully and efficiently as possible. At the same time the mining must, perhaps more than any other industry, concern itself with matters of safety to protect the men from accident and injury and to ensure smooth operation of the mine.

Besides its underground shafts and tunnels, every mine comprises extensive surface installations, including large buildings and other structures accommodating the mineral dressing and dispatch facilities, boiler and power-generating plant, winding gear, lamps and lighting equipment, dressing rooms and washrooms for the miners, stores, surveyors' office, management offices, etc. In addition, there are workshops that have to be fully equipped to carry out a wide variety of repairs to machinery and tools which are liable to suffer damage in the rough working conditions of the mine.

A well-established method for the mining of sedimentary deposits occurring in seams—coal, in particular—is known as "longwall working." In this method the coal is obtained from a continuous wall up to 200 yds. long, usually by removal of a web of coal about 5 ft. wide. In this way areas of several hundred acres are completely extracted. Two variants of the method are in use: in the "retreating" system, the roads are driven to the boundaries of the area to be mined, and the faces are worked retreating to the winding shaft; in the "advancing" system, the faces are opened up at the shaft and then advanced to the boundaries. In the United States the "room-and-pillar" method of coal mining is extensively used: roads are first made and from them rooms are driven; between 30 and 50% of the coal is mined in this way during the "first working"; subsequently the pillars of coal remaining are mined in the retreat, or "second working."

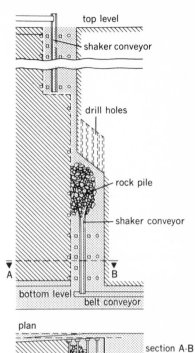

SEAM ROAD EXTENDING LONGITUDINALLY

top level

shaker conveyor

drill holes

rock pile

shaker conveyor

A   B

bottom level

belt conveyor

plan

section A-B

LONGWALL WORKING

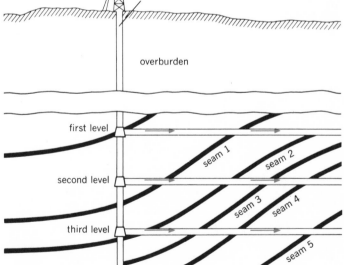

shaft

overburden

first level

seam 1

seam 2

second level

seam 3

seam 4

third level

seam 5

CROSSCUTS (AT RIGHT ANGLES TO STRIKE DIRECTION) OPEN UP A WHOLE GROUP OF SEAMS

73

Mechanical handling of coal coming out of the mine
Photo USIS

SHAFT SINKING

The construction of large and deep shafts is carried out by specialist firms, not by the mining company itself. In stable dry ground the excavation work is done by manual methods, with the aid of pneumatic picks and spades, augmented by drilling and blasting where hard rock is encountered. A multiblade grab or other mechanical device may be used for loading the loosened soil or rock into a heavy steel bucket, which is then winched to the surface (Fig. 1). Normally, shaft sinking and shaft lining proceed together, sinking being interrupted at intervals in order to line the newly sunk portion. Brick or concrete is used as a lining material, brickwork being more particularly used for round shafts in Britain and on the Continent.

In water-bearing strata the shaft lining is usually constructed from "tubbing," which consists of cast-steel segments (Fig. 3). The latter are about 1.3 m ($4\frac{1}{2}$ ft.) high and provided with ribs and flanges for strengthening and interconnecting them. They are bolted together to form rings which are installed one above the other, with lead gaskets in the joints, so that a closed watertight lining is obtained which is able to withstand pressure acting on it from the outside. The space between the lining and the wall of the excavation is filled with concrete. In loose water-bearing ground a shaft-boring technique may be employed, whereby it is possible to construct deep and wide shafts, e.g., up to about 500 m (1600 ft.) depth and 5 m (16 ft.) diameter. Boring is carried out with the aid of drilling mud, which helps to withstand the pressures (from the ground and from the underground water) which tend to collapse the shaft during construction. The cuttings from the drill are removed from the shaft bottom by suction through the hollow drill rod by means of special pneumatic pumps (mammoth pumps). The shaft lining, a cylinder fabricated from steel plate, is lowered into the shaft as excavation proceeds and is cemented in.

In the drop-shaft method of construction (Fig. 2), the brickwork or concrete lining is built up at the surface and sinks into the shaft—under its own weight, assisted by ballast loading—as excavation at the bottom proceeds. The bottom of the lining is provided with a cutting edge of steel to assist its penetration. Another technique that may be employed in water-bearing ground is cementation, which consists in sealing the cavities and fissures with "grout" (cement slurry—a fluid mixture of cement and water) which is injected under pressure through holes drilled into the strata concerned. The grout solidifies and stops the inflow of water, so that shaft sinking can be carried out in the ordinary way.

In soft waterlogged ground the so-called freezing process is sometimes employed. It is an expensive method because of the fairly elaborate equipment it requires (refrigerating plant, cooling tank, etc.). Pipes spaced about 1 yd. apart are sunk vertically into the ground at a distance of 2 or 3 yds. from the edge of the shaft to be excavated. Pipes of smaller diameter are installed concentrically inside these vertical pipes, and a freezing liquid (brine) is circulated through the inner pipes and flows back to the surface through the outer ones (Fig. 4). The temperature of the brine is about $-20°$ C. Ammonia is used as the refrigerating agent. A solid cylinder of frozen ground is gradually formed around each pipe, and when these frozen cylinders unite to form a solid ring round the ground to be excavated, shaft sinking can proceed in the usual way within the protection of this encircling "wall" of solidified ground. Sometimes the freezing is preceded by cement grouting if the ground contains wide fissures or cavities. When the shaft has been completed, freezing is stopped and the ground allowed to thaw. The pipes are then withdrawn. The freezing process has been used successfully for shafts up to about 600 m (2000 ft.) deep.

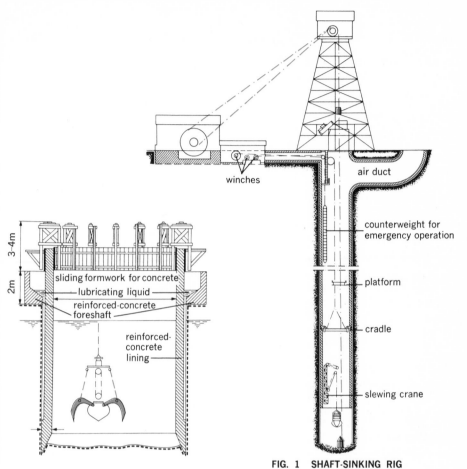

winches

air duct

counterweight for
emergency operation

platform

cradle

slewing crane

**FIG. 1   SHAFT-SINKING RIG
FOR A MAIN SHAFT**

3-4m

2m

sliding formwork for concrete

lubricating liquid

reinforced-concrete
foreshaft

reinforced-
concrete
lining

FIG. 2   DROP-SHAFT METHOD

**FIG. 3   SHAFT LINING WITH
CAST-STEEL SEGMENTS**

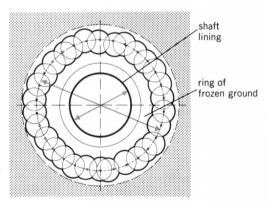

shaft
lining

ring of
frozen ground

FIG. 4   FREEZING PROCESS

77

WINDING

The term "winding" refers to the operations associated with hoisting the mined mineral to the surface. In modern mines winding is automated (controlled by electrical contacts) in conjunction with acoustic and visual signaling and various devices to ensure safety when men are being raised or lowered. All winding systems embody the counterweight principle, with two cages (or skips) moving in opposite directions—one ascending while the other descends. The basic features of the winding gear are the winding engine or motor, the headframe (usually a lattice steel structure, up to 200 ft. high, over the shaft), the winding rope and drum, the cages (or the skips), the intermediate gear whereby the latter are connected to the rope, and cage guides in the shaft.

Large-diameter shafts—of circular section up to 7 m (23 ft.) diameter—are normally equipped with two sets of winding gear; there are thus four hoistways (Fig. 1), in each of which a cage (or a skip) moves up and down. Steam-powered winding engines or electric winders are employed, the latter usually being driven by direct-current electric motors with Ward-Leonard control. Such motors may have power ratings of as high as 12,000 kW and hoist coal or other minerals at a rate of 10,000 tons per day from shafts 800 m (2600 ft.) in depth. The hoisting speed in deep shafts is about 22 m/sec. (70–75 ft./sec.) with a 30-ton payload. The winding operations are controlled by a device called a winding-speed regulator. It determines the hoisting speed in relation to the distance traveled and more particularly limits the acceleration of ascent and descent. In addition, every winding system includes a depth indicator, which consists essentially of a screw spindle along which a nut travels; the position of the nut on the spindle indicates the position of the cage in the shaft. This device is linked to an overwind-prevention device, which actuates a second brake (drop-weight brake) if the cage ascends too high and the counter-balancing cage consequently descends too low. In the event of overwinding, the cage is slowed down and braked by such means as thickening the cage-guide rods in the top part of the headframe.

Winding ropes are composed of several strands which in turn consist of cold-drawn steel wires of 2.5 mm (0.1 in.) diameter, with a tensile strength of 200 kg/mm^2 (127 tons/in.^{2}) (Fig. 4). Such ropes may be as much as 100 mm (4 in.) thick and have breaking loads of around 700 tons.

The cages that are raised and lowered in the shaft are multideck structures into which the tubs or mine cars are pushed and from which they are removed by mechanical means. The cages are also used for raising and lowering the miners. In Britain, cage winding is still predominant in coal mining. However, skip winding is progressively being introduced; it is already extensively used in the United States and in various Continental countries. A skip is a guided steel or aluminum-alloy box (Fig. 5) which is automatically filled at the bottom of the shaft and automatically discharged when it has been hoisted aboveground. The advantage of skip winding is that a skip can carry a relatively larger payload than a cage with tubs or cars; the proportion of payload to total load can be raised by nearly 40% by substituting skip for cage winding, and loading and unloading are faster. In the main, there are two systems of winding gear: drum winding and Koepe winding. Of these, drum winding is the more widely employed. The drum may be variously shaped: cylindrical, conical, cylindroconical. The object of the conical shape (Fig. 3) is to equalize the driving torque by using a smaller diameter of drum when exerting maximum rope pull to lift and accelerate the cage (or the skip). In Germany and Holland the Koepe system (Fig. 2) is generally preferred. In this system the massive drum is replaced by a wheel (pulley) with one peripheral groove. A single winding rope lies in this groove, and all controlling forces transmitted through the rope depend on the friction of the rope in the groove. The cages (or the skips) are suspended one on each end of the rope, which passes over the Koepe wheel. The system offers certain advantages and is more particularly suitable for winding heavy loads from deep levels.

78

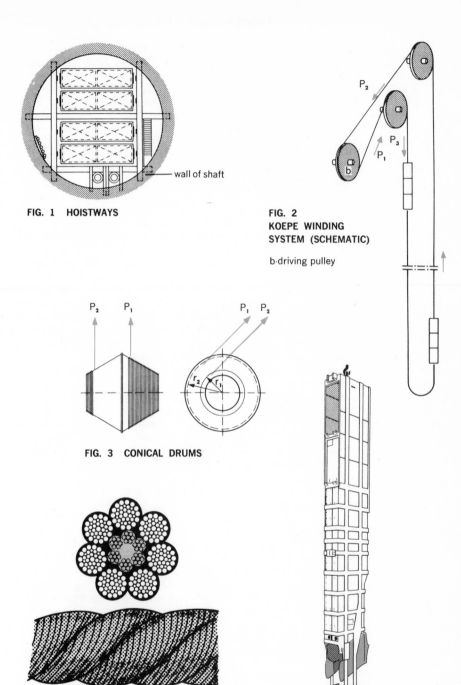

FIG. 1   HOISTWAYS

— wall of shaft

FIG. 2
KOEPE WINDING
SYSTEM (SCHEMATIC)

b-driving pulley

FIG. 3   CONICAL DRUMS

FIG. 4   WINDING ROPE

FIG. 5   SKIP

79

MINE VENTILATION

Ventilation in a mine serves three main purposes: to provide fresh air for respiration by the miners, to dilute any noxious gases that may be formed underground (including the fumes from the explosives used in blasting), and to lower natural heat of the rock. The underground temperature rises with increasing depth—on an average, about 1° C for every 30 m (100 ft.)—so that the deeper the mine, the hotter it generally is. In simple horizontal-tunnel mining it is usually sufficient to rely on natural ventilation by utilizing the difference in air pressure associated with the difference in level between two openings—the mine entrance and the top of a ventilation shaft (chimney effect, Fig. 1). Depending on the external temperatures prevailing at different times of the year, the direction of flow of the draft is subject to change. Diffusion (as distinct from draft) also plays some part in changing the air in a tunnel; thus, a large-diameter tunnel can be driven to a distance of several hundred feet without requiring artificial ventilation. The exhaust air from pneumatic tools is also helpful in promoting air circulation.

In deep mining it is often necessary to use fans, sometimes of very large size. In large coal mines fresh air may have to be drawn in at a rate of 20,000 m³ (700,000 ft.³) per minute. These fans are installed at the air-extraction shafts at the edge of the mined area—the main winding shaft or shafts, through which the fresh air is drawn in, being located in the central part of this area. With every method of ventilation the above-mentioned chimney effect is utilized as fully as possible: the fresh air descends by gravity to the lowest levels of the mine and is heated by the natural heat of the rock, so that it becomes specifically lighter and tends to rise. The rising air makes its way by various paths to the suction zone of the main extraction way or shaft, in which suction pressures up to 400 mm (17 in.) water gauge are maintained. Distribution of the fresh air over the various levels, main roadways, crosscuts, rooms and workings is assisted by ventilation doors (designed as air locks), stoppings, air crossings and other devices (Figs. 2 and 3).

Planning of a mine-ventilation system includes the preparation of so-called air-flow sheets—diagrams comprising data on airflow conditions. These diagrams are prepared for each section and for the mine as a whole, the data being checked against measurements of the actual flow underground. For reasons of safety the main flow has to be split up into the largest possible number of circulating currents, and it is essential to prevent "short circuits"—circumstances causing the air to take a shortcut and thus bypass certain parts of the mine. Parts that are not accessible to natural ventilation have to be provided with auxiliary ventilation. For this purpose air is piped to those parts through large-diameter ducts through which it is impelled by powerful fans. This auxiliary ventilation constitutes a separate system whose proper functioning has to be supervised and controlled with considerable care. It may operate by suction or by pressure (blowing) or a combination of both (Fig. 4).

Particularly in deep and hot mines—e.g., in South African gold mining—air conditioning (as distinct from mere ventilation) may be used to maintain the atmosphere of the workings at suitable temperature and humidity for men to work in. Because of the high cost involved, it is seldom used, however.

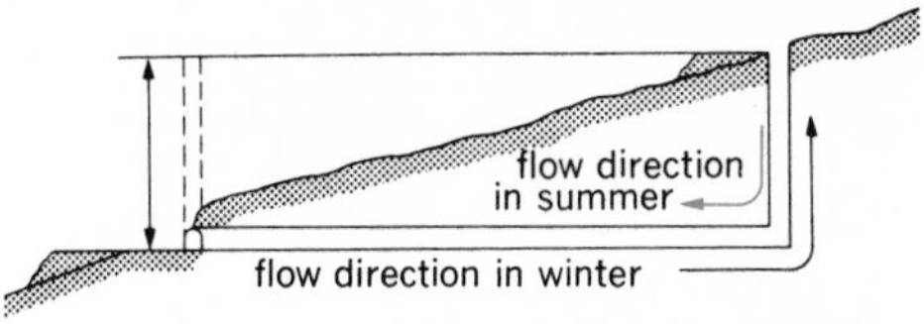

flow direction
in summer
flow direction in winter

FIG. 1   DRIFT MINE WITH VENTILATION SHAFT

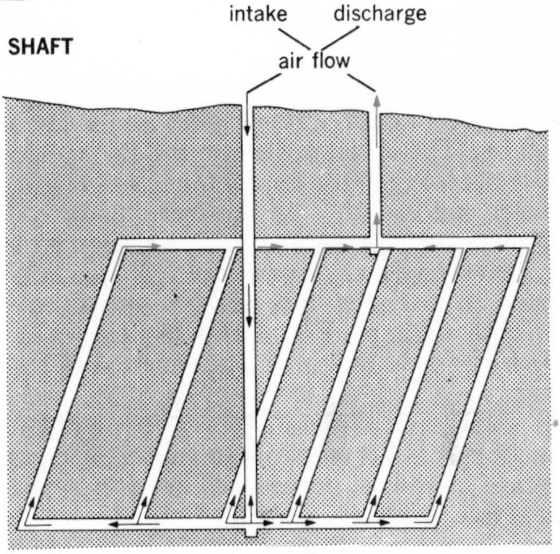

intake   discharge

air flow

FIG. 2   VENTILATING A MINE

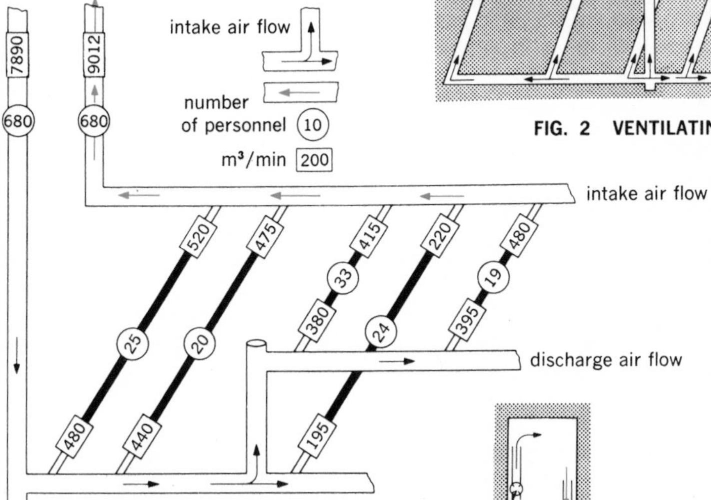

intake air flow

number
of personnel ⑩

m³/min ⟨200⟩

7890

9012

⟨680⟩   ⟨680⟩

intake air flow

⟨520⟩ ⟨475⟩   ⟨415⟩   ⟨220⟩   ⟨480⟩

⟨33⟩   ⟨19⟩

⟨380⟩   ⟨395⟩

⟨25⟩   ⟨20⟩   ⟨24⟩

discharge air flow

⟨480⟩   ⟨440⟩   ⟨195⟩

**FIG. 3   AIRFLOW SHEET FOR
A COAL MINE**

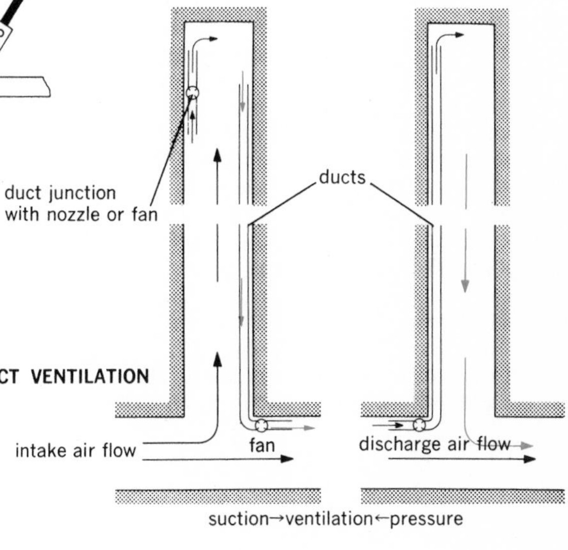

duct junction
with nozzle or fan

ducts

FIG. 4   DUCT VENTILATION

intake air flow ⟶   fan   discharge air flow ⟶

suction→ventilation←pressure

81

For every ton of coal removed from the working face, anything up to 200 m^3 (7000 ft.^{3}) of mine gas is released; the average amount in the Ruhr coal-mining district is 30 m^3 (about 1000 ft.^{3}). This gas consists of hydrocarbons, chiefly methane (CH$_4$), and is known as firedamp, more particularly when it occurs in an explosive mixture with air (when the gas concentration in the air is between 4.5 and 14.5%). Methane is a colorless, odorless and tasteless gas. Firedamp explosions have been the cause of many catastrophes and a vast number of deaths in the history of coal mining. The initial explosion is liable to ignite the cloud of coal dust that the blast disperses. When the air contains between 70 and 1000 grams of coal dust per cubic meter, it constitutes an explosive mixture. A coal-dust explosion produces carbon monoxide (CO), which is a serious danger to human life because of its toxicity.

Accordingly, the main object of research, supervision and legislation relating to safety in coal mines is to develop and improve the precautions against the occurrence of such mishaps. Essentially, the aim is to eliminate all possibility of ignition of such explosive mixtures. The emission of gas from the coal is a natural phenomenon associated with the constitution of the coal and adjacent strata (Fig. 1), and except in some rare circumstances where methane gas can be removed in advance by suction, it is not possible to reduce or effectively control this emission. The application of special procedures in extracting the coal, high speed of advance at the coal face, complete sealing off of old workings by suitable stowing (backfilling), etc., may have a favorable effect. It nevertheless remains essential to conform closely to safety regulations and to take all manner of technical precautions to prevent the occurrence of any spark or flame that might set off an explosion, including a strict ban on smoking. There remain potential sources of ignition in the use of explosives and electricity underground. Frictional heating of machinery and spontaneous-combustion phenomena, which may arise under certain conditions, are also hazards. An effective measure consists in keeping the workings supplied with fresh air in quantities large enough to ensure that the mine-gas concentration will at all times remain below the explosive level. The first important development in overcoming the firedamp menace was the invention of the safety lamp by Davey in 1816. The lamp, which burns a liquid fuel, is provided with an enclosure of metal-wire gauze above the glass (Fig. 2). If the air surrounding the lamp contains mine gas, the flame of the lamp will ignite the gas, but the latter will burn only inside the gauze enclosure; the flame will not ignite the gas all round the lamp. It is the high thermal conductivity of the gauze that arrests flame propagation. The lamp is used today as a detector for gas, which burns with a characteristic flame called a "gas cap" that appears when the flame in the lamp is lowered. The length of the gas cap provides an indication of the percentage of gas in the air (Fig. 3). A countermeasure against the formation of highly inflammable and therefore explosive coal-dust clouds consists in "dusting": i.e., specified quantities of stone dust (finely pulverized limestone or other nonsiliceous stone) are deposited throughout the mine, more particularly just before blasting is to take place. The cloud of dust thrown up by the explosion is rendered nonflammable by the presence of the stone dust. Stone dust is also used as a means of arresting the propagation of explosions. For this purpose a device called a stone-dust barrier (Fig. 4) is installed at "strategic" points in the mine. It may take the form of a light tilting platform on which a quantity of stone dust is placed. In the event of an explosion in the vicinity, the dust is flung off and forms a dense cloud which absorbs some of the energy of the blast and also exercises a cooling action which smothers the flame.

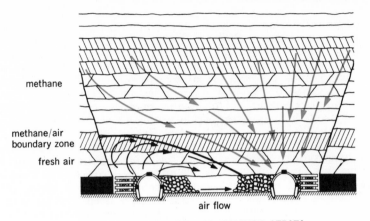

methane

methane/air
boundary zone

fresh air

air flow

FIG. 1 FLOW OF MINE GAS THROUGH STRATA

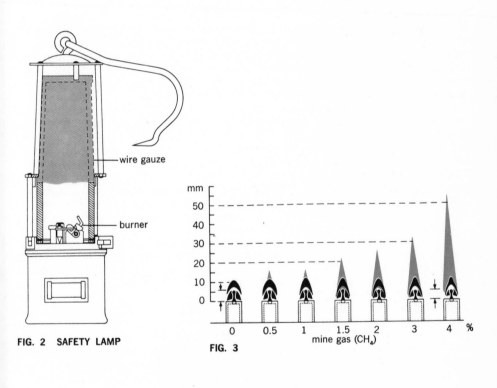

wire gauze

burner

FIG. 2 SAFETY LAMP

mm

50
40
30
20
10
0

0   0.5   1   1.5   2   3   4   %
mine gas (CH$_4$)

FIG. 3

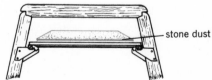

stone dust

FIG. 4 STONE-DUST BARRIER

83

MECHANIZATION AND AUTOMATION IN MINING

Because of the high proportion of wages in the cost of production, mechanization is more necessary in mining than in almost any other industry. On the other hand, because of the often difficult conditions in which the product—the mineral mined underground—must be obtained, the scope for mechanization of the actual "production" process is limited. Among the earliest developments in mine mechanization was the introduction of locomotives to replace manual or pony haulage. In present-day mining the operations of loading the mine cars, placing them in the cage at the winding shaft, discharging the cars at the surface, etc., are all performed automatically.

Underground haulage in mine cars and the like has in part been replaced by continuous conveying systems of various kinds (belt conveyors, steel-apron conveyors, chain conveyors, etc.), which can handle up to 600 or 700 tons of material per hour in the horizontal direction and at gradients up to about 12 degrees. Coordination of the various mechanical handling appliances is ensured by control centers operating with automatic interlocking optical and acoustic signaling systems in conjunction with measuring and monitoring equipment, overall control being assisted by remote indication (at the surface) of measured quantities, electronic data processing by computers, and a variety of other up-to-date aids.

Underground drilling is now performed by large crawler-mounted power drills equipped with high-alloy-steel- or tungsten carbide-tipped tools. These tools have swivel mountings and hydraulic feed mechanisms. They can drill blastholes at rates of up to 30 m (100 ft.) per minute. Blasting techniques too have been improved in recent years and are safer and more efficient.

Coal cutters are used to get most of the coal mined by longwall or other systems in Britain. A typical machine for longwall work has a jib provided with a cutting chain fitted with tungsten carbide-tipped cutter picks. The machine, which makes an approximately 5 ft.-deep horizontal cut, rests on the floor and hauls itself along by winding a wire rope on a drum.

Loaders and cutter-loading machines of American design were introduced into Britain chiefly during and after the Second World War. The majority of loaders employed in present-day mining are of two main types: (1) shovels which pick up and empty in sequence; (2) gathering machines with integral conveyors in continuous motion. Shovel-type mobile loaders have been developed since about 1925 and are now widely used in certain types of mining—e.g., ironstone mining. Some loading machines are illustrated in Figs. 1–3.

Mechanization has also been applied to the construction of the supports for underground workings. For example, a special type of anchor bolt for roof lagging is secured in a drilled hole by means of a screw thread and nut which expands the two halves of a tapered split bushing, so that the bolt is gripped firmly in the hole (Fig. 4). A more elaborate and important device is the fully mechanized remote-controlled hydraulic chock (Fig. 5), which is used to provide temporary support in situations where stability is very important, more particularly at the working face. It comprises four columns (hydraulic props) which are set at the corners of a steel base and are surmounted by a canopy or headframe. The device is advanced to a fresh position by means of a hydraulic cylinder whose movements, like those of the four props, are controlled by a system of valves.

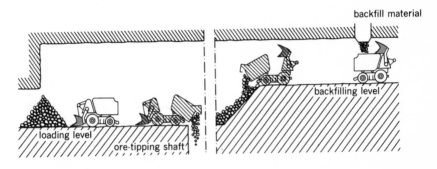

FIG. 1 SCRAPER-LOADER

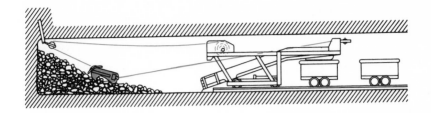

backfill material

backfilling level

loading level

ore-tipping shaft

FIG. 2 MOBILE SHOVEL LOADER

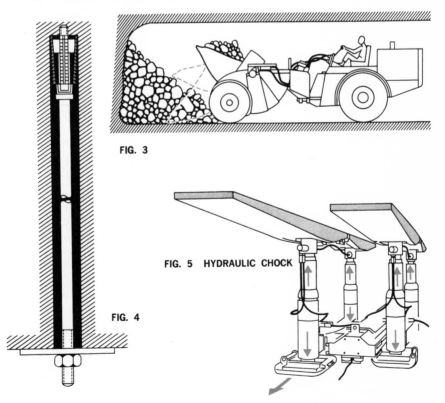

FIG. 3

FIG. 5 HYDRAULIC CHOCK

FIG. 4

85

PREPARATION OF ORES

Metalliferous ores straight from the mine are seldom directly suited for metal smelting. Quite often their metal content is too low (e.g., only 0.8% copper or 5% lead) for processing in the furnace, or they may be composed of minerals containing different metals requiring different kinds of metallurgical treatment. For these reasons, most ores have to undergo various preparatory processes, collectively referred to as "dressing," for the removal or separation of waste matter or other minerals, so that the concentration of the desired mineral is increased. The principal mineral-dressing processes are presented systematically on page 87. Some of the processes used more particularly in ore dressing are sorting (by hand); comminution (crushing and grinding); sizing (by screening); classifying (e.g., the grading of finely divided material by rates of settling); separation (e.g., by magnetism, electrical conductivity, specific gravity, etc.).

The preparation plants are usually located at the mines, so that only the processed ore, free of waste matter, has to be transported to the smelting works. In most cases preparation starts with crushing and grinding (Fig. 1). The degree of comminution (size reduction) to be applied will depend on the size of the ore lumps and on the requirements of the subsequent treatment to be applied. Sizing and classifying— i.e., grading the comminuted material according to particle size—are important operations in ore dressing. To relieve the crushing and grinding machines of unnecessary load, particles that have been sufficiently reduced in size are removed by screening (Fig. 5). Sizing of relatively coarse particles can most efficiently be performed by screening, and screens of many kinds are used for the purpose. Small particles (below about 1 mm in size) can usually be more suitably sized by classification based on different rates of settling of different particle sizes in water. For example, the Hardinge countercurrent classifier (Fig. 6) is a slowly rotating drum on the inner surface of which are located spiral flanges. As the classifier rotates, the coarser particles are settled out, moved forward by the spiral flanges, and repeatedly turned over in a forward motion, releasing any finely divided material mixed with them.

It is not possible, within the scope of this article, to describe all the many processes and types of equipment employed in the preparation of metalliferous ores. However, three important methods of treatment will be dealt with.

In *wet-mill concentration* the differences in specific gravity of different minerals are utilized for separating them. The metalliferous ores—sulphides and oxides— are as a rule specifically heavier than the waste material. Separation of the ore from the waste (or separation of different ores) may be effected in a settling classifier with the aid of water in motion, the underlying principle being that the differences in specific gravity are associated with different rates of settlement of the particles (Figs. 2 and 7).

Coarser particles, ranging in size from about 0.5 to 30 mm, can be settled out in a machine called a jig in which a horizontal stream of water is subjected to a rhythmical up-and-down motion. Finer-grained materials, approx. 0.3 to 0.5 mm in size, may be treated on a table concentrator—a slightly inclined plate on which the lighter material is separated from the heavier by a thin, shallow stream of water. This hydromechanical separating action may be augmented by the action of gravity developed by oscillating or jolting motions applied to the table (shaking and bumping tables, Fig. 4). These concentration processes are referred to as "tabling."

(more)

MINERAL DRESSING
(Survey of methods and processes for the preparation of minerals*)

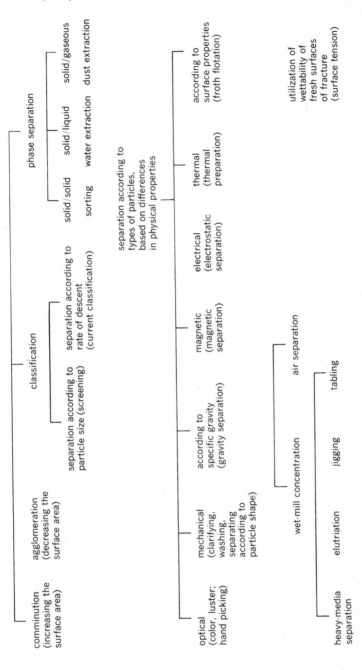

* according to Prof. Dr.-Ing. Gründer

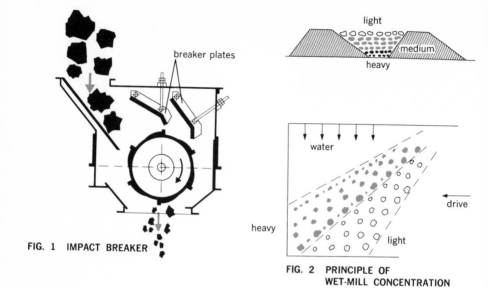

breaker plates

light

medium

heavy

water

heavy

drive

light

FIG. 1 IMPACT BREAKER

**FIG. 2 PRINCIPLE OF
WET-MILL CONCENTRATION**

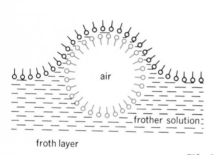

air

froth layer

frother solution

FIG. 3

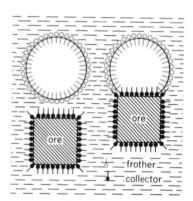

ore

ore

frother

collector

attachment of air bubble
to ore particle

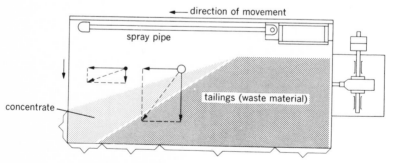

direction of movement

spray pipe

concentrate

tailings (waste material)

FIG. 4 SHAKING TABLE

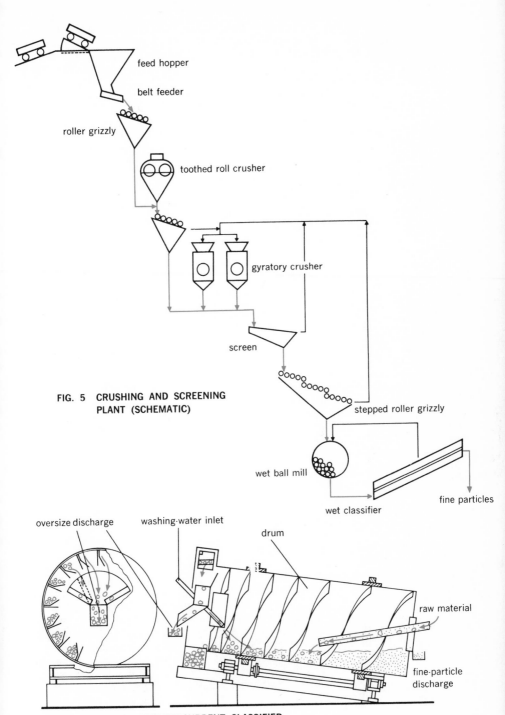

feed hopper

belt feeder

roller grizzly

toothed roll crusher

gyratory crusher

screen

**FIG. 5 CRUSHING AND SCREENING
PLANT (SCHEMATIC)**

stepped roller grizzly

wet ball mill

wet classifier

fine particles

oversize discharge

washing-water inlet

drum

raw material

fine-particle
discharge

FIG. 6 HARDINGE COUNTERCURRENT CLASSIFIER

Flotation is an important and widely used separation process which is based on the fact that some of the components in the comminuted minerals are wettable (hydrophilic), whereas others are water-repellent (hydrophobic). See Figs. 3 and 8. The hydrophobic particles have an ability to hold air bubbles by surface action, the nature of the film on the outside of the particles being the controlling factor. Finely divided air which is introduced into the "pulp," the mixture of solids and water in which flotation is performed, adheres in the form of bubbles to these particles, more particularly the metalliferous components of the pulp, and causes them to rise to the surface. Here they collect in a mass of froth and are removed by a skimmer device. The hydrophilic components remain behind in the pulp. As a rule, these are the worthless minerals (gangue), which are removed as tailings from the flotation machine.

The sulphides of heavy metals are readily floatable, and flotation is therefore an important method for the concentrating of copper, lead and zinc ores. A further development has been the selective flotation of two or more useful minerals, particularly the ores of different metals, which can thus be collected as separated "concentrates." This principle is, for example, applied to the preparation of sulphidic lead-zinc ores.

The floatability of minerals can be controlled by certain chemical additives called flotation agents. These are of various kinds:

Frothers, whose function is to produce froth by combining the air bubbles (introduced into the pulp by stirring or by the injection of compressed air) into a stable froth which will buoy up the ore particles. Oils and allied substances are used as frothers.

Collectors are substances that increase the water repellency and make the ore particularly receptive to the attachment of air bubbles. Collectors usually consist of synthetic organic compounds.

Other flotation agents help to regulate the process. So-called depressors can make hydrophobic minerals temporarily hydrophilic and can in this way help in the selective separation of one mineral from another by depressing one, thereby inhibiting its flotation. The "depressed" mineral can subsequently be made hydrophobic again by an activating agent. The various agents for regulating the flotation process in this manner are inorganic compounds, mostly salts.

Magnetic separation: If a comminuted and classified ore is brought into a magnetic field, the magnetic components (generally the useful metalliferous ore) can be extracted and thus separated from the nonmagnetic residual material. The treatment is carried out with the aid of magnetic separators, of which there are many kinds. A drum separator is illustrated in Fig. 9. This method of separation plays an important part, for example, in the concentrating of certain iron and manganese ores. Those substances which are attracted by a magnetic field are called paramagnetic. These are subdivided into strongly magnetic (ferromagnetic) and weakly magnetic substances. Various techniques have been devised for the separation of both categories of materials. In general, magnetic fields of greater intensity (high-intensity magnetic separators) have to be employed for dealing with weakly magnetic ores. In both categories "wet" and "dry" processes are employed, depending on whether or not water is used as an aid in the process. The magnetic properties of certain ferrous minerals can be enhanced by suitable preliminary heat treatment. For instance, in the case of siderite (a particular kind of iron ore, which is a carbonate— $FeCO_3$) the carbon dioxide can be expelled by heating the ore in a kiln. As a result, the carbonate is converted into the strongly magnetic compound named ferroso-ferric oxide (Fe_3O_4), which can readily be separated by magnetic action.

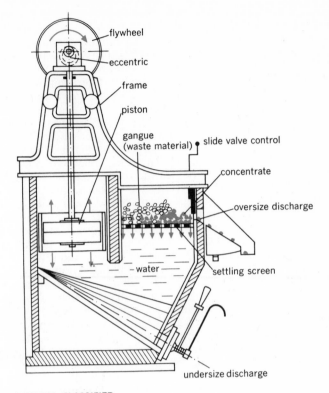

FIG. 7   SETTLING CLASSIFIER

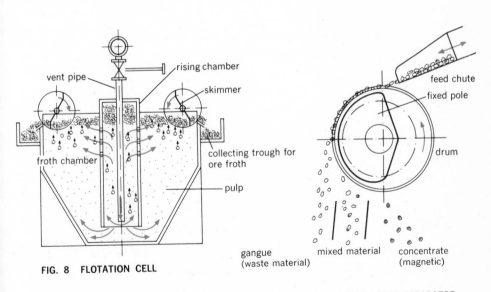

FIG. 8   FLOTATION CELL

FIG. 9   ELECTROMAGNETIC DRUM SEPARATOR

LEAD

The lead ore most commonly mined is galena, which is the sulphide of lead (PbS). It occurs intimately mixed with other metalliferous minerals, such as sphalerite (zinc sulphide), copper pyrites and iron pyrites. The ore has to be concentrated, e.g., by flotation (see page 91), in order to separate the galena from the sphalerite and other minerals that may be present. Subsequent treatment of the concentrate thus obtained consists in roasting followed by reduction in a vertical-shaft furnace, a form of blast furnace. Roasting is usually performed by heating the lead ores, blended with suitable fluxing minerals, on a traveling endless grate through which air is sucked. In this way the material is sintered—converted into lumps (called sinter) which are then mixed with coke and charged into the shaft furnace (Fig. 2). Air is forced into the furnace at the bottom. The coke, which serves as fuel and reducing agent, reacts with the sinter to reduce the oxides and yield liquid lead, which is, however, contaminated with other metals—silver, copper, zinc, tin, antimony, bismuth, arsenic, etc. The nonreduced components form a liquid slag which floats on the liquid metal. Preparing the charge and operating the furnace call for great skill. In particular, the charge must contain the correct proportions of iron, lime and silica to produce a liquid slag that can readily be separated from the metal; it is also essential to maintain the proper balance of coke and sinter.

When the impure liquid lead (known as "bullion") cools, some of the impurities, especially copper, separate out as drosses, which are further processed to extract the copper. Further removal of the copper may be effected by treatment of the bullion with sulphur. Antimony, tin and arsenic are removed by elective oxidation in a reverberatory furnace or by treatment of the bullion with chemical reagents to separate out these metals in the form of salt-type compounds. Desilverizing of the liquid lead is achieved by adding metallic zinc and raising the temperature sufficiently to dissolve it. On cooling, the zinc forms a dross or crust which contains nearly all the silver and other metallic impurities. The dross is skimmed off, and the silver is recovered from it in a separate process. The zinc is distilled off and used over and over again (Fig. 3). After desilverizing, the lead may have to be debismuthized, which is done by a process somewhat like desilverizing but using calcium and magnesium instead of zinc to form a dross with the bismuth.

An alternative method of treating the impure bullion is by electrolytic refining. The bullion is cast into plates which serve as anodes in electrolytic tanks. The electric current causes the lead at the anode to dissolve, and pure lead is deposited at the cathode. All these refining processes can produce pig lead of very high purity (99.999%!).

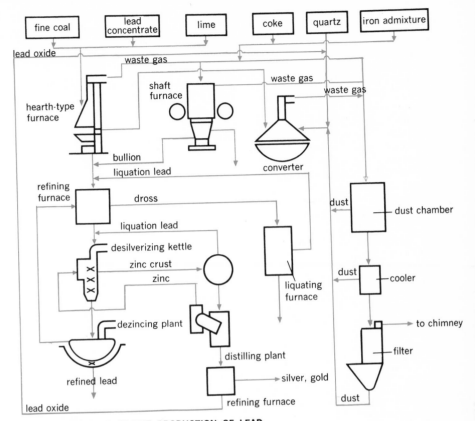

FIG. 1 PROCESSES IN THE PRODUCTION OF LEAD

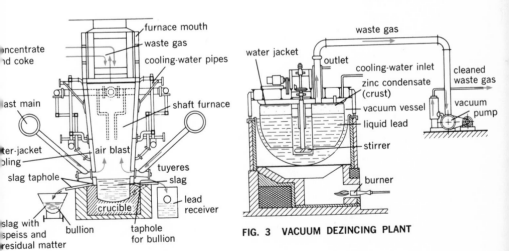

FIG. 2 SHAFT FURNACE FOR LEAD SMELTING

FIG. 3 VACUUM DEZINCING PLANT

COPPER

Most copper is obtained from sulphide ores. These are found admixed with large quantities of gangue (worthless material), and the initial content of copper may be very low (1 or 2%, sometimes only 0.7%). A concentrate containing 15 to 35% copper is produced by flotation (see page 91). For the purpose of eliminating some of the sulphur and certain impurities, the concentrate is usually roasted before smelting. Roasting is carried out in multiple-hearth furnaces, in which oxidizing reactions take place: sulphur is eliminated as the dioxide; metallic sulphides (iron and some copper) remain behind as oxides. The resulting mixture, known as calcine, contains the sulphides of iron and copper, together with gangue material and impurities. The next step consists in producing a molten artificial sulphide of copper and iron, known as matte, containing all the copper and the desired amount of iron. The smelting operation for producing the matte is generally carried out in a reverberatory furnace (Fig. 2), fired with oil, natural gas or pulverized coal. The charge is fed through the roof, and the molten material collects in a pool at the bottom. Slag, which rises to the top, is tapped off. The matte collects at the bottom of the pool and is likewise discharged through a taphole. The molten matte is fed to a converter (Fig. 3) in which the iron and sulphur are removed by oxidation, which is effected by blowing air through the molten mass and is based on the fact that copper has a lower affinity for oxygen than has iron or sulphur. The reactions in the converter occur in several stages. First the iron oxidizes and forms a slag with silica, which has been added to the charge; this slag is tapped off, the copper then being present as the sulphide. Further oxidation results in the formation of metallic copper with a small amount of copper oxide and other impurities. The converter in which the process is performed is a large revolving refractory-lined drum.

The copper obtained in the converter is subjected to further refining treatment, which consists in fire refining (in furnaces) followed by electrolytic refining. Fire refining is done in small reverberatory furnaces or in revolving furnaces similar to the copper converter. Air is blown through the molten material to oxidize all impurities; the oxides rise to the surface and are skimmed off. Then follows a reduction process which is performed by forcing the ends of green logs into the molten metal to form highly reducing gases. The copper obtained as a result of this treatment is called tough pitch. For further refining, it is cast into anodes for electrolytic refining cells (Fig. 4). The system most widely used is known as the multiple system, comprising separate anodes and cathodes; the latter consist of thin sheets of high-purity copper (so-called starting sheets). When an electric current is passed through the cells, copper is dissolved from the anodes and is deposited in a very pure form on the cathodes. When these have grown to a thickness of about $\frac{1}{2}$ inch they are replaced by fresh starting sheets. About four starting sheets are used for each anode, until the latter has been completely consumed. An electrolytic refinery may comprise hundreds of refining cells, each using perhaps thirty or more anodes. The cathodes are melted down and cast into suitable shapes for market.

Ore treatment may, alternatively, be carried out by hydrometallurgical processes in which the ore is treated with a solvent that dissolves the copper and leaves the undesirable material unaffected. This principle is applied more particularly to the oxide ores of copper, or to sulphide ores after suitable roasting, sulphuric acid being used as the leaching solvent. Elaborate washing, filtration and purification of the leach solution are associated treatments. The copper is recovered from the solution by precipitation (displacement of copper from the copper sulphate by metallic iron that is added to the solution) or by electrolysis (using insoluble anodes and copper cathodes, which are high-purity starting sheets).

94

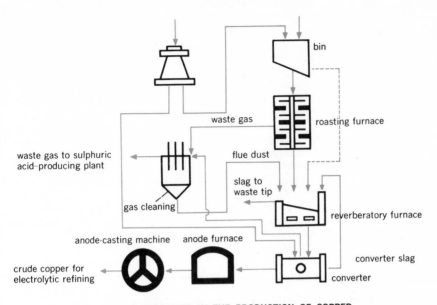

bin

waste gas

roasting furnace

waste gas to sulphuric
acid-producing plant

flue dust

slag to
waste tip

gas cleaning

reverberatory furnace

anode-casting machine   anode furnace

converter slag

crude copper for
electrolytic refining

converter

FIG. 1   PROCESSES IN THE PRODUCTION OF COPPER

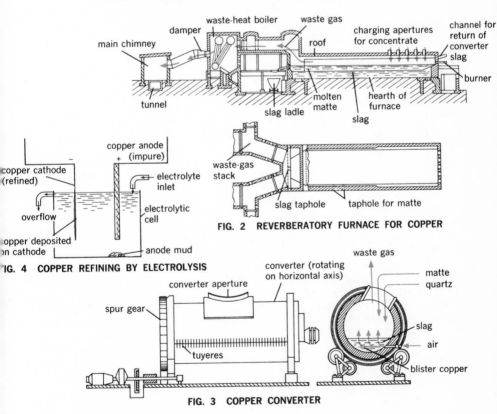

waste-heat boiler   waste gas

damper   charging apertures   channel for
                                          for concentrate   return of
main chimney   roof   converter
                                                                slag

                                                                burner

tunnel   molten   hearth of
            slag ladle   matte   furnace
                                                     slag

FIG. 2   REVERBERATORY FURNACE FOR COPPER

copper anode
+ (impure)

copper cathode   waste-gas
(refined)   electrolyte   stack
                   inlet

overflow   electrolytic
                   cell
                              slag taphole   taphole for matte

copper deposited
on cathode   anode mud   FIG. 2   REVERBERATORY FURNACE FOR COPPER

FIG. 4   COPPER REFINING BY ELECTROLYSIS

waste gas

converter (rotating
on horizontal axis)   matte
converter aperture   quartz

spur gear   slag

                             air
tuyeres
                             blister copper

FIG. 3   COPPER CONVERTER

95

ZINC

The chief ore of zinc is sphalerite (ZnS), also known as zinc blende, which usually occurs in association with galena (PbS) and smaller quantities of other metallic sulphides. Concentrates with more than 50% zinc are produced by flotation (see page 91). From these the zinc can be obtained by various thermal reduction processes or by leaching and electrolysis. In every case the process must be preceded by complete roasting to convert zinc sulphide into zinc oxide and thereby make it leachable or reducible with carbon. From low-grade zinc ores and from intermediate products containing zinc, such as flue dusts from lead and copper smelting, it is possible to obtain zinc oxide by the so-called rotary process: the material containing zinc is heated under reducing conditions in a long rotary kiln (a tubular cylindrical furnace which is inclined and revolves on its longitudinal axis; the raw material is fed in at the upper end and gradually makes its way down to the lower end, acquiring a progressively higher temperature on the way). In the kiln the zinc is volatilized; in the upper part the zinc vapor is burned to zinc oxide, which leaves the kiln along with waste gases and is collected in a bag-filter plant. Zinc production by "dry" processing presents particular difficulties because zinc has a low boiling point (906° C) and therefore occurs only in the gaseous form at the temperature necessary for effecting the reduction (1300° C). For this reason reduction has to be carried out in closed vessels or furnaces in which the zinc vapor can be condensed in the absence of air. For thermal reduction the concentrate is roasted—a treatment that may be carried out in two stages (multiple-hearth furnace followed by sintering on a traveling grate) or in a single-stage operation in which a proportion of the roasted material is fed back to the sintering machine. Sintering is necessary for transforming the material into suitable lumps to allow air to flow through it during the subsequent reduction process.

Reduction of the zinc oxide can be done by various methods. In the so-called standard process, reduction is effected in horizontal retorts in a retort furnace or distilling furnace (Fig. 2), which comprises a lower part containing regenerative chambers for preheating the gas and combustion air and an upper part in which retorts, arranged in tiers one above the other, are heated by the hot-flame gases. A retort of this kind is a rectangular distilling vessel, about 6 or 7 ft. long and about 1 ft. square in cross section. It is made of fireclay and has only a short service life, having to be renewed every four to six weeks. The retorts are charged with crushed sintered material, intermediate products containing zinc, and coke breeze (as the reducing agent). This mixture is fed into the retorts by high-speed belt conveyors; hand charging is still employed in some zinc-processing plants, however. When the retorts have been charged, their mouths are provided with so-called condensers, likewise made of refractory material, and the furnace is heated up to about 1300° C, at which temperature reduction of the zinc oxide takes place according to the reaction $ZnO + C \rightarrow Zn + CO$. The zinc vapor escapes from the retorts and is collected in the condensers as liquid metal. At the end of about 20 hours the process has been completed; the liquid zinc and zinc dust are then removed from the condensers, and the residual matter is removed from the retorts by special machines. Cleaning out the retorts and recharging them takes about 4 hours, so that the whole cycle can be repeated every 24 hours. In a more recent development of the process a single large condensing chamber is used instead of individual condensers.

(more)

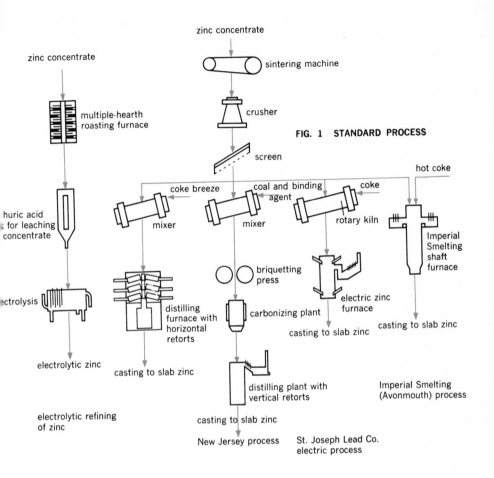

zinc concentrate

zinc concentrate

sintering machine

multiple-hearth
roasting furnace

crusher

FIG. 1 STANDARD PROCESS

screen

hot coke

huric acid
for leaching
concentrate

coke breeze

coal and binding
agent

coke

mixer

mixer

rotary kiln

Imperial
Smelting
shaft
furnace

ectrolysis

briquetting
press

electric zinc
furnace

distilling
furnace with
horizontal
retorts

carbonizing plant

casting to slab zinc

casting to slab zinc

electrolytic zinc

casting to slab zinc

distilling plant with
vertical retorts

Imperial Smelting
(Avonmouth) process

electrolytic refining
of zinc

casting to slab zinc

New Jersey process

St. Joseph Lead Co.
electric process

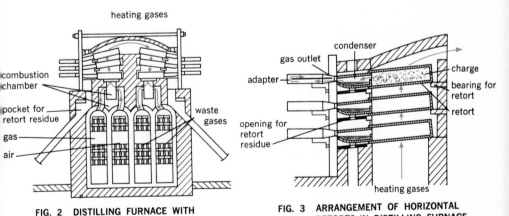

heating gases

combustion
chamber

pocket for
retort residue

gas

air

waste
gases

condenser

gas outlet

adapter

opening for
retort
residue

charge

bearing for
retort

retort

heating gases

**FIG. 2 DISTILLING FURNACE WITH
HORIZONTAL RETORTS (SECTION)**

**FIG. 3 ARRANGEMENT OF HORIZONTAL
RETORTS IN DISTILLING FURNACE**

97

Zinc (continued)

In the New Jersey process (Fig. 4), reduction is effected in large vertical retorts about 14 m (45 ft.) high and of rectangular cross section, lined with silicon-carbide bricks in the hottest parts. The advantage over the horizontal retort method is that reduction can be performed as a continuous operation. The charge consists of briquettes made of a mixture of zinc oxide material (roasted blende) and bituminous coal. The briquettes are fed automatically to the retort, the residual matter being extracted by a screw conveyor at the bottom. The mixture of carbon monoxide and zinc vapor is discharged from the top of the retort into a condenser, where the metal is precipitated in liquid form.

There have been many attempts to utilize electricity for the smelting of zinc. The St. Joseph Lead Co. (U.S.A.) has developed a successful method of reducing zinc in an arc furnace (Fig. 5). The process is similar in principle to the retort method, except that the heat is now supplied by the electric arc. Another fairly recent development is the method employed at Avonmouth (Great Britain), which has significantly affected the metallurgical processing of lead as well as zinc. In this method, known as the Imperial Smelting process, the two metals are produced simultaneously from the oxides of zinc and lead in a shaft furnace. The process is especially valuable for dealing with ores in which sphalerite and galena occur in intimate association with each other. The furnace is charged with coke and a mixture of roasted lead and zinc ores, prepared by a pressure sintering process. In the furnace, which is really a form of blast furnace, the lead oxide is reduced to molten metallic lead, which collects at the bottom. The zinc oxide is likewise reduced and forms zinc vapor, which is extracted at the top of the furnace along with the combustion gases. The vapor is passed to a condenser in which the cooling medium is molten lead, in which the zinc dissolves. The zinc-in-lead solution is then passed into a separator in which, on cooling, a layer of liquid zinc forms on top of the lead (this separation is due to the fact that the solubility of zinc in lead diminishes at lower temperatures). The lead is returned to the condenser, and the zinc is further processed by refining.

The refining of zinc—i.e., the removal of the remaining impurities (chiefly lead and cadmium)—is effected by redistillation in a furnace comprising two columns constructed of silicon-carbide trays placed one above the other. The lower part of the first column is heated. Impure zinc is fed continuously into the top of the column and is vaporized as it flows down through the heated trays. After further purification by refluxing in the upper part of the column, the zinc vapor (still containing cadmium, but free of other impurities) is passed to a condenser, whence it is fed to the top of the second column, in which all the cadmium is driven off. Zinc of 99.995% purity is condensed and drawn from the bottom.

Another widely used method of zinc production is by the leaching of roasted zinc concentrates with acid and then depositing the zinc by electrolysis from the solution thus obtained.

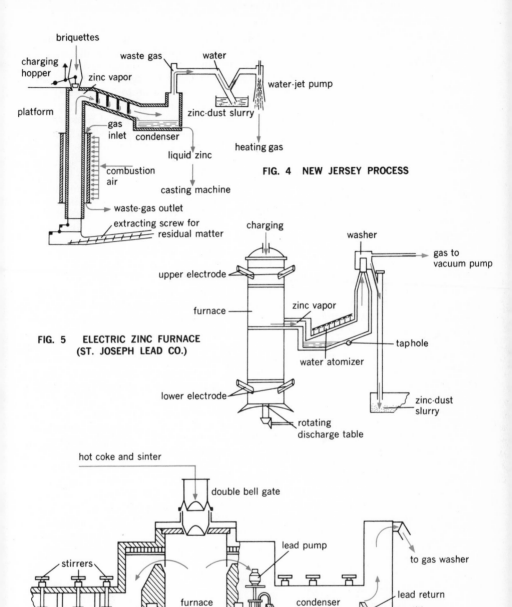

FIG. 4 NEW JERSEY PROCESS

- briquettes
- charging hopper
- zinc vapor
- waste gas
- water
- water-jet pump
- zinc-dust slurry
- platform
- gas inlet
- condenser
- liquid zinc
- heating gas
- combustion air
- casting machine
- waste-gas outlet
- extracting screw for residual matter

FIG. 5 ELECTRIC ZINC FURNACE (ST. JOSEPH LEAD CO.)

- charging
- washer
- gas to vacuum pump
- upper electrode
- furnace
- zinc vapor
- taphole
- water atomizer
- lower electrode
- zinc-dust slurry
- rotating discharge table

FIG. 6 IMPERIAL SMELTING PLANT

- hot coke and sinter
- double bell gate
- lead pump
- to gas washer
- stirrers
- furnace
- condenser
- lead return
- partition, open at base
- liquid lead-zinc mixture
- zinc trough
- hot-air bustle pipe
- hot-air blast
- water-cooled trough
- zinc
- tuyeres
- zinc overflow
- water jacket
- slag, stone and speiss
- tank for separation of lead and zinc
- crucible
- crude lead

99

ALUMINUM

Aluminum (or aluminium, as it is called in Britain) is one of the most abundant elements on earth, and its oxide is present in clay, kaolin and many other mineral formations. Mainly for economic reasons, aluminum is almost exclusively produced from bauxite, which is a residual clay formed in tropical regions by the chemical weathering of basic igneous rocks. It contains 55 to 65% aluminum oxide (alumina) together with varying amounts of iron oxide, silica and titanium oxide. Preparation of bauxite is carried out in two stages: first, pure aluminum oxide (Al_2O_3) is produced, which is then decomposed into aluminum and oxygen by an electrolytic treatment.

The principal method of making aluminum oxide from bauxite is the Bayer process (Fig. 1). The bauxite is dried, ground and treated with caustic soda solution in an autoclave. As a result, the aluminum is dissolved as sodium aluminate $(NaAlO_2)$, while iron oxide, titanium oxide and silica remain undissolved in the residue (known as "red mud"). The solution is filtered, and the aluminum is precipitated from it as aluminum hydroxide $Al(OH)_3$, which is separated by filtration and then calcined to aluminum oxide in a rotary kiln. The purified aluminum oxide is dissolved in molten cryolite—a sodium-aluminum fluoride (Na_3AlF_6)—and electrolyzed with direct current. This is done in an electrolytic cell (Fig. 2), which is essentially a tank lined with carbon bricks and provided with carbon anodes. The carbon lining forms the negative pole (cathode). Under the influence of the electric current the oxygen of the Al_2O_3 is deposited on the anodes, while the molten aluminum is deposited on the lining. In particular, the metal accumulates at the bottom of the cell. More aluminum oxide is stirred into the electrolyte from time to time and the molten metal removed. Currents of very high intensity are used (up to 100,000 amps. at 5 or 6 volts). A cell may be 20 ft. long, 6 ft. wide and 3 ft. deep. A modern processing plant may comprise a large number of such cells. The ordinary commercial aluminum obtained in this process may be up to 99.9% pure, which is sufficient for most purposes. In some cases, however, it is necessary to increase the purity by refining.

The principal refining method in present-day use is by three-layer electrolysis (Fig. 3), which is carried out in a cell provided with a carbon-lined bottom and magnesite-lined walls. In this type of cell the carbon bottom forms the anode, while a graphite electrode forms the cathode. To increase its specific gravity, the aluminum to be refined is first alloyed with copper or some other metal and is introduced into the cell in the molten condition. Over it is a layer of molten salt which is specifically lighter than this alloy, but heavier than pure aluminum. The passage of an electric current causes pure aluminum to go to the cathode, with the result that it accumulates as a layer floating on the molten salt. This aluminum, which has a purity of 99.99%, is removed from time to time and cast into suitable shapes for commercial purposes.

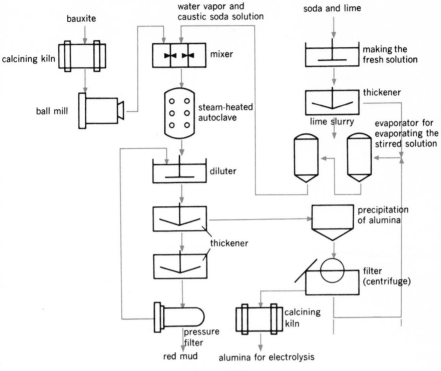

bauxite

water vapor and
caustic soda solution

soda and lime

calcining kiln

mixer

making the
fresh solution

ball mill

steam-heated
autoclave

thickener

lime slurry

evaporator for
evaporating the
stirred solution

diluter

thickener

precipitation
of alumina

filter
(centrifuge)

pressure
filter

calcining
kiln

red mud

alumina for electrolysis

FIG. 1   FLOW SHEET OF THE BAYER PROCESS

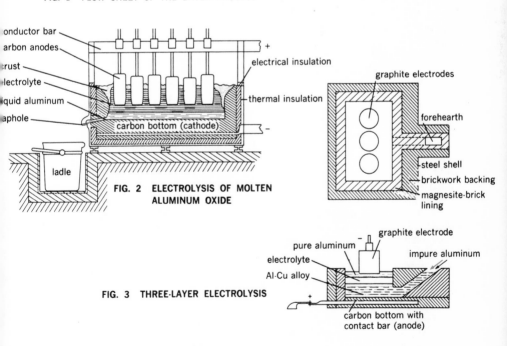

conductor bar
carbon anodes
crust
electrolyte
liquid aluminum
taphole

electrical insulation

thermal insulation

carbon bottom (cathode)

ladle

**FIG. 2   ELECTROLYSIS OF MOLTEN
ALUMINUM OXIDE**

graphite electrodes

forehearth

steel shell
brickwork backing
magnesite-brick
lining

pure aluminum
electrolyte
Al-Cu alloy

graphite electrode

impure aluminum

FIG. 3   THREE-LAYER ELECTROLYSIS

carbon bottom with
contact bar (anode)

101

ROASTING OF ORES AND CONCENTRATES

The ores or the concentrates of the heavy metals copper, lead, zinc and nickel (but not iron and tin) consist mainly of the sulphides of those metals. To enable the sulphides to be reduced with carbon or dissolved with dilute acids, total or partial removal of the sulphur is necessary. This is achieved by roasting, which is a heat treatment carried out in an oxidizing atmosphere and which conforms to the following general reaction:

$$MeS + 1\tfrac{1}{2}O_2 \rightarrow MeO + SO_2$$

(where Me denotes any bivalent metal). Thus, roasting results in the formation of the metallic oxide and sulphur dioxide gas, which may be processed to sulphuric acid. Once the roasting process has been initiated by ignition, it produces its own heat and generally requires no additional fuel. Arsenic and antimony, when present, are likewise removed by roasting. In a wider sense, roasting may also denote the process of driving off the carbon dioxide from carbonate ores; this process is more particularly referred to as calcining.

Depending on the further treatment that the roasted material will undergo, roasting is so controlled that all the metal is transformed into its oxide (dead roasting) or that, alternatively, only a proportion of the metal is oxidized while the rest remains combined with sulphur (partial roasting). The roasting process can, moreover, be regulated by varying the temperature and the air-supply rate in such a way that the sulphate of the metal is formed; or its chloride can be formed by the addition of chloride salts or chlorine gas.

There are many different types and varieties of roasting furnace. The multiple-hearth furnace (Herreshoff furnace, Fig. 1) has a number of annular-shaped hearths mounted one above the other. Each hearth has rabble arms driven from a common center shaft. The material for roasting is charged at the periphery of the top hearth; the arms push it inwards to the center, where it falls to the next hearth; here it is moved to the periphery and falls to the next hearth; and so on.

In the process known as flash roasting, the finely pulverized sulphide material is roasted in a special kind of fluidized-solids reactor (Fig. 2). Sulphur dioxide and the metallic oxide are formed. The material for roasting is introduced into the top of the combustion chamber along with a stream of preheated air. A swirling motion is imparted to the gases in the chamber, so that the larger particles settle in the hopper bottom.

The same general principle of roasting the finely divided material while it is in suspension in an air stream is applied in the fluosolids process (Fig. 3). Air is blown in through a bottom grate, and the finely pulverized material in the reactor is thus kept in a state of turbulent suspension. The material in this condition forms a "fluidized bed." The roasted material is discharged through an overflow pipe. Some of it is carried along as dust with the exhaust gas and is collected in a dust filter.

A widely employed machine for the roasting or calcining of a variety of materials is the rotary kiln (Fig. 4), which consists of a slightly inclined cylindrical steel tube which rotates on its longitudinal axis and is lined with refractory material. The charge to be roasted or calcined is fed in at the upper end and is progressively heated in the course of its journey down to the other end of the kiln. The kiln is fired from the lower end, where an oil, gas or pulverized-coal burner is installed.

The roasted material obtained from the above-mentioned processes is in the form of a powder. For further treatment in the shaft furnace, however, a lumpy charge material is required. The powder can be agglomerated by a process called sintering, whereby the particles become caked together by partial fusion (in addition to undergoing roasting), so that a porous mass called sinter is formed. This can be done on a sintering belt (such as the Dwight-Lloyd machine illustrated in Fig. 5) which comprises a traveling endless grate on which a bed of ore or concentrate is placed. Air is sucked or blown through the bed. Roasting is initiated by a gas, oil or pulverized-coal flame in an ignition hood under which the grate passes.

102

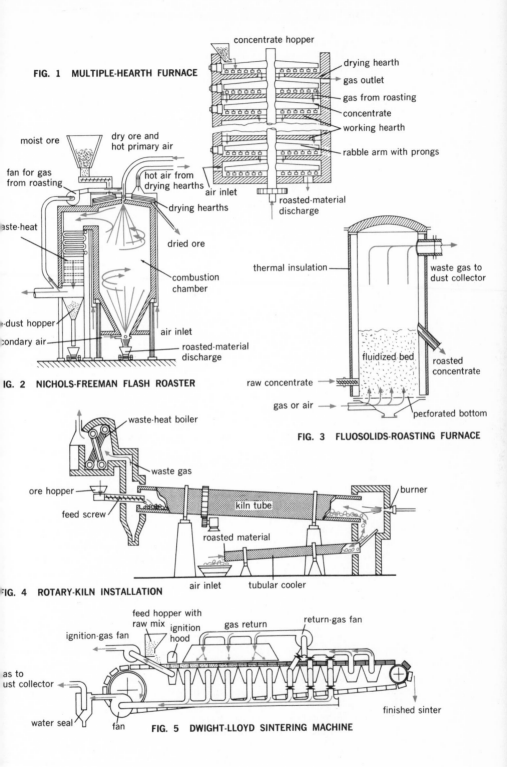

FIG. 1   MULTIPLE-HEARTH FURNACE

concentrate hopper

drying hearth

gas outlet

gas from roasting

concentrate

working hearth

rabble arm with prongs

moist ore

dry ore and hot primary air

fan for gas from roasting

hot air from drying hearths

air inlet

drying hearths

roasted-material discharge

waste-heat

dried ore

combustion chamber

-dust hopper

condary air

air inlet

roasted-material discharge

thermal insulation

waste gas to dust collector

fluidized bed

roasted concentrate

raw concentrate

gas or air

perforated bottom

IG. 2   NICHOLS-FREEMAN FLASH ROASTER

FIG. 3   FLUOSOLIDS-ROASTING FURNACE

waste-heat boiler

waste gas

ore hopper

feed screw

kiln tube

burner

roasted material

air inlet

tubular cooler

IG. 4   ROTARY-KILN INSTALLATION

feed hopper with raw mix

ignition hood

gas return

return-gas fan

ignition-gas fan

as to ust collector

water seal

fan

finished sinter

FIG. 5   DWIGHT-LLOYD SINTERING MACHINE

103

INGOT CASTING

An intermediate operation between the smelting of metals and their further treatment is casting. The metal may be cast in the form of large ingots for subsequent working by forging, rolling, stamping, etc., or the castings may be smaller ingots or billets—especially for nonferrous metals—which are more convenient to handle and are afterwards recast or are eventually formed into castings for machine parts or other components that require only a small amount of finishing treatment of one kind or another. The principal casting processes in industrial use are as follows:

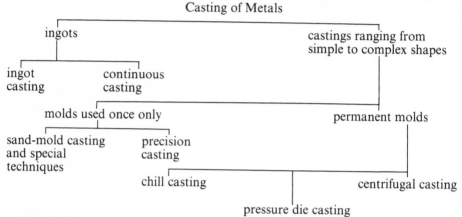

Casting of Metals

The choice of method will depend upon the melting point and the casting properties of the metal or alloy concerned and, in the case of final castings, also upon the purpose for which the casting is to be employed, the desired mechanical and technological properties, the requisite precision and surface condition, the number of castings to be produced, the question of economy, and other considerations.

Steel and nonferrous-metal ingots for further working are normally cast in ingot molds made of cast iron. These molds are usually filled from the top, either directly from the furnace through a pouring spout or from a ladle. In such cases the molten metal may be poured through a runner, a kind of long funnel, which is withdrawn before the ingot solidifies. Alternatively, bottom (or uphill) pouring may be used, to reduce turbulence during pouring. This is illustrated in Fig. 1, where the arrangement known as group casting is presented—i.e., several ingot molds are filled simultaneously through one runner. In the procedure shown in Fig. 2 the molten metal is poured direct from the ladle into the mold. The latter is at first held almost in the horizontal (tilted-over) position and is gradually swung back to the upright position as pouring proceeds, while the ladle is progressively tilted farther over. This technique too is aimed at reducing turbulence and thus producing a better-quality ingot. In order to achieve uniform quality and not too coarse a structure of the metal on solidification, and moreover to obviate such defects as segregations, pipes and blowholes, the ingots are generally cooled with water. The water may be circulated in the walls of the molds, or the molds may be sprayed with water, or they may be immersed bodily in water. This last-mentioned principle is applied in the casting of nonferrous-metal ingots to produce a fine-grained and uniform structure. In this process an electrically heated jacket, which is provided with a pouring aperture, is placed over the thin-walled ingot. When the mold has been filled with metal, it is slowly lowered into a tank of cooling water. A development of this method is the multiple-immersion process (Fig. 3), in which several ingot molds, each enclosed by a heated jacket, stand in a casting pit. The metal is poured into the molds through distributor channels and long runners. The latter are withdrawn when the molds have been filled, and the heated jackets are then slowly removed and the pit is flooded with water.

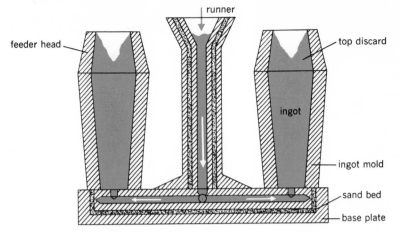

FIG. 1　GROUP CASTING BY THE
BOTTOM-POURING METHOD

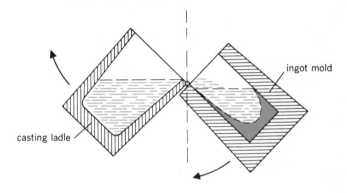

FIG. 2　TILTING-MOLD CASTING

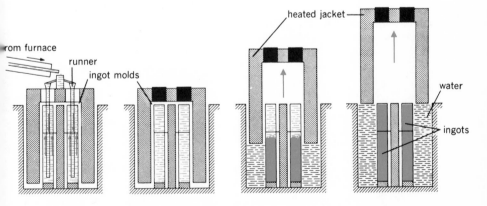

FIG. 3　MULTIPLE-IMMERSION CASTING

CONTINUOUS CASTING

More than a century ago Bessemer patented a proposed method of obviating the intermediate stages between the molten crude metal and the semifinished product. According to his invention, the steel would be cast between two water-cooled rollers and be pulled out in the form of a solid plate (Fig. 1). Since those days there have been a large number of proposals based on this fundamental idea, but its technical realization presented great difficulties which proved insurmountable until the first major breakthrough was achieved, not long before the Second World War. The first metal for which continuous casting was successfully employed was aluminum, which, because of its low melting point and its favorable casting and solidification properties, presented the least difficulty. At the present time, vertical continuous casting is in fact the most commonly used method for the production of ingots, tubes and other sections of this metal and its alloys. The principle of the aluminum-casting process was developed by Junghans: the metal is molded into a billet (or other desired barlike casting) in a mold that is open at the top and bottom and is of the appropriate square, round or rectangular cross-sectional shape (Fig. 2, page 109). When casting commences, the bottom of the mold, which is made of copper or aluminum and is water-cooled, is at first closed by a retractable table. When the billet has solidified in the mold, the table is lowered and the billet can now be slowly withdrawn from the mold. When the billet, which is cooled by water spraying, has reached a certain desired length, it is cut off by a saw or a cutting torch. If the billet is suitably held by withdrawal rollers above the cutting device (Fig. 3), casting can proceed continuously, the flow of liquid metal into the mold being controlled by a float-operated mechanism. The temperature and flow rate of the metal, the mold temperature, the flow rate of the cooling water and the speed of descent of the billet must all be accurately interadjusted. With several molds side by side, the installation can be designed to produce a number of billets simultaneously. Tubes and other hollow sections can likewise be produced by continuous casting. For this purpose the mold is provided with a suitably shaped water-cooled core.

From the vertical continuous-casting process various horizontal processes have been developed, in which the mold is installed sideways in relation to the holding furnace and the billet is withdrawn horizontally by withdrawal rollers (Fig. 4). The continuous casting of aluminum was followed by basically similar processes for copper and its alloys, though substantial modifications were needed: graphite molds cooled at the base are employed, and casting is carried out under protective gas shielding.

Whereas the continuous-casting processes for aluminum and copper have already reached an advanced stage of technical perfection, those for iron and steel are still under development. The great difficulties to be overcome arise particularly from the fact that because of the smelting procedures employed, iron becomes available in sudden large quantities and therefore has to be cast relatively quickly. There is a

(more)

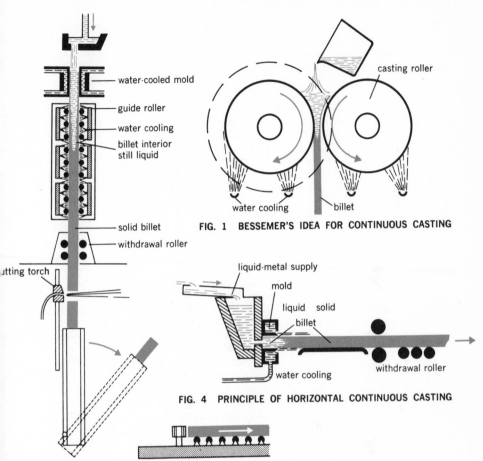

water-cooled mold

guide roller

water cooling

billet interior
still liquid

casting roller

solid billet

withdrawal roller

water cooling

billet

FIG. 1 BESSEMER'S IDEA FOR CONTINUOUS CASTING

utting torch

liquid-metal supply

mold

liquid   solid

billet

water cooling

withdrawal roller

FIG. 4 PRINCIPLE OF HORIZONTAL CONTINUOUS CASTING

IG. 3 VERTICAL CONTINUOUS CASTING

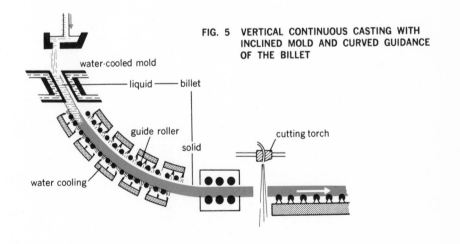

**FIG. 5 VERTICAL CONTINUOUS CASTING WITH
INCLINED MOLD AND CURVED GUIDANCE
OF THE BILLET**

water-cooled mold

liquid —— billet

guide roller

cutting torch

solid

water cooling

further complication in that iron has a high heat content and fairly poor thermal conductivity, so that rapid dissipation of heat is difficult to achieve, while the high working temperature also gives rise to technical difficulties. Some of the problems have been overcome, and there already exist a number of continuous-casting plants in industrial operation. In these plants the steel is cast in a copper mold of considerable height which performs a very rapid short, periodic up-and-down motion, whereby the dissipation of heat is assisted and the billet is prevented from sticking in the mold. It also helps to prevent the solidified outer layer of the billet from breaking open, which would cause liquid steel to flow out of the interior. Because of the relatively long time it takes for the interior of the billet to solidify, the requisite height of construction for an installation of this kind is generally greater than that needed for a continuous-casting installation for light alloys. To overcome this problem, installations have been developed in which the billet, after being cast in the vertical position, is curved sideways to the horizontal position and passed to conveyor rollers. This lateral deflection of the billet may be effected by means of a heavy deflecting roller just after the billet emerges from the water-cooling zone or by means of a curved arrangement of the guiding rollers and appropriate design of the mold (Fig. 5, page 107). Installations for the continuous casting of spigot-and-socket cast-iron pipes are in operation, though these pipes are still unusually manufactured by centrifugal casting (see page 120).

In the above-mentioned processes, which operate with stationary molds, the billet slides in relation to the mold. Various types of continuous-casting machine for strips, bars, wires and other small steel sections have been developed in which the mold travels along with the billet until the latter has completely solidified. Molding may be achieved by means of a rotating water-cooled wheel or roller which is provided with a groove closed by a metal band (rotary process, Fig. 7). Alternatively, a "caterpillar" mold is used, consisting of a pair of belts provided with half molds which are temporarily brought together in the casting zone, where they are filled with liquid metal and travel along with the billet until the latter has completely solidified and leaves the machine (Hazelett process, Fig. 6). By means of rolling and drawing devices installed behind the casting machine it is thus possible to produce strip or wire in a continuous operation. Further shaping treatments may be added: e.g., stamping or deep-drawing devices, whereby sheet-steel products can be manufactured continuously.

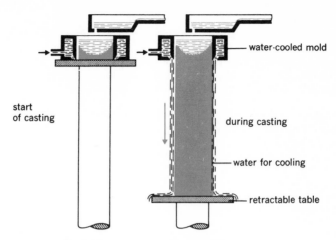

FIG. 2 SEMICONTINUOUS CASTING OF ALUMINUM

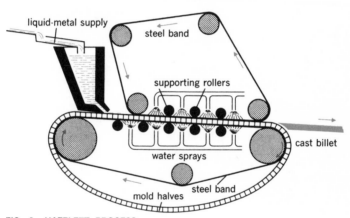

FIG. 6 HAZELETT PROCESS

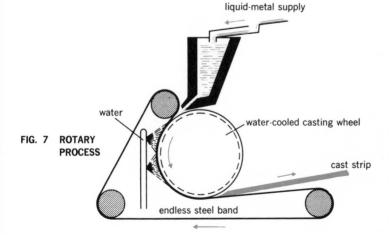

FIG. 7 ROTARY PROCESS

METAL CASTING

Sand Casting
The numerous processes for the casting of metals can be divided into two main groups: casting with expendable molds (sand casting, shell molding, etc.) and casting with permanent molds which can be reused a large number of times (chill casting, pressure die casting, etc.). In either case it is necessary to make a model of the casting to be produced. Such a model is called a "pattern" in founding. The mold is then produced from the pattern. Wood, plaster, metal and plastics are materials used for pattern making. Except for very simple castings, the pattern will generally comprise two or more parts: the actual pattern and the cores which will form the cavities and recesses in the casting.

In casting with expendable molds, the individual pattern parts are first made by hand or by mechanical means and then assembled. The molding materials—i.e., those used for constructing the actual molds in which the metal will be cast—are usually mineral substances such as sand, cement, fireclay, plaster, etc., in conjunction with bonding agents (sulphite solution, oil, water glass, synthetic resins, etc.) which give the molds the necessary strength and dimensional accuracy. The bonding action may be achieved by drying or by chemical consolidation (curing). In dry-sand molding the mold is baked; in green-sand molding the mold is used with sand in the damp ("green") condition. The metal is poured from above into an open mold. Closed molds, which are the more usual kind, are filled through a special system of channels (called runners or gates) which are generally so contrived that the metal enters at a low point and rises in the mold. When the metal has solidified and cooled, the casting is removed from the mold, and the runners and risers (which ensure that the mold is properly filled and compensated for shrinkage) are detached from the casting. The latter is then cleaned up by abrasive blasting, tumbling, grinding and cutting.

Sand casting can be used for all the common metals. There are many sand-casting processes and special processes derived from this method. These are known by various names such as box molding, open sand molding, pit molding, template molding, etc. The most widely employed method for making comparatively small castings is box molding (Fig. 1). In this method the pattern is embedded in the sand (or other mold material) within a molding box which usually comprises an upper and a lower part, the sand being compacted by ramming, pressure or vibration. Then the box is opened, the pattern removed, the cores inserted, the box closed again and casting carried out. For the casting of very large, heavy and intricate components the pit molding process is employed. Here the mold is built up in a casting pit. To give the sand greater strength when used as a mold material for large castings, cement may be added to it (cement-sand method). For symmetrically shaped castings the mold is sometimes formed by means of a template, a metal plate cut to the desired profile for producing a certain shape when it is moved along—e.g., slid along a guide track or rotated on a pivot (as in Fig. 2).

(more)

110

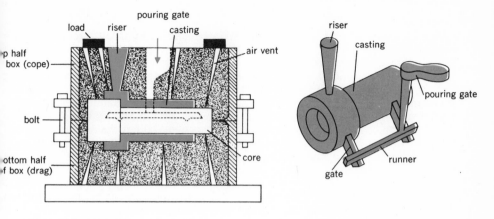

FIG. 1   BOX MOLDING

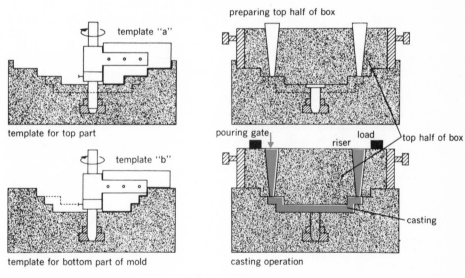

FIG. 2   TEMPLATE MOLDING

111

Shell Molding

A substantial saving of mold material may be effected by using a molding box whose shape roughly corresponds to that of the pattern it encloses, so that only a relatively thin layer of material is needed. The molding sand (or other mold material) is introduced into the box by a blowing device and is compacted to form a shell-like mold around the pattern. In plaster molding, the pattern made of metal or plastic is surrounded by a paste of gypsum plaster which is removed when it has set and is then assembled to form the mold which will receive the metal. With plaster it is possible to make molds of high precision, but this material has the disadvantage of having only low permeability to gas, which may give rise to difficulties in casting. This drawback can be overcome by the addition of foaming agents which increase the porosity of the plaster.

An important advance was achieved with the shell molding process, invented by Croning and patented in 1944 (Figs. 3 and 4). Its principle consists in making a thin "shell"—only a few millimeters thick—around a pattern and then assembling the parts of the shell to form the mold for the metal. A suitable mold material is a mixture of 95% fine quartz sand and 5% synthetic resin and a hardening agent. Alternatively, a sand whose grains have been precoated with a resin may be used, the advantage of this technique being that segregation of the material is thereby prevented. The metal parts that make up the pattern are mounted on a metal base plate, and together they are heated to about 250° C. Mold material is heaped on the pattern or deposited on it by a blowing device. The temperature causes the mold material to form a thin adherent coating ("shell") on the pattern by melting the resin constituent in immediate contact with the pattern. The rest of the mold material (in which the resin has not melted, so that the material is still of a loose granular constitution) is then removed, and the shell is cured by heating for a short time to 450° C. With the help of the hardening agent the shell thus attains the necessary strength to serve as a mold to receive the metal and is detached from the pattern (Fig. 3). The hollow core is produced by a similar method (Fig. 4). The halves of the shell and the cores are assembled to form the mold and are gripped in special holding devices or are glued together with a special adhesive. For casting, a number of molds may be arranged in stacks or installed side by side in a box, the voids between the molds being packed with steel balls to hold them firmly in position. When the casting metal is poured, the resin in the shell is burned away by the heat released from the metal so that only the sand remains, which can afterwards be easily shaken or knocked off the solidified casting.

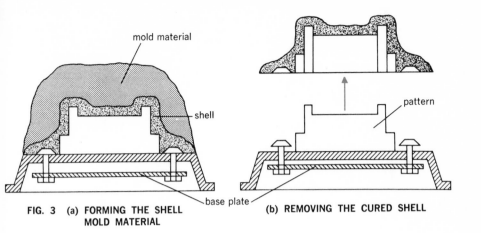

FIG. 3   (a) FORMING THE SHELL
         MOLD MATERIAL

(b) REMOVING THE CURED SHELL

Croning's shell-molding process

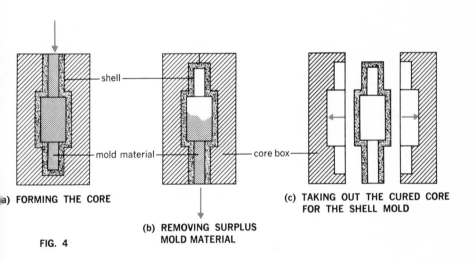

a) FORMING THE CORE

(b) REMOVING SURPLUS
   MOLD MATERIAL

(c) TAKING OUT THE CURED CORE
    FOR THE SHELL MOLD

FIG. 4

113

PRECISION CASTING

The processes under the heading of "precision casting" differ from sand casting and shell molding in that the molds they employ consist of only one part—i.e., are not assembled from two or more parts—while the pattern itself is expendable each time a casting is made. Precision casting processes offer considerable freedom to the designer and produce castings of a superior surface finish and a high degree of dimensional accuracy. Among other purposes, they are used for the casting of metals and alloys that are difficult to machine, since the castings generally require little or no finishing treatment. Such castings are used in precision engineering, clock-making, the manufacture of metal ornaments, and other fields of industrial production.

The principle is as follows. From an original pattern (usually of metal) an impression or master mold is made in which a second pattern (the expendable working pattern of wax or some similar material) is cast. This second pattern is embedded in mold material and is then melted out, so that a cavity is left into which the metal for the actual casting can be poured.

The most widely used precision casting technique is the "lost-wax," or "investment molding," process. When the original metal pattern has been made, the first step is to make a master mold, which may consist of two or more parts and be provided with cores. It is usually made of a low-melting metal alloy which is easily workable, though in certain cases, especially where very large numbers of castings are required, steel may be used for the master mold. The latter is filled with molten wax, which is allowed to solidify and is then removed. Thus a wax pattern similar to the original is obtained. In some cases a number of wax patterns may be joined together in a treelike assembly, so that a corresponding number of castings can be produced in one operation. This is represented in the accompanying illustrations. The wax pattern (or "tree" of patterns) is immersed in a wet slurry or paste consisting of a fine-grained refractory mold material and a bonding agent, so that the wax pattern becomes coated with this mixture. The wax pattern is now taken out of the paste bath and the coating is built up to a greater thickness by having strewn on grains of a coarser mold material. The coating, which closely envelops the wax pattern and reproduces every detail of its shape, is called the "investment." The pattern thus "invested" is placed, with the pouring gate downwards, in a special box, which is filled up with more mold material. The complete mold is then heated, causing the wax to melt and run out. This is followed by baking the mold at about 1000° C for several hours, so that it becomes hard and strong. The metal is cast in the mold while the latter is still hot. Filling the mold may be done by gravity, pressure, or centrifugal means. Finally, when the metal has solidified, the mold is broken up.

There are many variants of the lost-wax process. For instance, plastics may be used instead of wax; or the wax may be removed with solvents instead of being melted out. In the Mercast process (used in the United States), mercury is used for filling the master mold at normal temperature. Then this mold is cooled to −40° C, causing the mercury to solidify. The "frozen" mercury pattern is removed from the master mold and dipped a number of times in a special investment mixture, so that it receives a multilayer coating which forms the final mold. The temperature is allowed to rise, and the mercury liquefies and is retrieved from the mold, which is then baked.

nal pattern   wax pattern

injecting wax into the
master mold

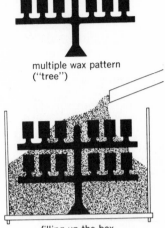

multiple wax pattern
("tree")

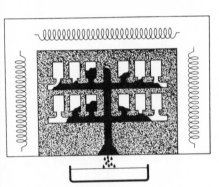

wax pattern immersed
in investment mixture

filling up the box
with mold sand

melting out the wax and
baking the mold

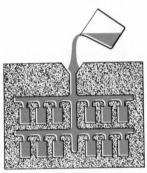

casting the metal

sandblasting and
detaching the castings

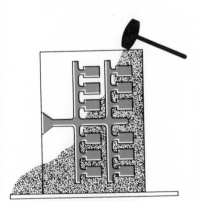

destroying the mold
to release the casting

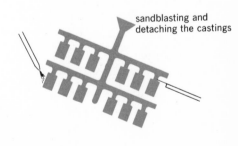

finished castings

115

GRAVITY DIE CASTING

With sand casting and shell-mold casting the mold has to be broken up after each casting operation. On the other hand, in the process known as die casting, the mold, called a "die," is made of metal and is used a large number of times. It is, of course, more expensive to make than an expendable "once-only" mold. An intermediate technique is the use of semipermanent molds made of fireclay or gypsum plaster, from which a limited number of castings can be obtained. The most widely used die-making materials are steel, cast iron and heat-resisting alloys of iron. For particular purposes other materials are sometimes employed for the dies, e.g., copper, aluminum or graphite. A die can produce castings with a smooth and clean surface and high dimensional accuracy, requiring little or no final machining or other finishing treatment. The service life of a die, in terms of the number of castings that can be produced from it, depends on such factors as the thermal shock resistance of the die material, the casting material, the temperature at which it is poured, and the casting method employed.

A great many details have to be taken into consideration in designing the pattern from which the die is made. Thus, in designing the pouring-gate system and risers it must be borne in mind that the walls of the mold exert a quenching (sudden cooling) action upon the molten metal so that this solidifies much more rapidly than in sand casting. In addition, the die must be provided with fine channels at the joints and with air-vent holes and thus enable the air displaced by the casting metal to escape from the interior of the die. (In a sand mold the air can escape through the porous mold material.) Also, the die must be so constructed that it will not restrain the shrinkage that occurs when the metal cools and solidifies and will allow the casting to be easily removed. Shrinkage presents particular difficulties in designing the cores which form the cavities and recesses in the casting. Normally such cores are made of steel or special alloys. Sometimes compressible sand or shell cores are used, however.

To prevent the casting metal from sticking to the die, the latter may be given an internal coating of clay, chalk or bone ash with water glass as a binder, this mixture being applied to the die by brushing, spraying, or immersion.

In the case of simple castings the metal may be poured into the open die from the top (Fig. 3). Usually the die is a closed and rather complex assembly of two or more parts, however (Fig. 1), sometimes comprising a number of cores. It must be so designed that the molten metal will flow quickly, without turbulence, into all parts of the die. For the casting of metals with a low melting point it may be necessary to use a heated die (to prevent premature solidification), and for metals with a high melting point the die may have to be artificially cooled after each casting operation. Slowly tilting the die during casting, in order to reduce turbulence and help the metal to flow smoothly, is an expedient that is employed particularly for heavy castings (Fig. 2). For the production of awkwardly shaped or very thin-walled castings a vacuum may be applied to facilitate the filling of the die. "Slush casting" is a technique used for making hollow ornamental castings: the molten metal is poured into a die, and when a solid shell of sufficient thickness has formed, the remaining liquid is poured out.

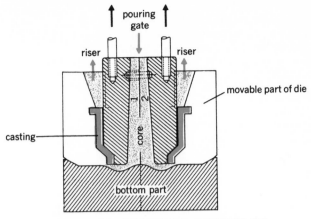

FIG. 1 GRAVITY DIE CASTING WITH MULTIPART DIE

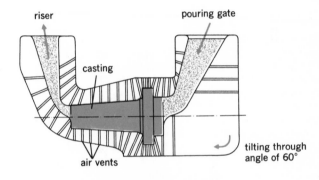

FIG. 2 TILTING DIE-CASTING TECHNIQUE

FIG. 3 GRAVITY DIE CASTING WITH ONE-PIECE DIE

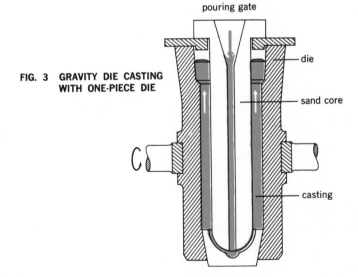

117

PRESSURE DIE CASTING

Pressure die casting makes possible the economical quantity production of intricate castings at a rapid rate. Such castings, which may comprise various holes, recesses, screw threads, etc., are characterized by high dimensional accuracy, good surface finish, and economy of metal; they require little or no final machining. The principle on which pressure die-casting processes are based consists in forcing molten metal into a mold (the "die") under considerable pressure. The machines used for the purpose operate on one of two systems: hot-chamber machines (for metals with a low melting point) and cold-chamber machines (for metals with a high melting point). In the first-mentioned type of machine (Fig. 1) the metal is kept liquid in a crucible inside the machine, and the pressure chamber that delivers the metal into the die is located in the metal bath. Such a machine may be pneumatically operated or, more frequently, develop the pressure by the action of a ram. The casting metal for a cold-chamber machine is kept liquid in a holding furnace from which it is transferred to the pressure chamber (which may be integral with the die or separate from it) by means of a scoop or a special automatic device and is forced into the die by means of a ram. Depending on the arrangement of the ram, a distinction can be made between "vertical" (Fig. 2) and "horizontal" (Fig. 3) pressure die-casting machines. The simplest machines are hand-operated, but fully automatic machines are more usually employed, which make possible high rates of production. A complete cycle of operations comprises closing the die, forcing the molten metal into it, withdrawing the cores, opening the die, ejecting the casting and (if necessary) shearing off the sprue, deburring the casting, and cleaning the die. The number of cycles per hour that a casting machine can attain will depend on the size and shape of the castings and on the casting metal used. Thus, with zinc alloys it is possible, within a given period of time, to produce about seven times the number of castings that can be made with brass. There are fully automatic machines which can turn out small zinc-alloy castings at a rate of more than 1500 cycles per hour. In pressure die casting, precision-made dies, sometimes of intricate multipart design and therefore very expensive, are employed, which are exposed to severe working conditions characterized by high pressures and a large number of successive variations in temperature. For the production of zinc and zinc-alloy castings the dies may be made of unalloyed steel; however, for aluminum, magnesium, copper and the alloys of these metals the dies are usually made of hot-work tool steel, which has greater durability.

A more recent development is vacuum die casting, which has hitherto been applied chiefly in the United States, Great Britain and Holland. It produces castings which have an even better surface finish than ordinary pressure die castings. There are two systems: either the die is enclosed within a hood which evacuates the air, or the holding furnace (in which the casting metal is kept molten) is so installed under the casting machine that on evacuation of the air from the die, the metal is sucked into the die and is compacted in it. A process for making iron castings based on this latter principle has been developed.

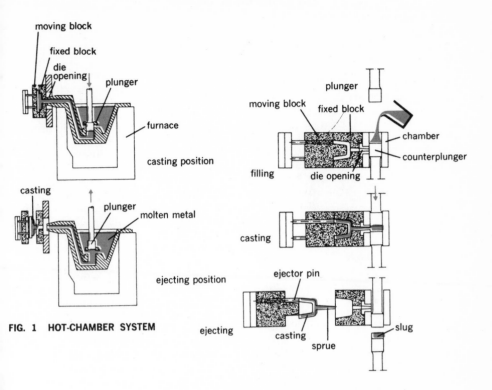

FIG. 1 HOT-CHAMBER SYSTEM

FIG. 2 VERTICAL COLD-CHAMBER SYSTEM

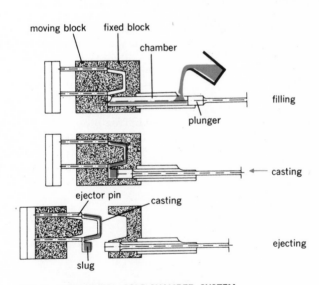

FIG. 3 HORIZONTAL COLD-CHAMBER SYSTEM

CENTRIFUGAL CASTING

"Centrifugal casting" comprises a number of processes in which the centrifugal force set up by the rotation of a part of the casting installation is utilized to shape the casting, fill the mold, and help solidify and strengthen the metal. A distinction can be made between "vertical" centrifugal casting (Fig. 1) and "horizontal" centrifugal casting. The first-mentioned process is essentially a pressure-casting technique employing rotation about a vertical axis; it produces good filling of the mold, high dimensional accuracy, and a high-strength dense structure of the casting metal. This method is used for casting of components that are too difficult to produce satisfactorily by static casting methods because their sections are too thin or for other reasons: e.g., gears, piston rings, impellers, propellers, bushings and railway wheels. Horizontal centrifugal casting is used mainly for making long hollow castings, such as pipes, gun barrels, sleeves, etc. The mold rotates at high speed about a horizontal (or nearly horizontal) axis, the molten metal being fed into the interior of the mold and distributed around it by centrifugal action. Rotation is continued until solidification is complete. The external diameter of the casting corresponds to the internal diameter of the mold; the internal diameter of the casting can, however, be varied by appropriately proportioning the amount and feed rate of the casting metal. An advantage of the centrifugal process is that it produces a sounder and more uniform casting than static means. The mold is usually made of steel or cast iron; nonmetallic linings may be used.

An important application of horizontal centrifugal casting is the manufacture of pipes, especially cast-iron pipes. It provides an economical method capable of an advanced degree of mechanization. The two main methods of centrifugal casting are in a water-cooled mold by the Briede–de Lavaud process (Fig. 2) and in a sand-lined mold by Moore's process (Fig. 3). For the manufacture of spigot pipes, a sand core is inserted at the end of the mold (to form the enlarged socket) and is subsequently destroyed when the pipe is demolded. The first-mentioned method employs a slightly inclined mold which can move longitudinally. The molten iron is introduced into the mold through a long duct from a tilting ladle containing the correct amount of casting metal to form the pipe. When the mold has reached a certain speed of rotation, the molten iron is admitted to it, and the mold is moved slowly forwards (to the right in Fig. 2) while the feed duct remains stationary, so that uniform distribution of the metal along the mold is achieved. Moore's method uses a rotating mold with a sand lining, which protects the metal shell of the mold so that water cooling is not necessary. The sand itself is applied to the mold wall and compacted by centrifugal action. The inlet duct is short because, with a sand lining, solidification of the casting takes a relatively long time (no rapid cooling); proper filling of the mold is thus ensured. This process has the advantage of not requiring a wide range of molds of different diameters, since any desired pipe diameter can be produced simply by varying the thickness of the sand lining.

Centrifugal methods are also used for the production of composite castings (see page 124).

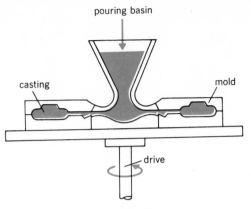

FIG. 1 CENTRIFUGAL CASTING

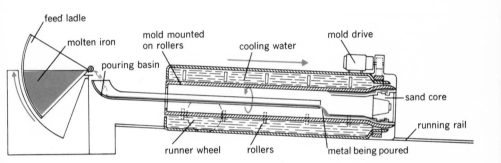

FIG. 2 BRIEDE–DE LAVAUD PROCESS

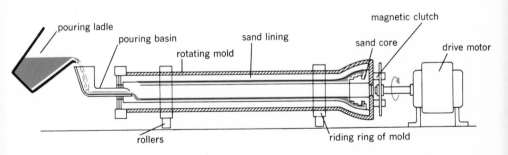

FIG. 3 MOORE'S PROCESS

121

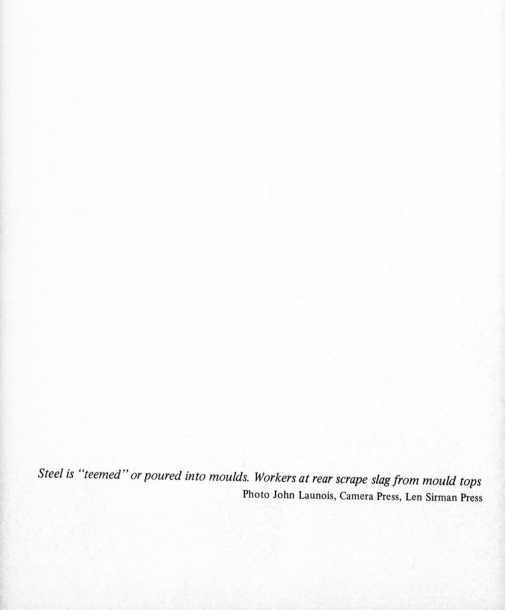

Steel is "teemed" or poured into moulds. Workers at rear scrape slag from mould tops
Photo John Launois, Camera Press, Len Sirman Press

COMPOSITE CASTING

"Composite casting" refers to a large number of processes in which molten metal is cast on to a solid metal component, so that the two subsequently form one integral unit. In this way the favorable mechanical or other technological properties of one metal can be combined with those of another. For example, bearings may be made from an outer shell of strong metal with a lining of special low-friction metal cast inside it, or a metal possessing high strength may be given a cast-on covering of corrosion-resistant metal, or an expensive metal may be combined with a cheaper metal for economy.

The mechanical connection of the two metals can be promoted by means of interlocking devices such as dovetailing, grooves, recesses, etc., which form a physical "key," or by shrink fitting or by bond established as a result of diffusion at the interface of the two metals so that local interpenetration occurs. The bond may be further strengthened by heat treatment (annealing) or by the interposition of special bonding layers of metal at the junction.

In the simple case of a bearing comprising an outer steel shell and a metal-alloy lining, the shell is preheated and the molten lining metal (with a lower melting point than steel) is cast inside it. In the integral-casting process developed by Mascher (Fig. 1) the steel shell is first given a coating of zinc and then, while it is still hot, is filled with molten lining metal (lead bronze) in a compound iron-and-sand mold. The zinc coating serves to establish a strong bond between the lining and the shell. Another technique is represented by the salt-bath displacement process, in which the bearing shell and the mold for forming the lining within it are together preheated in a salt bath, which also has the function of protecting the metal against oxidation. When the required temperature has been reached, the bearing metal is poured, displacing the salt. In the immersion process (Fig. 2), which is used, for example, for making bushings provided with bearing metal on both sides or for the production of relatively large castings, the bearing shell enclosed within the mold is heated in a salt bath and is then lowered into a bath of molten bronze in which the bronze displaces the salt in the mold.

Centrifugal casting techniques are extensively used for the production of thick-walled composite bearings (Figs. 3 and 4). The steel outer shell is heated in a salt bath or is zinc-coated; it is then gripped in a centrifugal casting machine, and when the latter has reached the requisite speed of rotation, the molten metal is introduced into it. In the case of a composite bearing built up from different metals in concentric layers, an intermediate bonding layer of tin is applied to the first layer of metal after it has solidified. Then the second layer is cast. In another technique for the casting of bearings the appropriate quantity of casting metal in the form of chips or granules, together with a fluxing agent, is fed into the mold, which is closed at both ends. The mold is then rotated while it is heated externally, so that the casting metal melts and is distributed in the mold by centrifugal action.

The Al-Fin process, a patented American method for the composite casting of light metal alloys in combination with steel or cast iron, is becoming increasingly important in the motor industry and other industries. In this process the steel basic component, whose surface has been thoroughly cleaned and degreased, is heated in molten aluminum at about 750° C, so that it becomes coated with an iron-aluminum compound (Fe_2Al_5) which in turn becomes covered with a layer of pure aluminum. The component is then placed in the mold and the metal is cast so quickly that the aluminum coating is still liquid, so that this coating and any adhering oxides are, as it were, washed away by the molten casting metal, which can now bond itself firmly to the underlying layer of Fe_2Al_5.

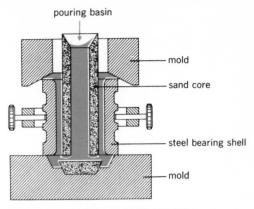

FIG. 1   MASCHER'S INTEGRAL-CASTING PROCESS

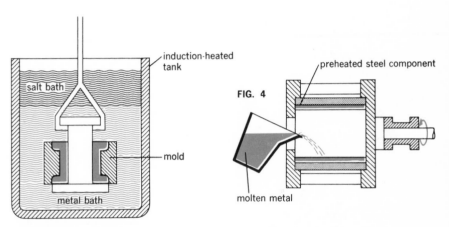

FIG. 2   IMMERSION PROCESS (MOLTEN BRONZE WITH OVERLYING SALT BATH)

FIGS. 3 and 4 CENTRIFUGAL COMPOSITE CASTING

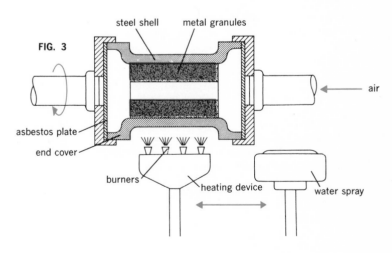

125

This process, in which articles and components are produced by agglomeration of fine metallic powder, is employed in cases where other methods of shaping – such as casting, forging and machining – are impracticable or where special material properties have to be achieved. By way of example, three techniques for the extrusion of metallic powders are indicated in Fig. 2. The materials used in powder metallurgy (metallic powders or, for some purposes, mixtures of metallic and nonmetallic powders) are shaped by cold pressing at room temperature between steel dies, which produces initial adhesion of the particles. This is followed by heating of the compacts in a nonoxidizing atmosphere (sintering) to obtain final cohesion. The dies usually consist of two parts thrusting against each other, and each part may be subdivided to produce the required shape (Fig. 4). Another technique is isostatic pressing: the powder is pressed in a closed flexible container (rubber, plastic) under liquid pressure.

The function of the sintering treatment is to bond the powder particles of the compact into a coherent mass. As a rule, the sintering temperature is somewhat below the melting point of the powder, or the temperature may be so controlled that fusion of certain constituents of the powder mixture is achieved. Sintering as a subsequent separate treatment may be dispensed with by pressing of the powder at elevated temperature or by subjection of cold-pressed compacts to hot shaping – e.g., by drop forging, rolling or extrusion. In certain cases it is advantageous to process the powder in a protective metal envelope which provides mechanical strength and/or protection against oxidation (Fig. 2c). To prevent oxidation, hot pressing or sintering is usually carried out under the protection of a shielding gas or in a reducing atmosphere.

Shaping of the powder is generally done by the application of pressure. However, in the so-called slip casting process, a technique adopted from the ceramics industry (Fig. 1), the powder is mixed with a suitable liquid suspension medium to form a "slip" (a thick suspension), which is put into a mold (a, Fig. 1). The liquid is absorbed by the walls of the mold, usually consisting of gypsum plaster (b). Then the shaped component is removed from the mold, dried and sintered (c). The powders used in powder metallurgy are produced by comminution of solid materials, by atomizing of molten materials in a stream of gas or water (Fig. 3), or by chemical processing. It is essential to obtain particles that are suitably graded in size and are of regular shape and surface condition, so that they interlock and adhere properly when compressed.

The technique has numerous applications. It is used in the production of high-melting-point metals such as tungsten and molybdenum. For instance, pure tungstic oxide is prepared from the ore and then reduced to tungsten powder, which is cold-pressed and sintered. Another important application of powder metallurgy is the manufacture of hard-metal cutting and working tools in which cemented carbides – e.g., tungsten carbide – are incorporated: cobalt and carbide powders are mixed together, pressed and sintered, so that the cobalt fuses. Metals produced by powder-metallurgy techniques are characterized by their fine porosity, a fact that is utilized for making filters and bearings, more particularly porous bronze bearings that can soak up oil like a sponge and require no subsequent lubrication. Copper-tungsten and similar combinations produced by powder metallurgy are used as electrical-contact materials. Permanent-magnet alloys are also produced by such techniques. There are many other applications, including the combination of metallic with nonmetallic materials to produce high-temperature-resisting materials (so-called "cermets").

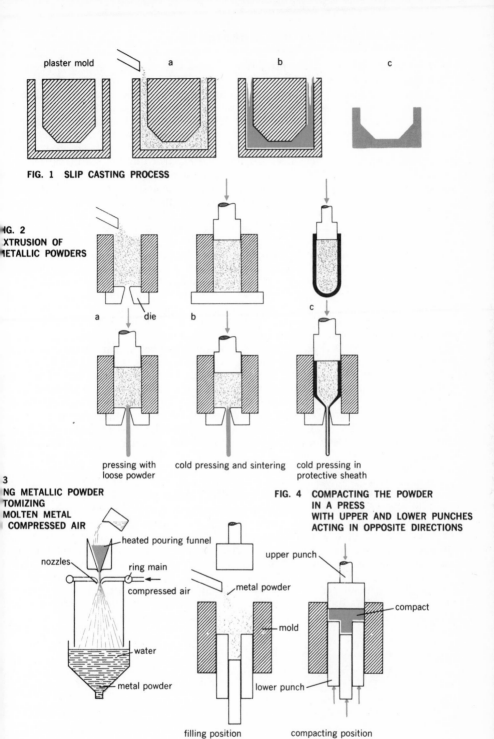

plaster mold   a   b   c

FIG. 1   SLIP CASTING PROCESS

FIG. 2
EXTRUSION OF
METALLIC POWDERS

a   die   b   c

pressing with   cold pressing and sintering   cold pressing in
loose powder   protective sheath

3
NG METALLIC POWDER
TOMIZING
MOLTEN METAL
COMPRESSED AIR

FIG. 4   COMPACTING THE POWDER
IN A PRESS
WITH UPPER AND LOWER PUNCHES
ACTING IN OPPOSITE DIRECTIONS

heated pouring funnel

nozzles

ring main

compressed air

metal powder

upper punch

compact

water

mold

metal powder

lower punch

filling position   compacting position

127

FORGING

One of the most important properties of metals is their deformability. The term "malleability" denotes the ability to be mechanically deformed by forging, rolling, extrusion, etc., without rupture and without significant increase in resistance to deformation. Metals such as lead and tin are malleable at ordinary temperatures, whereas others, such as iron, become malleable only when heated. The term "ductility" denotes the ability of metals to be mechanically deformed when cold. In the course of such deformation most metals become progressively more resistant to deformation; this latter effect is called work hardening (or strain hardening). A distinction is to be made between cold-forming and hot-forming processes. The former are usually associated with work hardening and are performed at room temperature. Hot-forming processes involve heating the metal above a certain temperature to make it malleable.

Forging is an important hot-forming process. It is used in producing components of all shapes and sizes, from quite small items to large units weighing several tons— e.g., heavy crankshafts. The metal, which is preheated to the appropriate forging temperature in a forge fire, in a forging furnace or by induction, is deformed mainly by upsetting (compressive deformation) between impact surfaces or pressure surfaces. In the process the metal flows in the direction of least resistance, so that generally lateral elongation will occur unless restrained. The most important forgeable materials are steel and steel alloys. Certain nonferrous metals and alloys are also shaped by forging.

Hand forging tools (Fig. 1) comprise variously shaped hammers, such as light and heavy sledgehammers (respectively wielded with one hand or both hands), the square flatter, the cross-peen hammer, various auxiliary hammers, etc. The base on which the work is supported during forging is the anvil, which is provided with a hardened steel face and terminates at one end or both ends in a horn, or beak, used for bending work. Various accessories can be inserted into the holes in the anvil. For holding the work, the smith has at his disposal a range of tongs and pincers with a variety of jaw shapes, together with other devices for gripping and handling larger pieces.

For the semimechanized forging of small to medium-sized components, forging hammers powered by various means are employed. The feature common to all of them is that, like the hand forging hammer, they utilize the energy of a falling weight to develop the pressure needed for shaping the metal. Larger components are forged by means of forging presses operated by steam or compressed air or by hydraulic or electric power. Largely automatic forging machines are used for the quantity production of engineering parts. The manufacture of intricately shaped forgings from bar material in very large quantities may be carried out by forging rollers (Fig. 5, page 131). These are matched rotating rollers or segments of rollers which have impressions sunk in their surfaces. The metal blank is rolled into these impressions as the rollers turn. Whereas the rollers of rolling mills rotate continuously, forging rollers perform only one revolution per shaping operation.

(more)

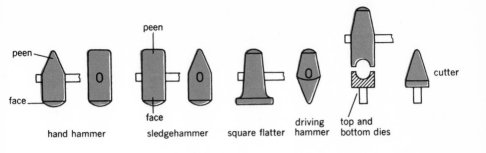

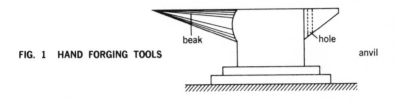

FIG. 1 HAND FORGING TOOLS

anvil

FIG. 2 HAMMER-FORGING OPERATIONS

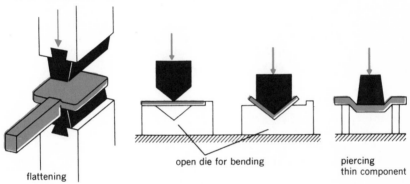

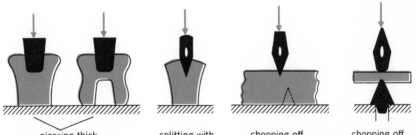

129

Forging (continued)

A distinction may be made between open-die forging, usually in the form of hammer forging, and closed-die forging. In hammer forging (Fig. 2), which is essentially derived from the traditional craft of the blacksmith, the component is shaped by hammer blows aided by relatively simple tools. These may include open dies—i.e., dies that do not completely enclose the metal to be shaped. One of the basic operations of hammer forging is the elongation of a piece of metal by stretching with hammer blows (Fig. 3), causing it to become thinner and longer. In hand forging the work piece is usually turned 90° after each blow, in order to forge it thoroughly and prevent its lateral expansion. A tube can be forged by flattening the metal longitudinally or tangentially around a mandrel. The opposite of elongation is upsetting, which produces compressive shortening. For example, the diameter of a bar can be increased uniformly or locally by heating and hammering axially.

More important is closed-die forging (Fig. 4), very widely used for mass production in industry, in which the metal blank is shaped by pressing between a pair of forging dies. The upper die is usually attached to the ram of a forging press or a forging hammer, while the lower die is stationary. Together they form a closed die. Closed-die forging can produce components of greater complexity and accuracy, with a better surface finish, than the more traditional methods not using closed dies. The dies are made of special heat-resistant and wear-resistant tool steels. A piece of hot metal sufficient to slightly overfill the die shape is placed in the bottom die, and the top die is forced against it, so that the metal takes the internal shape of the die. In hammer forging, several blows are struck in quick succession, forcing the metal evenly into the die impressions. The surplus metal forms a "flash" at the meeting surface of the upper and lower dies. This is subsequently trimmed off by special tools fixed in a press, the forging being forced through a hollow tool which cuts off the flash. Closed-die forging is used for the rapid production of large numbers of fairly small parts and also for very large components. For the latter—e.g., modern jet-aircraft components (including complete wing and airframe units)—giant hydraulically operated presses are used, which can develop forces of 50,000 tons and more. Such presses are highly complex pieces of machinery, equipped with elaborate electronic and other controlling and monitoring instruments. Forgings produced in closed dies are known as "drop forgings" or "stampings." For some purposes the forging operation is performed in two stages, the blanks first being treated in preliminary shaping dies and then formed in final shaping dies.

FIG. 3 DRAWING OUT METAL BY HAMMERING

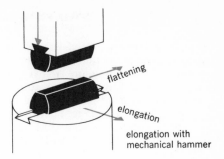

elongation with peen of hammer

flattening

elongation

elongation with
mechanical hammer

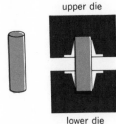

longitunal and tangential flattening
of a tube around a mandrel

FIG. 4 CLOSED-DIE FORGING

upper die

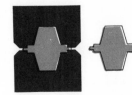

lower die
in the die

forging completed

forged
article

trimming off
the flash

finished
product

metal blank

FIG. 5 FORGING ROLLS

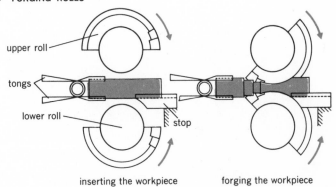

upper roll

tongs

lower roll

stop

inserting the workpiece

forging the workpiece

COLD EXTRUSION OF METALS

In cold extrusion, which is used for the manufacture of special sections and hollow articles, the material is generally made to flow in the cold condition by the application of high pressure, which forces it through the cavity enclosed between a punch and a die. A distinction is to be made between "forward" extrusion (Fig. 2), in which the extruded metal flows in the direction of movement of the punch, and "backward" extrusion (Fig. 1), which is characterized by the opposite direction of flow. The two techniques may be used in simultaneous combination (Figs. 3 and 4). Cold extrusion can be used with any material that possesses adequate cold workability—e.g., tin, zinc, copper and its alloys, aluminum and its alloys—and it is for these metals that the process is most widely adopted. Low-carbon soft-annealed steel can also be cold-extruded. If the product cannot be fully shaped in a single operation, the extrusion process may be performed in several stages. The solid or hollow products that can be made by cold extrusion are relatively limited in size.

The initial stock from which cold extrusions are produced consists of round blanks, lengths cut from bars, or specially preformed blanks. The punches and dies used in cold extrusion are subject to severe working conditions and are made of wear-resistant tool steels—e.g., high-alloy chromium steels. To reduce friction, the tool surfaces are polished. In the cold extrusion of steel the blank may additionally be given a phosphate coating to minimize friction.

A widely used special cold-extrusion method is impact extrusion. It is used for making collapsible tubes of lead, tin, zinc and aluminum—e.g., toothpaste tubes. Zinc battery cans are also produced in this way. A pointed punch descends swiftly on to a disc-shaped blank arranged in a die, causing the metal to flow upwards and around the punch.

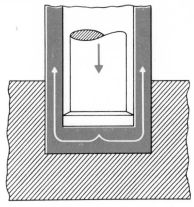

FIG. 1 BACKWARD EXTRUSION

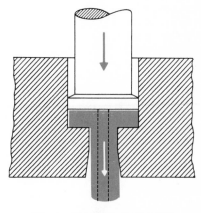

FIG. 2 FORWARD EXTRUSION

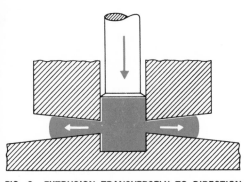

FIG. 3 EXTRUSION TRANSVERSELY TO DIRECTION
OF PUNCH MOTION

FIG. 4 COMBINATION OF FORWARD
AND BACKWARD EXTRUSION

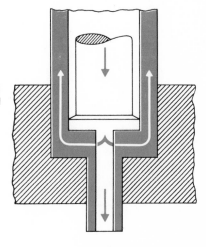

HOT EXTRUSION OF METALS

Extrusion is a hot-working process which, like forging, rolling, etc., uses the good deformability of heated metallic materials for shaping them. The most important aspect of the process is that it enables considerable changes of shape to be achieved in a single operation and provides a means of dealing with metals and alloys whose physical structure renders them unsuitable for shaping by other methods. Besides, with extrusion it is possible to form complex sections that cannot be produced in other ways. Finally, extrusion also offers economic advantages in that the dies are relatively inexpensive and are interchangeable, so that one extrusion machine can be used for the production of a wide variety of sections.

A metal billet heated to the appropriate temperature is fed into the cylindrical container of the extrusion press and is forced by the action of a ram through a steel die whose orifice has the desired shape to produce the solid or hollow section. The metal emerges from the die as a continuous bar, which is cut to the required lengths. Extrusion products are therefore essentially "linear" in character, in the sense that shaping is confined to the cross section only. The process is therefore eminently suitable for the production of barlike and tubular objects. A distinction is to be made between "direct" extrusion (Figs. 1 and 2, showing production of solid and hollow sections respectively) and "inverted" extrusion (Fig. 3), in which the extruded metal flows in the opposite direction to the movement of the ram, the extrusion die being in the ram itself.

Most metals and alloys can be shaped by extrusion. At first the process was confined to nonferrous metals and has now in fact largely superseded other methods for the shaping of such metals. Cable sheathing, lead pipe and aluminum-alloy structural sections are typical of such extrusion products. The extrusion of steel presented difficulties because of the heavy wear on the dies and the high working temperatures and stresses. However, these difficulties have been overcome, and extrusion is used, for example, in the production of stainless steel tubes. In the Ungine-Séjournet method the steel billet is coated with glass powder, which melts and forms a viscous heat-insulating and lubricating layer between the die and the extruded metal.

For making tubular sections, a mandrel is arranged in the die orifice (Fig. 2), and during extrusion the metal flows through the annular space so formed. Hollow billets are used for tubes, or solid billets are first pierced in the extrusion operation. Extrusion machines are generally hydraulic presses, with capacities ranging from about 500 tons to about 7500 tons. Graphite grease is commonly used for lubrication between metal and tools.

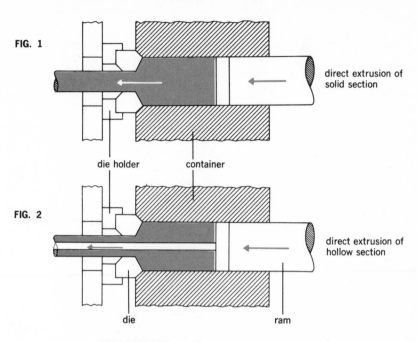

FIG. 1 direct extrusion of solid section

die holder   container

FIG. 2 direct extrusion of hollow section

die   ram

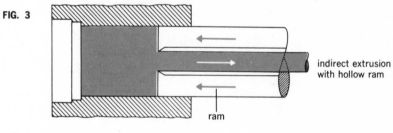

FIG. 3 indirect extrusion with hollow ram

ram

examples of extruded sections

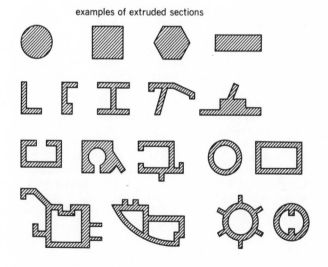

135

CUTTING AND MACHINING OF METALS

Forging, rolling, extrusion, etc., are metal-shaping processes that do not involve the removal of metal by means of cutting tools. On the other hand, many important shaping processes are based on cutting and similar operations. The tools used are made of special steels (tool steels), hard metals (cemented carbide alloys), oxide ceramic materials, and diamonds.

In this article the principles of the various methods are briefly outlined, without detailed descriptions of the machines used for performing the shaping operations. For each of these methods a whole range of tools has been developed, each type of tool being employed for a particular purpose. In chiseling (Fig. 1), the cutting edge of the tool is driven into the surface of the workpiece by the action of blows. To ensure even and regular removal of the chips it is essential to hold the chisel correctly and take care that it does not slip on the metal surface or dig too deeply into it. Chiseling is used chiefly for cutting off and for the removal of edges, burrs, fins, etc.

Planing, shaping and slotting (Fig. 2) are machining operations comparable to chiseling, characterized by the removal of the chips in one direction, the tool being moved to and fro or up and down in relation to the workpiece. In sawing (Fig. 3) the removal of metal is effected by a series of saw teeth. With power-driven band saws and circular saws, cutting can be performed in a continuous operation. The shape, spacing and number of teeth vary greatly for different saws. Large-diameter circular saws may have interchangeable teeth or interchangeable segments comprising a number of teeth. Sawing is used mainly for cutting off and for cutting plate material of not too great a thickness. Thick pieces of metal can, while still hot from the furnace, be cut with hot sawing machines or with cutting discs. The latter achieve very high cutting rates, cutting being effected by melting of the metal due to frictional heating. Band-type cutting devices are based on the same principle of heat generated at the cutting surface.

Another important basic process is filing (Fig. 4). By using suitably shaped files it is possible to cut metal to any desired shape. The actual cutting is performed by the teeth of the file. Roughing out the shape is first done by means of coarse files, followed by finishing with finer files. Files are available in a great variety of shapes, sizes and grades. They are classified and named according to sectional shape (e.g., half-round, square, triangular, round), length, and the relative fineness of cut of the teeth. With regard to fineness, the following classes of file are distinguished: bastard, second-cut, smooth, dead smooth. If there is only one series of parallel teeth, the file is known as a single-cut file; if the first series is intersected by a second and finer series, so as to form diamond-shaped teeth, the file is a so-called double-cut.

A broach (Fig. 5) is a tapered tool provided with a series of cutting teeth which are lower at one end of the tool than they are at the other. Broaching is mainly employed for machining out holes or other internal surfaces, but can also be used for external surfaces and for burnishing already-formed holes. The cut starts with the smaller teeth, which enter the hole, and finishes with the larger teeth, which bring the hole to the finished size. Fig. 5 shows an internal broach. Its cross-sectional shape may be round, rectangular, etc., depending on the desired shape of the hole. The broaching operation is performed by a machine that pulls or pushes the broach through the workpiece.

Turning (shown in Fig. 6) is one of the most important machining processes. It is the process of reducing the diameter of material held in a lathe. The workpiece is attached to a driven spindle and, while rotating, is brought into contact with a cutting tool. The position of the tool in relation to the axis of rotation can be varied so as to cut the workpiece to the desired shape. In longitudinal turning, the tool is moved

(more)

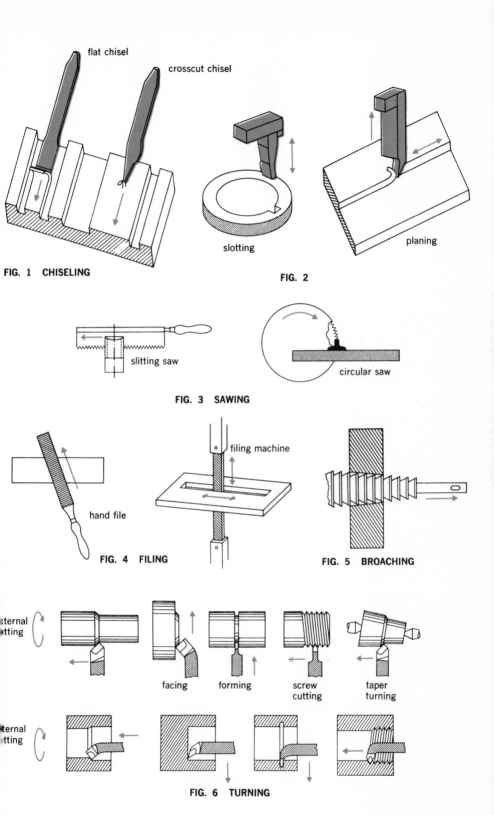

flat chisel

crosscut chisel

FIG. 1 CHISELING

slotting

planing

FIG. 2

slitting saw

circular saw

FIG. 3 SAWING

hand file

filing machine

FIG. 4 FILING

FIG. 5 BROACHING

external cutting

facing forming screw cutting taper turning

internal cutting

FIG. 6 TURNING

137

parallel to the axis of rotation, so that cylindrical shapes are obtained. A screw thread can be cut by a tool forming a spiral groove. In transverse turning (also known as facing) and in forming, the tool is moved at right angles to the axis. Workpieces of any desired tapered or other axially symmetrical shape can be produced by suitable combinations of longitudinal and transverse tool movements. Turning tools are available in a wide range of shapes and types. The cheapest are made of high-carbon steel, hardened and tempered. Alloys known as high-speed steels are used for tools that can be operated at much higher cutting speeds. In so-called tipped tools the cutting tip is made of a special hard material—e.g., a cemented carbide, particularly tungsten carbide.

Drilling (Fig. 7) is a rotary cutting operation for producing holes. The tool most widely used for the purpose is the twist drill, provided with helical cutting edges, which rotates and is fed forward into the material under pressure. The combination of rotary and feed motion cuts away chips of the material, which are removed from the hole. For drilling a hole in a solid workpiece, it is necessary first to make an indentation for the center of the drill to revolve in. A tool called a center punch is used for the purpose. It is advisable first to use a smaller drill and then follow up with a drill of larger diameter. Counterboring (Fig. 8) is a process related to drilling and is employed to form a cylindrical hole of large diameter at the end of an existing hole—e.g., to receive the head of a screw or bolt. If the enlarged hole is formed with tapered sides, the process is called countersinking.

Milling (Fig. 9) is another important machining process, in which the workpiece is shaped by means of a rotating cutter provided with a number of teeth. Usually the work is fed against the teeth, the work-feed direction (in relation to the cutter) being longitudinal, transverse or vertical. Milling machines are very versatile and can be used for a great variety of work, including screw-thread cutting. In circular milling the cutter and the workpiece are both rotated; in straight milling the cutter rotates while the workpiece performs a straight feed motion.

Grinding (Fig. 10) is the operation in which an abrasive wheel or disc is used to remove metal. It is employed as a finishing treatment to give parts already machined the necessary precision by the removal of excess material. It is also employed as a machining process in its own right—e.g., for roughly forged or cast parts or for the shaping of hard materials. Centerless grinding is used for small cylindrical parts and is performed between two grinding wheels. Grinding wheels are made from artificial abrasives, usually of the aluminum oxide or the silicon carbide type, embedded in suitable bonding agents. Wheels are available in a vast number of different combinations of abrasive, grain size, type of bond, hardness of bond, and structure.

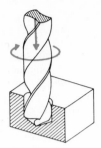

FIG. 7   DRILLING

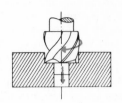

FIG. 8   COUNTERBORING

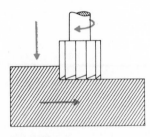

face milling

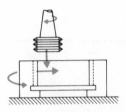

thread milling

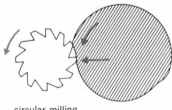

circular milling

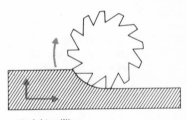

straight milling

FIG. 9   MILLING

cylindrical grinding

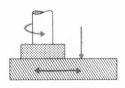

face grinding

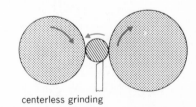

centerless grinding

FIG. 10   GRINDING

139

PRESSURE WELDING

Welding is the joining of metals by the application of heat and/or pressure, with or without the addition of a similar metal (filler metal). A welding technique may be designated according to the purpose for which it is used, or the procedure employed (manual or automatic welding), or the nature of the heat source (gas welding, electrical-resistance welding, arc welding, welding based on chemical reactions. etc.). As regards the purpose, a distinction is to be made between connective welding— i.e., the forming of joints and connections—and build-up welding (or surfacing), which is the process of reconditioning damaged or worn engineering components by the application of weld metal or the protection of components against corrosion or wear by the application of an armoring layer of more resistant metal (hard surfacing). As to the nature of the welding process itself, a distinction may be made between pressure welding and fusion welding.

In pressure welding, the parts to be joined are first locally heated at the place where the joint is to be formed and are then squeezed together in the plastic state so that they are united. In general, no filler metal is employed. Cold pressure welding makes use of high pressure, without the help of heat, to unite the parts. Related to this process are ultrasonic welding and explosion welding.

The oldest welding technique, still used in art ironwork and smith's work, is forge welding. This is the process of joining steel or iron parts by heating them in a forge until they reach a plastic state and are then united by hammering, by pressure, or by rolling.

In gas pressure welding (Fig. 1) the parts to be joined are heated by a gas-and-oxygen flame and are united by the exertion of continuous or of impact-type pressure. This principle is applied, for example. in the manufacture of small-diameter tubes from steel strip (Fretz-Moon process). By means of a special die, called a bell, and shaping rollers the continuous strip is formed into a tube. The edges of the strip are heated to welding temperature by gas burners, and the edges are pressed together and united by pressure rollers. In the case of arc pressure welding and the special techniques derived from it. the heat is generated by an electric arc briefly produced between the parts to be joined. which are then united by impact action. In the resistance pressure-welding process (Fig. 2) the heat is generated by the resistance encountered by an electric current which is passed through the material, especially the high resistance at the contact faces of the parts to be joined. The current is applied through electrodes or generated in the parts by induction. Heating based on electrical resistance is, for example, utilized in the process known as resistance butt welding (Fig. 2a): the two parts to be joined end to end are gripped, in contact with each other, in copper jaws which serve as electrodes for the passage of current across the joint. When the metal at the joint has reached a sufficiently high temperature, the current is switched off and the contact pressure is increased to unite the parts.

(more)

140

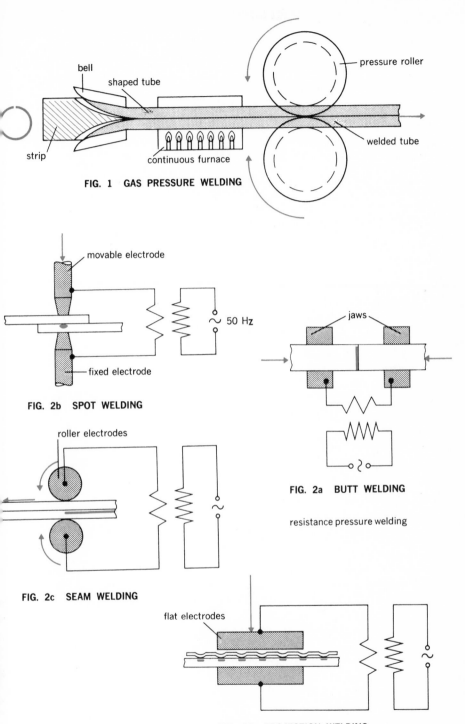

FIG. 1   GAS PRESSURE WELDING

FIG. 2b   SPOT WELDING

FIG. 2a   BUTT WELDING

resistance pressure welding

FIG. 2c   SEAM WELDING

FIG. 2d   PROJECTION WELDING

Similar in principle to resistance butt welding is spot welding (Fig. 2b, p. 141), which is a method of uniting by means of localized welds and is employed more particularly for sheet metal and wire. The sheets are gripped between copper electrodes through which a heavy current is passed; fusion occurs at the spots where the electrodes are thus applied. Seam welding (Fig. 2c, p. 141) is the process of closing a seam by a continuous resistance weld formed between two copper-roller electrodes. The principle is the same as in spot welding. The process called projection welding (Fig. 2d, p. 141) is used mainly for joining sheet-metal parts: prior to welding, projections are raised on the surfaces of the sheets, and the welds occur at these places. The current is introduced through flat electrodes.

Resistance pressure welding is widely used in the manufacture of tubes. More particularly, three techniques are employed. In all three, the initial material is a continuous strip of steel sheet preformed into a tubular section, but as yet with an open joint. In the conventional resistance-welding process of tube manufacture (Fig. 3) the tube is heated at the joint with low-voltage high-intensity alternating current by means of a large-diameter copper-roller electrode. The heated edges of the joint are then forced together by pressure rollers and thus united. With this process it is possible to produce tubes of 6 mm to 500 mm diameter and 0.6 mm to 10 mm wall thickness. A newer process is contact-electrode high-frequency welding, using alternating current of 100 to 450 kilocycles/sec. which is supplied to the edges of the joint through sliding contact electrodes. The method is employed mainly for welding the longitudinal seams of thin-walled tubes and other hollow sections. A third process widely employed in present-day tube manufacture is induction welding (Fig. 4), in which the joint is heated by induction produced by a medium-frequency (10 kilocycles/sec.) alternating current. The inductor is in the form of a coil which encloses the tube or is a linear inductor placed on the joint.

In the process known as thermit pressure welding, the heat is generated by a chemical reaction between powdered aluminum and iron oxide that develops a temperature of 3000° C. The aluminum powder is converted into aluminum oxide, and molten iron is formed by the reduction of the iron oxide. A recently developed method is friction welding (Fig. 5). The parts to be joined are mounted, with the joint faces in contact with each other, in a device somewhat like a lathe. One of the parts is then set in rotation. The friction generates heat, and when the requisite welding temperature has been reached, the rotating part is stopped and the two parts are then forced together with increased pressure so that they unite. Explosion welding (Fig. 6) is a form of cold pressure welding in which the pressure is produced by the shock wave from the detonation of an explosive. It is sometimes used for the joining of thin overlapping plates. The plates are gripped together and are covered with a "buffer layer" of rubber sheet and a layer of a special explosive, which is detonated electrically. Another new method is ultrasonic welding (Fig. 7), which is effected by high energy concentrations developed at the joint by ultrasonic vibrations, in combination with pressure.

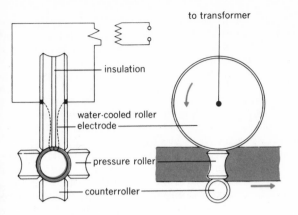

to transformer

insulation

water-cooled roller
electrode

pressure roller

counterroller

**FIG. 3   TUBE MANUFACTURE BY
RESISTANCE WELDING**

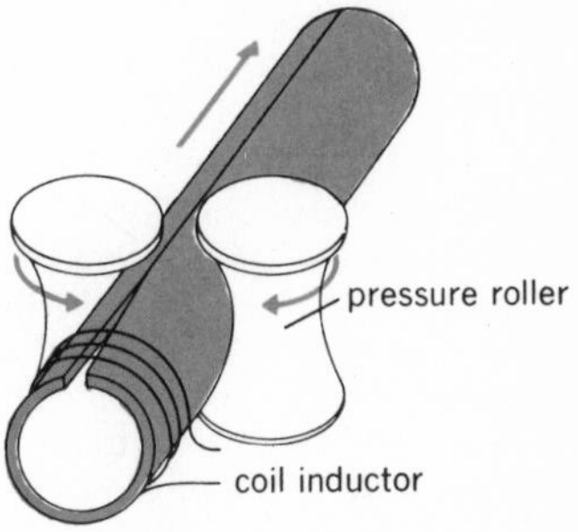

pressure roller

coil inductor

FIG. 4   INDUCTION WELDING

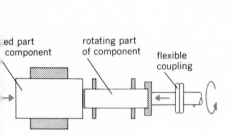

ed part
component

rotating part
of component

flexible
coupling

FIG. 5   FRICTION WELDING

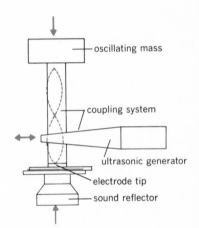

oscillating mass

coupling system

ultrasonic generator

electrode tip

sound reflector

FIG. 7   ULTRASONIC WELDING

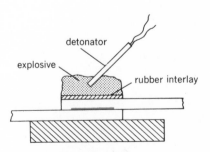

detonator

explosive

rubber interlay

FIG. 6   EXPLOSION WELDING

FUSION WELDING

The term "fusion welding" is applied to processes in which metals are heated to the temperature at which they melt and are then joined without hammering or the application of pressure. The joint can be formed without the use of a filler metal, but usually a filler metal in the form of a wire or rod is employed to fill the joint. Normally the filler metal has the same composition as the parent metal, but may contain alloying metals to improve its fluidity in the molten condition or to produce a fine-grained weld structure. The wire or rod of filler metal may be sheathed in a special coating. Such coatings perform one or more of various functions: serve as a flux, remove oxides or other disturbing substances that may be present, improve the wettability of the material surface, protect the weld against external influences, prevent excessively rapid cooling, and (in arc welding) stabilize the arc. The composition of the coating depends more particularly on the material to be welded and on the welding method. Mixtures of oxides of iron, manganese and titanium, alkaline-earth carbonates, fluorite, and organic compounds are used for coatings. Sources of heat employed in fusion welding are gas, electricity, chemical reactions, etc. Gas welding (Fig. 1) uses a flame produced by the burning in oxygen of acetylene (oxyacetylene welding) or sometimes another fuel gas (e.g., propane, butane, hydrogen) to heat and liquefy the metal at the joint to be welded. This is a very widely employed method of welding iron, steel, cast iron, and copper. The flame is applied to the edges of the joint and to a wire of the appropriate filler metal, which is melted and runs into the joint.

A fairly recent development is the electroslag process (Fig. 2), in which the metal at the joint is melted in an electrically conducting (ionized) molten-slag bath whose temperature is above the melting temperature of the metal. The welds are executed as vertical welds; with this method it is, for instance, possible to form butt welds in very thick plates quickly and economically. The current is supplied to the slag bath through bare metallic electrodes, which melt away and provide the filler metal. The molten filler metal sinks in the slag, fills the gap of the joint and slowly solidifies in it, from the bottom upwards. The gap is bridged by water-cooled copper shoes which, together with the faces of the joint, form a mold for the molten metal. The shoes move upwards along the joint during welding.

The most important and most widely used fusion-welding technique is arc welding, which employs an electric arc to melt the parent metal and the filler metal. The latter may be provided in the form of an electrode which melts away or it may be melted thermally—i.e., without carrying the welding current. The general technique can be subdivided into three categories: open-arc welding, covered-arc welding, and gas-shielded-arc welding. Open-arc welding by Benardos' method (Fig. 3a) employs direct current, the arc being formed between the parent metal and a carbon electrode. In Zerener's method (Fig. 3b) the arc is formed between two carbon electrodes; the heat of the arc is concentrated on the workpiece by the action of a magnetic coil. The method now most widely used was originated by Slavjanov (Fig. 3c): the arc is formed between a metallic electrode, which gradually melts away to supply the filler metal, and the workpiece.

(more)

144

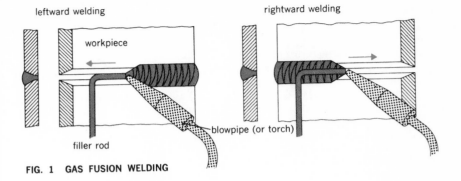

FIG. 1   GAS FUSION WELDING

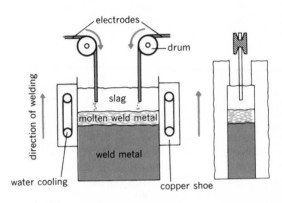

FIG. 2   ELECTROSLAG WELDING

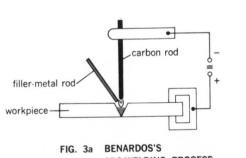

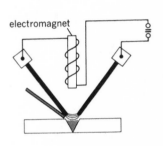

FIG. 3a   BENARDOS'S
ARC-WELDING PROCESS

FIG. 3b   ZERENER'S
ARC-WELDING PROCESS

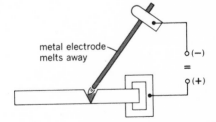

FIG. 3c   SLAVJANOV'S ARC-WELDING PROCESS

Fusion Welding (continued)

The process known as firecracker welding (Fig. 4) is an example of a covered-arc method. A heavily coated electrode is laid horizontally on the joint to be welded and is covered with an insulating layer of paper and a covering bar of copper or some other metal. The workpiece is connected to one pole and the electrode is connected to the other pole of a current source. An arc is struck between the end of the electrode and the joint, and burns along the length of the electrode. Another form of covered-arc welding is submerged-arc welding (Fig. 5). The flux is supplied separately in the form of powder which blankets the arc. The powder melts and protects the molten filler metal from atmospheric contamination. Any powder not melted is recovered by suction and reused. When cool, the fused powder forms a slag, which peels off the weld.

Shielded-arc welding is based on the principle of protecting the molten filler metal by an envelope of chemically inert gas, which may be helium (heliarc process), argon (argonarc process) or carbon dioxide. In atomic-hydrogen welding (Fig. 6a) the heat liberated by monatomic hydrogen when recombining into molecules is used to fuse the metal. An alternating-current arc is maintained across two tungsten electrodes. A stream of hydrogen gas is passed through the arc, in which the hydrogen molecules are split up into atoms. Outside the actual arc these atoms recombine into molecules. This produces great heat, which melts the parts to be welded and unites them, with or without the addition of a filler metal. The inert-gas tungsten-arc process (Fig. 6b) and the inert-gas metal-arc process (Fig. 6c) are two shielded-arc welding processes that are used both for manual techniques and for automatic welding by mechanized equipment.

Thermit welding (Fig. 7) has already been referred to in connection with pressure welding. It is also used as a fusion-welding process, more particularly for iron and steel castings and forgings. The source of heat is not electricity or gas but a chemical reaction that produces intense heat (3000° C): the combustion of a mixture of aluminum powder and iron oxide by which the aluminum is converted into aluminum oxide and the iron oxide is reduced to molten iron (or steel). The parts to be joined are surrounded by a sand-lined mold. The powder mixture is packed in a conical crucible and ignited. The molten iron flows in and around the joint, where it fuses with the preheated parent metal.

146

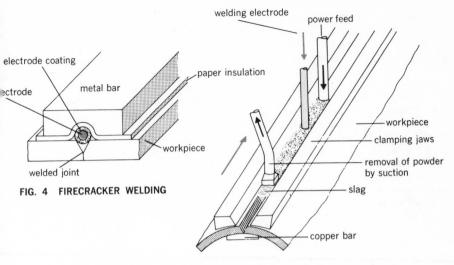

FIG. 4 FIRECRACKER WELDING

FIG. 5 SUBMERGED-ARC WELDING

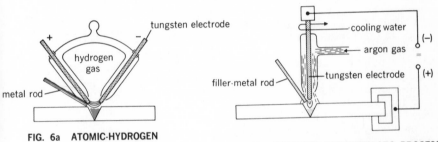

FIG. 6a ATOMIC-HYDROGEN
WELDING PROCESSES

FIG. 6b INERT-GAS TUNGSTEN-ARC PROCESS

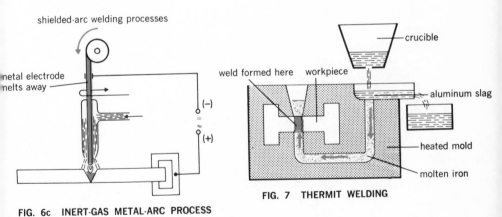

FIG. 6c INERT-GAS METAL-ARC PROCESS

FIG. 7 THERMIT WELDING

147

SOLDERING

Soldering is the process of joining metal parts by means of a molten filler metal (solder) whose melting point is lower than that of the metals to be joined. The latter are wetted by the molten filler without themselves being melted (as in welding). The solder is employed in the form of rods, wires, strips, sheets, granules, powder or paste. In contrast with welding, different metals can be joined by soldering. A distinction is made according to the type of solder employed: (1) soft solders (usually a mixture of lead and tin); (2) hard solders, which comprise brass solders (copper-zinc alloys), silver solders, copper solders, nickel-silver solders, solders for light alloys, etc. The solder must be suitably chosen in relation to the metals to be joined. In particular, the melting point of the solder should be well below that of the metals. In soft soldering, the heat may be supplied by a soldering iron (Fig. 1) or a blowpipe. Another method consists in placing the assembled work on a plate along with a piece of solder and flux. The work is then heated in a furnace, so that the solder melts, and is then allowed to cool. This last-mentioned technique may also be used in hard soldering. More usually the heat to melt a hard solder is supplied by a blowpipe (Fig. 2) or torch. In certain cases heat generated by electrical resistance is used. The term "brazing" is applied more specifically to a form of hard soldering using brass (i.e., a copper-zinc alloy) as the jointing medium. A flux is generally employed in conjunction with the latter. In brazing, borax is used as a flux; it serves as a means of preventing the formation of an oxide coating on the joint faces, as a cleaning agent, and as a "wetting agent" to aid the flow of the molten metal. In some cases a shielding gas may be used to prevent oxidation of the faces of the joint. Dip brazing is a technique in which the assembled parts to be joined are immersed in the molten jointing medium (Fig. 3). It is widely used in industrial mass-production processes. In other industrial techniques the workpiece, provided with solder at the joint, is heated to the appropriate soldering temperature by immersion in a salt bath (Fig. 5) or an oil bath. In another method, the molten solder is poured through the highly heated joint until the metal cools and unites the two parts (Fig. 4). In electrical-resistance soldering (Fig. 6), the solder, flux and workpiece are heated between tungsten or copper electrodes. Induction soldering (Fig. 7) utilizes a high-frequency alternating current to induce a heating current in the workpiece. A more recent method is ultrasonic soldering, which is used, for example, for the soldering of aluminum. The ultrasonic vibrations are transmitted by a nickel rod through the solder on to the surface of the workpiece, destroying the oxide film on the aluminum.

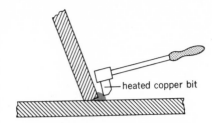

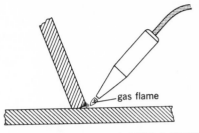

FIG. 1 SOFT SOLDERING WITH A SOLDERING IRON
(OR SOLDERING BIT)

heated copper bit

FIG. 2 HARD SOLDERING WITH A BLOWPIPE

gas flame

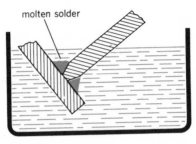

molten solder

FIG. 3 DIP BRAZING

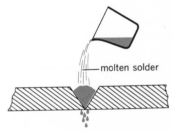

molten solder

FIG. 4 SOLDERING WITH MOLTEN METAL

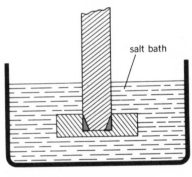

salt bath

FIG. 5 SALT-BATH SOLDERING

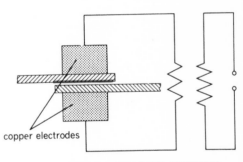

copper electrodes

FIG. 6 RESISTANCE SOLDERING

FIG. 7 INDUCTION SOLDERING

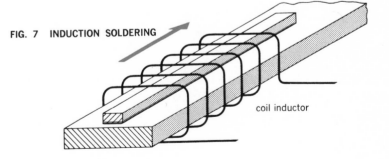

coil inductor

149

By means of a wide variety of techniques, sheet metals can be given all sorts of complex hollow shapes and sections. The equipment employed for this type of work ranges from simple hand tools to elaborate power-operated automatic machinery. Sheet-metal work usually starts with a basic preliminary operation such as cutting, slitting, perforating, etc., performed with tools that exercise a shearing action. Many kinds of shearing devices are available for these purposes. These may be simple hand shears, which are scissorslike cutting tools of various shapes and sizes, or hand-operated bench shears for heavier-gauge materials. There are several kinds of power-driven shearing machines. In general, such a machine comprises a fixed blade and a movable blade. The term "punching" refers to operations performed with the aid of a punching machine (or press) and comprising blanking (the shearing of a metal blank from the sheet), piercing (the cutting of a hole in a metal article with tools fitted in the machine), and clipping (removal of surplus metal).

A wide range of shaping operations coming under the heading of folding and bending are done on presses and similar machines, as well as such operations as stamping, crimping, beading, seaming, grooving, etc. These processes are used for the shaping or stiffening of metal sheets, the forming of tubular sections of circular or other shape, and numerous other purposes.

Angles and sections of all kinds can be formed by bending (Fig. 1) or folding (Fig. 2). Coiling (Fig. 3) is the process of coiling over the edge of a sheet-metal component to increase the strength or to provide a suitable edge finish. It can be done by a coiling or rolling tool on a press. Cylindrically shaped articles such as tubes can be produced on a roll-forming machine (Fig. 4). Press forming operations include cupping (Fig. 5), which denotes the conversion of a blank into cup form, and embossing (Fig. 5), by which a particular design (for decorative or strengthening purposes) can be produced on a partly finished component. Cupping is often merely the first stage in an operation called forming, in which an appropriate tool is employed to give the article its final shape. Seaming (Fig. 6) is used mainly for the joining of sheet-metal parts and is, for example, often applied to joints in metal roofing. The seam is formed by bending over the adjacent edges to produce an interlocking, which is strengthened by hammering the seam to flatten it. Flanging (Fig. 7) is the process of forming a flange on a sheet-metal component. Beading (Fig. 8) is the process of making depressions for the purpose of stiffening, embellishment, etc.; it may be done by means of suitably shaped rollers.

(more)

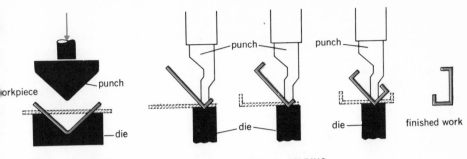

FIG. 1 BENDING

FIG. 2 FOLDING

workpiece — punch — die

punch — die — finished work

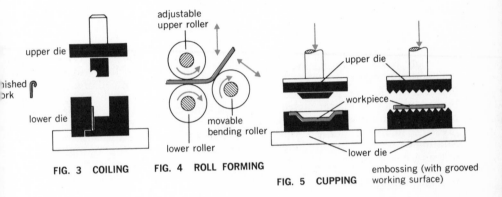

upper die

finished work

lower die

FIG. 3 COILING

adjustable upper roller

movable bending roller

lower roller

FIG. 4 ROLL FORMING

upper die

workpiece

lower die

FIG. 5 CUPPING

embossing (with grooved working surface)

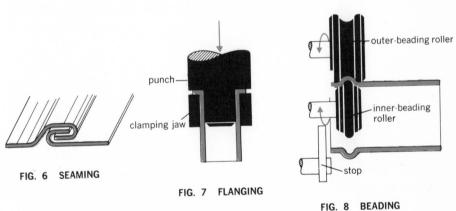

FIG. 6 SEAMING

punch

clamping jaw

FIG. 7 FLANGING

outer-beading roller

inner-beading roller

stop

FIG. 8 BEADING

Deep drawing (Fig. 9) is the forming of sheet or strip metal into a cup-shaped component by a process of shaping followed by drawing. It is extensively employed in the automobile and aeronautical industries and in other industries for the production of hollow objects of various kinds, ranging from cartridge cases to washing-machine tubs. The process is usually associated with metals possessing good ductility, such as copper, brass, aluminum, cupronickel and mild steel. The principle of deep drawing consists in clamping a metal blank over a die opening and then forcing it through the opening by means of a punch. A cup-shaped shell of reduced thickness is thus formed. A lubricant is used. The depth of shell that can be drawn in a single operation depends on the tensile strength and thickness of the metal. As a rule, one or more redrawing operations are necessary to obtain the finished component. Between successive operations the cup is annealed, cleaned and lubricated. A somewhat similar technique is used in the process called stretch forming, in which the blank is strained beyond its elastic limit over a form tool or stretch block by the application of a tensile load, so that plastic deformation takes place (Fig. 10). In another technique the sheet metal is shaped by being distended in a mold under radial internal pressure (Fig. 10). In the process called "marforming" (Fig. 11) the displacement of a rubber pad under high pressure makes it conform to the contour of a die block placed between it and the table of the press. It is a technique by which shallow components can be manufactured cheaply. In "hydroforming" a rubber diaphragm supported by hydraulic pressure is used instead of a solid rubber pad. Yet another method of sheet-metal forming is by utilizing the force developed by an explosion acting through a liquid or gaseous medium (Fig. 12). Spinning is the process of forming a hollow shape by the application of lateral pressure to a rapidly revolving blank on a lathe, so that the metal assumes the shape of a former which is rotating with it. Deformation is effected by a combination of bending and stretching, pressure being exerted by means of a steel forming tool worked by an operator (Fig. 13) or by means of a mechanically controlled roller (Fig. 14). This latter process is known more particularly as "flow forming" or "flow turning": thick-gauge material is made to flow plastically by pressure rolling in the same direction in which the roller is traveling.

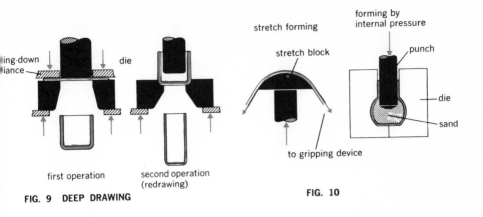

FIG. 9   DEEP DRAWING

first operation

second operation
(redrawing)

stretch forming

stretch block

to gripping device

forming by
internal pressure

punch

die

sand

FIG. 10

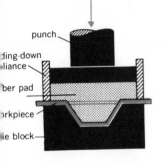

FIG. 11   MARFORMING

punch

holding-down
appliance

rubber pad

workpiece

die block

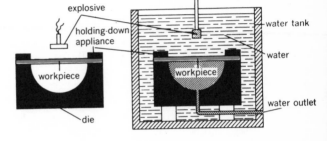

FIG. 12   EXPLOSION TECHNIQUES FOR DEEP DRAWING

explosive

holding-down
appliance

water tank

water

workpiece

die

water outlet

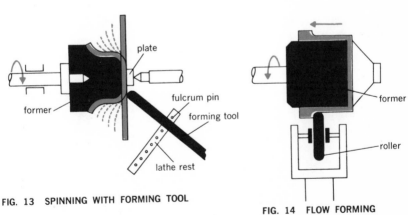

FIG. 13   SPINNING WITH FORMING TOOL

plate

former

fulcrum pin

forming tool

lathe rest

former

roller

FIG. 14   FLOW FORMING

153

GALVANIZING

Among the various metallic coatings applied to iron and steel to provide protection against corrosion, zinc plays a very important part. The process of applying the zinc coating is called galvanizing. It is very extensively employed for products such as bar, tube, strip, wire and sheet as well as for all manner of articles and utensils such as buckets, watering cans, washtubs, garbage cans, etc. The most commonly applied process is hot-dip galvanizing, in which the zinc coating is obtained by immersion of the materials or articles in a bath of molten zinc. The zinc combines with the iron, so that iron-and-zinc-alloy crystals are formed which provide a firmly adhering coating (Fig. 1). The characteristic crystalline surface patterns presented by hot-dip coatings are known as "spangles"; their size and shape are influenced by the surface condition of the steel, the impurities present in the bath, the rate of cooling, etc. Less widely used zinc-coating processes are electrogalvanizing, metal spraying (see p. 156), and sherardizing.

For successful hot-dip galvanizing, the steel must be free of oil, grease, dirt, scale, and corrosion products. Preparatory treatment may comprise some or all of the following: degreasing with a suitable solvent, pickling with acid, rinsing, treatment with a flux, and drying. The object of pickling is to remove any oxide film by the action of hydrochlorie or sulphuric acid. Castings to which molding sand still adheres may have to be subjected to mechanical cleaning treatments such as grit blasting or tumbling, the latter being an operation in which small articles are mixed with an abrasive and rotated in a cylindrical drum. The flux, usually a mixture of zinc chloride and ammonium chloride, serves to remove any remaining traces of impurities and increases the wettability of the steel surface. In "wet galvanizing" (Fig. 3) the flux is deposited in molten form on the zinc bath, and the metal to be galvanized is introduced into the bath through the layer of flux. In "dry galvanizing" (Fig. 2) the metal components are first dipped in a solution of flux and are then dried, so that they become precoated with a thin film of flux, which melts in the zinc bath. The molten-zinc bath is kept at a temperature of 450°–470° C. Certain metals such as tin and aluminum may be added to the bath; they promote fluidity, and tin imparts brightness to the coated metal.

Sherardizing is a process for forming intermetallic compounds of iron and zinc on a steel surface by heating it in the presence of zinc dust below the melting point of the zinc. This heating is done in a sealed container packed with zinc dust and continuously rotated. The process is used more particularly for small articles such as bolts, nuts, chains, valves, etc.

The Sendzimir process (Fig. 4) is used for the galvanizing of steel strip. The strip is unwound from a coil (1). At (2) the oil or grease adhering to it is removed by oxidation (heating). In the next stage (3) the strip is annealed and the oxides are reduced by ammonia. Then follows cooling to 500° C (4) and immersion of the strip in the zinc bath (5), which is kept molten at about 450° C by the temperature of the steel strip. On leaving the bath, the strip is cut (6) or coiled (7).

154

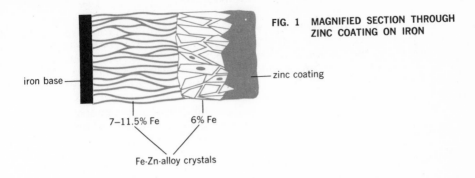

FIG. 1 MAGNIFIED SECTION THROUGH ZINC COATING ON IRON

iron base

zinc coating

7–11.5% Fe   6% Fe

Fe-Zn-alloy crystals

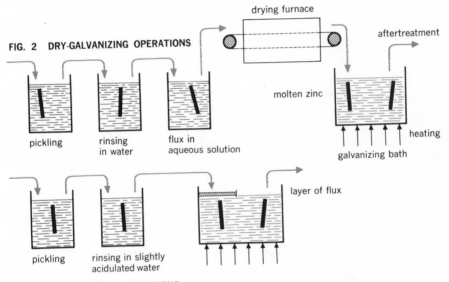

drying furnace

aftertreatment

FIG. 2 DRY-GALVANIZING OPERATIONS

molten zinc

pickling   rinsing   flux in
             in water   aqueous solution

heating

galvanizing bath

layer of flux

pickling   rinsing in slightly
             acidulated water

FIG. 3 WET-GALVANIZING OPERATIONS

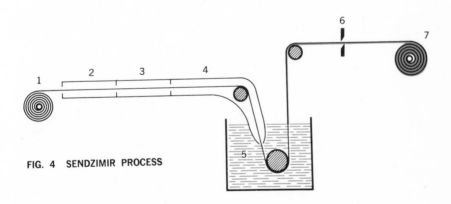

6

7

1   2   3   4

5

FIG. 4 SENDZIMIR PROCESS

METAL SPRAYING

Metal spraying, or metallizing, is a process for applying protective coatings to iron and steel. It consists in spraying particles of molten metal on to the surface to be treated and can be used with most of the common metals, including aluminum, copper, lead, nickel, tin, zinc, and various alloys. The coating metal, in the form of a wire, is fed into a spray gun in which it is melted by the combustion of a fuel gas— e.g., a mixture of oxygen and acetylene. A spray gun of this kind (Fig. 1) comprises two rollers which are powered by an air turbine (driven by compressed air) or an electric drive and which feed the wire through the central part of a special nozzle. The gas at the nozzle is ignited; the wire is melted on emerging from the nozzle; the molten metal is "atomized" by compressed air and is projected at high velocity against the surface to be coated. In another type of spray gun (not illustrated) the wire is melted in a combustion chamber in the head of the gun. Although the particles of molten metal are cooled instantly, the impact causes them to adhere firmly to the steel surface, provided that it has been cleaned and roughened thoroughly, as by machining or by sandblasting. Special measures may have to be taken in certain cases to ensure good bonding of the sprayed metal to the steel surface. A special adhesion-promoting intermediate layer may be provided, the steel component may be preheated, or a subsequent heat treatment (after spraying) may be applied. A process known as fuse bond may be employed, in which the surface is roughened by low-voltage electric arcs. In a somewhat different technique, the metal to be sprayed is fed to the spray gun not in the form of wire, but as powder supplied from a container by suction or blowing (Fig. 2). This method is generally used in cases where the metal to be sprayed cannot be drawn into a wire—e.g., hard alloys— or has a high melting point.

Metal spraying is a very versatile technique, offering advantages of flexibility and portability. Thus it can be applied in the field to steel bridges, storage tanks, pylons, etc. For such structures, zinc spraying is most extensively used. Spraying is used not only for the application of thin coatings as protection against corrosion, but also for building up surfaces—e.g., for reconditioning worn or damaged parts, for filling holes and cavities, and for the application of friction surfaces to bearings. The metallized coating can be built up to any reasonable thickness and can be filed, turned, ground and polished. Coatings of lead, aluminum, silver or stainless steel are sometimes used for providing protection against corrosion in special apparatus employed in the chemical and foodstuff industries. Steel or hard-alloy coatings are used as wearing surfaces: for instance, light-alloy pistons can be surfaced with a sprayed steel coating. In the electronics and telecommunication industries, metallic coatings are applied to nonmetallic materials to make them electrically conductive.

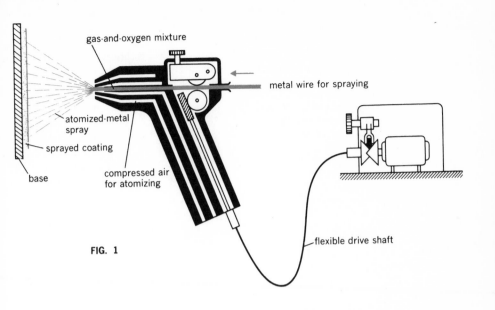

gas-and-oxygen mixture

metal wire for spraying

atomized-metal spray

sprayed coating

base

compressed air for atomizing

flexible drive shaft

FIG. 1

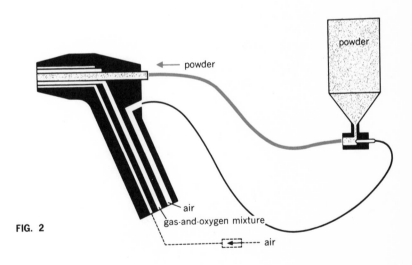

powder

powder

air

gas-and-oxygen mixture

air

FIG. 2

ELECTROFORMING

Electroforming is the process of producing or copying an object by electrodeposition of a metallic coating within a mold, from which it is afterwards removed so that the finished product is a hollow shell. Alternatively, a metallic coating may be deposited on the exterior of a nonmetallic solid object.

First a mold is produced from the model to be copied (a). The mold may consist of a nonmetallic substance or sometimes a low-melting-point alloy. A suitable substance used for the purpose may be celluloid, wax or stearin, which is poured over the model and is removed when it has set. Gypsum plaster, gutta-percha and plastics are also used for mold making. Plastics, in particular, have the advantage of producing molds that have a long service life—i.e., can be reused a large number of times. Molds may comprise one, two or three parts, depending on the complexity and shape of the model.

The next operation consists in making the surface of the mold electrically conductive (b). This can be done by brushing it with fine graphite powder, or with metallic powder such as copper, suspended in a thin lacquer. Alternatively, very finely divided copper, silver or some other metal may be deposited by chemical reduction or by vaporization in a vacuum. A mold made of a metallic substance must be provided with a bond-breaking layer before electrolysis, so as to enable the electroformed shell subsequently to be stripped from the mold and not remain adhering to it. The electrodeposition of metallic coatings is done with the aid of direct current on the principle of electrolysis in an acid or an alkaline salt solution containing the metal to be deposited. The mold is connected to the negative pole and thus forms the cathode; the anode, connected to the positive pole of the current source, usually consists of a plate of the metal to be deposited and is gradually consumed (c). Various auxiliary techniques are applied—such as the use of internal anodes, masking, etc.—to ensure that a uniform and smooth metallic coating is formed. By the addition of special substances it is possible to enhance the smoothness, fineness and luster of the coating. When a coating of the desired thickness has been attained, the shell is rinsed, removed from the mold (d) and, if necessary, given a finishing treatment. Next, the shell may be given a backing or filling of low-melting-point alloy, or some other material, to strengthen it.

Electroforming is used for a variety of purposes: e.g., making copies of archeological or art objects, printing plates, metal master discs in the manufacture of phonograph records, embossing dies, templates, molds for casting, and many objects used in mechanical and electrical engineering.

158

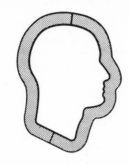
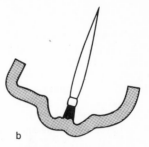

object to be copied

a

forming the mold

b

making the mold electrically conductive by brushing it with graphite powder

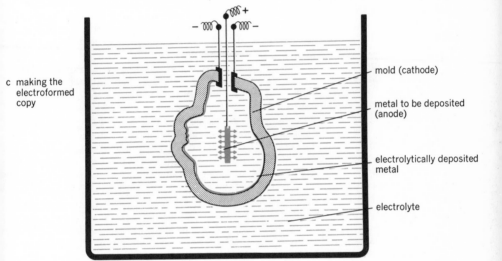

c making the electroformed copy

mold (cathode)

metal to be deposited (anode)

electrolytically deposited metal

electrolyte

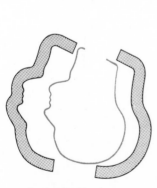
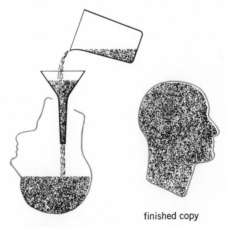

d removing the electroformed copy from the mold

e filling the copy

finished copy

ELECTROPLATING

Electroplating is the process of producing a metallic coating on a surface by electrodeposition—i.e., by the action of an electric current. Such coatings may perform a mainly protective function, to prevent corrosion of the metal on which they are deposited: e.g., plating with zinc (electrogalvanizing) or with tin; or a decorative function: e.g., gold or silver plating; or both functions: e.g., chromium plating. The principle of electroplating is that the coating metal is deposited from an electrolyte—an aqueous acid or alkaline solution—on to the base: i.e., the metal to be coated (Fig. 2). The latter forms the cathode (negative electrode), while a plate of the metal to be deposited serves as the anode (positive electrode). A low-voltage direct current is used; the anode is gradually consumed. Various substances (addition agents) are added to the electroplating bath to obtain a smooth and bright metal deposit. These are principally organic compounds, usually colloidal. Sometimes the objects to be plated are coated with two or more layers of different metals; for example, chromium plating cannot suitably be applied directly to a zinc-sprayed base; a coating of copper followed by a coating of nickel must be applied intermediately before the chromium is deposited.

To obtain a good and firmly adhering coating it is necessary to subject the objects or components to a thorough cleaning. This may be achieved by mechanical treatment—e.g., sandblasting, grinding, wire brushing, scraping, etc.; or by physical methods such as degreasing with organic solvents; or by chemical methods such as pickling with acid, or degreasing by the action of alkalies (saponification); or by electrocleaning, which is a method of cleaning by electrolytic action (more particularly the scrubbing action exercised by the evolution of gas at the surface of the metal). Wetting agents or emulsifiers may be added. The vats for electroplating baths differ greatly in size, shape and lining material (glass, lead, etc.), depending on the size and shape of the components to be plated and on the chemical character of the bath. Electroplating is normally done with direct current. However, particularly with cyanide copper baths, improved smoothness and uniformity of the coating can be obtained by means of the so-called periodic-reverse process, in which the polarity is periodically reversed, so that the metal is alternatively plated and deplated.

Steel strip is plated with zinc or with tin by continuous and largely automated high-speed processes. The electrolytic tin-plating process illustrated schematically in Fig. 3 comprises the following operations: electrolytic cleaning in dilute sulphuric acid, pickling, electrodeposition of tin, melting of the coating to give it a brilliant surface, chemical dipping in chromate solutions, oiling, shearing. The steel strip travels through the installation at a speed of about 25 m/min. (80 ft./min.). A continuous zinc-plating installation is illustrated schematically in Fig. 4.

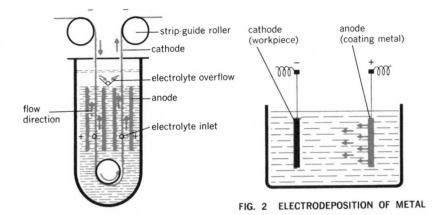

FIG. 2 ELECTRODEPOSITION OF METAL

FIG. 1 ELECTROGALVANIZING CELL

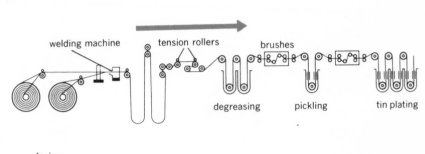

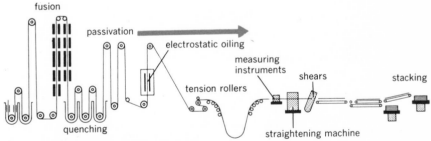

FIG. 3 ELECTROLYTIC TIN-PLATING PLANT
FOR STEEL STRIP

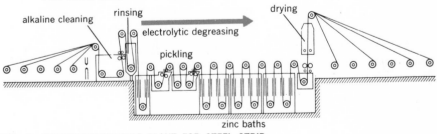

FIG. 4 ELECTROGALVANIZING PLANT FOR STEEL STRIP

Besides manually operated valves, an important part is played by valves and similar devices actuated by some form of auxiliary power such as electricity, compressed air or hydraulic pressure.

A solenoid valve is a combination of a valve with an electromagnet which provides the power to operate it. The valve disc is connected by a rod to the core of the magnet. Functionally there are three main types of solenoid valve. In the first type (Fig. 1) the core of the magnet and the valve disc are pulled upwards against the force of a spring when the magnet is energized. When the current is switched off and the magnet thus de-energized, the spring thrusts the disc against the valve seat, thereby closing the valve. In the valve shown in Fig. 2, the pressure of the fluid is utilized to control the valve. When the magnet is energized, the valve disc is lifted clear of the primary control passage, and the space above the differential piston is brought into communication with the valve outlet. The pressure over the differential piston is thus reduced. Since the amount of fluid that can flow through the narrow compensating passage is smaller than the amount that flows through the primary control passage, a difference in pressure is developed, causing the differential piston to be lifted off the valve seat. On removal of the pressure, the primary control passage is first closed. Pressure now builds up again above the differential piston, so that this piston is thrust downwards. The valve closes. To function properly, valves of this kind require a certain minimum pressure difference between valve inlet and outlet. In the third type of solenoid valve (Fig. 3) a magnetically operated three-way valve and a piston valve form a unit. Control is effected with the aid of pressure supplied by an auxiliary source of power. While the valve is in the closed position the magnet is de-energized and the bypass passage is in communication with the outlet. There is then no pressure in the space under the piston. When the magnet is energized, the auxiliary pressure is admitted under the piston, so that the latter rises, causing the valve to open (left-hand diagram in Fig. 3).

A diaphragm valve (Fig. 4) is controlled by the action of a diaphragm which is actuated by liquid or pneumatic pressure. A magnetically operated three-way valve or changeover valve is connected to the space over the diaphragm. While the magnet is de-energized, access to this space is closed, the diaphragm being held in the closed position by the compression spring. When current flows through the magnet, compressed air is admitted to the space over the diaphragm and develops the force needed to thrust the diaphragm downwards (against the pressure of the spring and the pressure of the fluid acting against the valve disc), thereby causing the valve to open.

In long pipelines with high rates of flow it is undesirable to effect valve closure abruptly in a single stage, as this will cause sudden pressure buildup which may harm the pipeline or the fittings and measuring devices installed in it. This can be avoided by employing two valves, one in the pipeline itself and the other in a bypass pipe of smaller bore. On closure of the main valve there remains a flow of 10–20% in the bypass, which can then be closed as a final stage of the closing operation. Alternatively, a double-diaphragm valve (Fig. 5) may be used, which closes in two stages. It may be equipped with quick-action air-relief valves (as shown in Fig. 5) or with magnetically operated changeover valves. Release of the air pressure may be effected either manually or automatically by closing the control pipelines. Valves of this kind are widely used in industrial processes, especially automatic processes with centralized control: e.g., for the delivery of predetermined quantities of fluid.

(more)

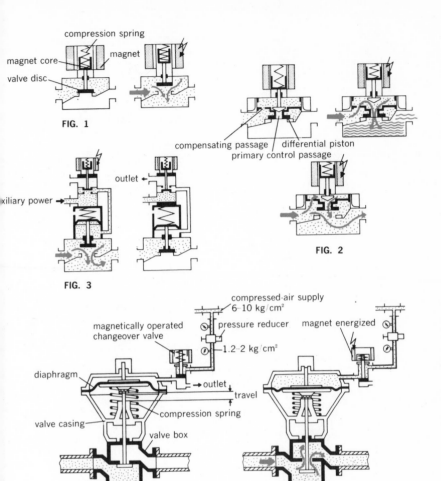

FIG. 1

compression spring

magnet core
magnet

valve disc

compensating passage / differential piston
primary control passage

FIG. 2

outlet ←

xiliary power →

FIG. 3

compressed-air supply
6–10 kg/cm²

magnetically operated
changeover valve

pressure reducer

magnet energized

1.2–2 kg/cm²

diaphragm

→ outlet

travel

valve casing

compression spring

valve box

FIG. 4   DIAPHRAGM VALVE WITH MAGNETICALLY OPERATED CHANGEOVER VALVE

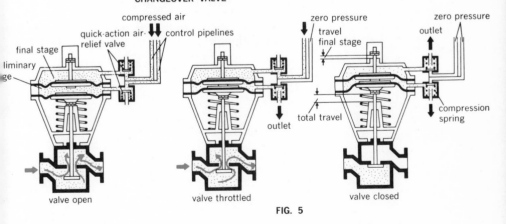

compressed air

quick-action air-
relief valve

control pipelines

zero pressure

zero pressure

final stage

liminary

ge

travel
final stage

outlet

outlet

total travel

compression
spring

valve open

valve throttled

valve closed

FIG. 5

163

Power-Operated Valves (continued)

Besides the disc-type valves described in the foregoing, other types of valve, such as sluice valves and flap valves, can likewise be power-operated.

The sluice valve illustrated in Fig. 1 is provided with an electric motor for raising and lowering the gate. Alternatively, a hydraulic drive system may be used to do this. The hydraulic actuating cylinder is mounted directly over the valve and is connected to the valve gate by means of a rod. The hydraulic fluid (oil, for instance) is admitted into the cylinder either over the piston (to close the valve) or under it (to open the valve).

There exist many types of valve for a variety of specific purposes—e.g., in pipelines, in refineries, for water turbines, for hot gases, etc. An important type is the annular measuring valve (Fig. 2). The rate of flow through the valve is measured in terms of the difference in pressure between the two points where the two small side pipes are connected to the valve casing, these pipes being connected to a manometer. The inlet casing, the upstream end of the gate, and the diffuser are so shaped that a reliable flow-rate measurement is obtained over almost the entire range of valve-gate movement from closed to fully open. The gate may be actuated manually or with the aid of electric or hydraulic power and is held in the desired position by means of a self-locking worm drive. Such valves, with or without flow-measuring facilities, are used in water engineering as valves for pipelines, pumping stations, etc. In such circumstances they often have to perform the additional function of a nonreturn valve in the event of pump failure or as a check valve to protect the pump itself from reverse flow. For this purpose a special quick-action closing mechanism may be employed (Fig. 3). It is electrically connected to the pump-drive motor and functions as follows. The electromagnet is normally energized, the clutch is engaged, and the self-locking worm drive holds the valve gate in the position to which it has been set. In the event of a power failure, the magnet becomes de-energized and the clutch is automatically disconnected by spring action. The connection to the worm drive is broken, the drop weight descends and—through the agency of a crank mechanism—moves the gate to the closed position. To slow down the final stage of closure and thus avoid too sudden a pressure buildup, an oil braking cylinder (dashpot) is provided, whose braking action can be controlled by means of valves in the oil-bypass pipes.

Another important class of valves is formed by the flap valves, of which the automatically acting check valve (Fig. 4) is a particular type. It comprises a disc, or gate, which is pivoted at its upper end and is held open by the flow; but if the flow reverses, the weight of the disc and the movement of the fluid force the disc on to the seat. In the butterfly valve (Fig. 5) the closing element is a circular disc pivoted along a diameter. Closure is effected manually, electrically or hydraulically. Such valves are used, for example, in the penstocks to the turbines of hydroelectric power stations. They may be equipped with quick-action closing devices of the type shown in Fig. 3.

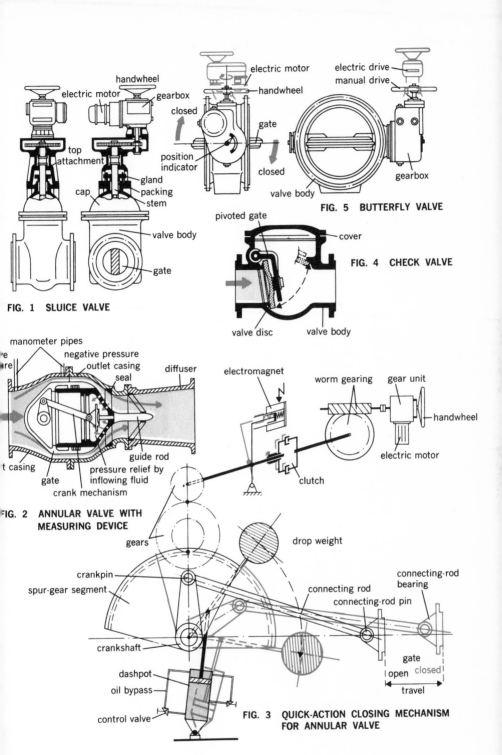

electric motor — gearbox

handwheel

top attachment

gland packing — cap — stem

valve body

gate

FIG. 1 SLUICE VALVE

electric motor — handwheel

closed

gate

position indicator

closed

valve body

FIG. 5 BUTTERFLY VALVE

electric drive — manual drive

gearbox

pivoted gate — cover

FIG. 4 CHECK VALVE

valve disc   valve body

manometer pipes

negative pressure outlet casing

seal   diffuser

t casing

gate   guide rod

pressure relief by inflowing fluid

crank mechanism

FIG. 2 ANNULAR VALVE WITH MEASURING DEVICE

electromagnet   worm gearing   gear unit

handwheel

electric motor

clutch

gears   drop weight

crankpin

spur-gear segment

connecting rod

connecting-rod pin

connecting-rod bearing

crankshaft

gate

open   closed

travel

dashpot

oil bypass

control valve

FIG. 3 QUICK-ACTION CLOSING MECHANISM FOR ANNULAR VALVE

SCREW THREADS

Screw threads are used for the purpose of fastening (screws and bolts) and for the transmission of motion: e.g., a rotating screw spindle imparts a longitudinal motion to a nut mounted on it. A screw thread conforms to a helix, a space curve that may be conceived as the hypotenuse of a right triangle wrapped round a cylinder (Fig. 1) to form either a right-hand or a left-hand thread, according to the direction of wrapping. Depending on the shape of the groove, various types of screw thread are distinguished (see Fig. 5). A single-thread screw may be conceived as a cylinder with one continuous helical groove. The "pitch" of the thread is the distance, measured in the axial direction, between two corresponding points on adjacent turns of the thread; it is the distance a nut would travel in one complete revolution. For particular purposes a multiple thread may be employed—e.g., a double or a triple thread, which may be conceived as respectively two or three independent but parallel helical grooves around a cylinder.

Consider a body on an inclined plane (Fig. 2). If the angle of inclination α is gradually increased, the body will begin to slide down the plane when this angle reaches a particular value $\alpha = \rho$, called the angle of friction. The magnitude of the angle of friction depends on the material and surface condition (roughness, smoothness) of the inclined plane and of the body, but is independent of the weight or loading of the latter. A screw thread may be regarded as a helical inclined plane, while the nut corresponds to the object placed on the plane. For the nut to be self-locking, so that it will not slacken and move along the thread of its own accord, the thread should have a slope α which is smaller than the angle of friction ρ (screws and bolts for fastening). On the other hand, a screw thread for the transmission of motion should preferably have a larger value of α. In the absence of friction the amount of work done in moving a body up an inclined plane (Fig. 3) would be $G \times h$, where G is the load and h is the vertical distance traveled. If there is friction, the amount of work will be greater, namely, $G \times H$ (H greater than h), as though the plane were inclined at a steeper angle which exceeds α by an amount ρ. Obviously, for a thread with a small angle α the relative effect of friction (corresponding to the angle ρ) is greater than for a threader with a large α (compare left-hand and right-hand diagram in Fig. 3). To achieve good efficiency a screw thread for the transmission of motion should therefore have a large α and consequently a large pitch.

Increased friction, to achieve self-locking, can also be achieved by sloping the flanks of the threads. From Fig. 4 it is apparent that for a V-shaped screw thread the loading perpendicular to the plane of the thread (the normal force N) is greater than for the square thread shown in the right-hand diagram. Since the friction force is proportional to the normal force, screw threads for the transmission of motion should preferably have the flattest possible flanks (square threads) to minimize friction, whereas fastening screws should have V-shaped threads for maximum friction.

Various forms of thread are shown in Fig. 5. Most threads employed in engineering are of V form, some are square, and some are modifications of a V or square. In the Whitworth, or English Standard, thread, the angle made by the two flanks of the thread is 55°. In the metric thread and the Sellers (American) thread it is 60°. Knuckle threads (rounded threads) are used in cases where damage, clogging with dirt, or corrosion is liable to occur; the characteristic shape is a semicircle instead of a V. The Acme thread with an angle of 29° between the flanks is a standardized thread of trapezoidal shape. The buttress thread is used in cases where large forces act in the longitudinal direction of the screw.

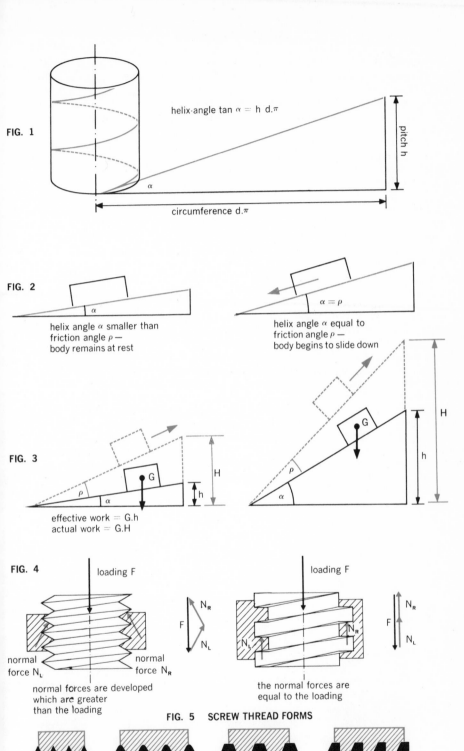

FIG. 1

helix-angle tan $\alpha = h \; d.\pi$

pitch h

circumference d.π

FIG. 2

helix angle α smaller than
friction angle ρ —
body remains at rest

$\alpha = \rho$

helix angle α equal to
friction angle ρ —
body begins to slide down

FIG. 3

effective work $=$ G.h
actual work $=$ G.H

FIG. 4

loading F

normal
force N_L

normal
force N_R

normal forces are developed
which are greater
than the loading

loading F

the normal forces are
equal to the loading

FIG. 5 SCREW THREAD FORMS

vee thread   knuckle thread   Acme thread   buttress thread

167

SCREW CUTTING

Screw threads can be produced in various ways: by hand with the aid of such devices as a screw tap, a die plate or a screw die, or by mechanical methods which comprise turning (on a lathe), milling, rolling, pressing or casting. Which of these methods is most suitable in any particular case will depend on the number of screw-threaded components to be produced, the desired precision of the thread, and the quality of surface finish to be attained.

Screw cutting for a limited number of components can be done cheaply and simply by hand with a screw tap (Fig. 1) or a screw die (Fig. 2). The tool is rotated by hand, the workpiece being gripped in a vise. Alternatively, the workpiece may be gripped in the chuck of a lathe and rotated, while the tap or die is guided by the tailstock. The screw tap cuts an internal thread in a hole drilled beforehand. The screw die cuts an external thread on a rod or bolt and is held in a device called a stock, which has handles for manipulation. A simpler device is the die plate, which is merely a steel plate provided with threaded holes of various sizes for cutting screw threads.

A higher degree of precision can be obtained with machine-cut screw threads, especially those produced on a lathe. For the majority of screwed work a tap is used for internal threading (Fig. 3, showing the thread being cut in a nut) and a die head is used for external threading. The die head, a device that is clamped to the lathe, comprises a cylindrical body containing chasers for cutting the thread. Greater precision can be attained with a single-point cutting tool (Figs. 4 and 5). On the lathe the required pitch of the screw thread is obtained by gearing the lead screw up to the main spindle of the lathe by means of a train of gears. The lead screw is a long threaded rod extending along the lathe and serving as a master screw for cutting screw threads. The gearing enables screws of varying pitch and diameter to be cut, by varying the speed of rotation of the lead screw. When the lathe is started, the lead screw rotates and, by means of a nut that engages with it, moves the saddle (which carries the cutting tool) along the lathe at a definite rate, so that the tool cuts a thread of the requisite pitch. When the tool reaches the end of the workpiece, the lead screw is disengaged, the tool withdrawn, and the saddle returned to its starting position ready to take another cut. Instead of a single-point tool a so-called chaser is sometimes used; this tool has a serrated cutting edge to produce the screw-thread profile.

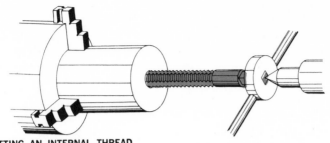

FIG. 1   CUTTING AN INTERNAL THREAD
WITH A SCREW TAP

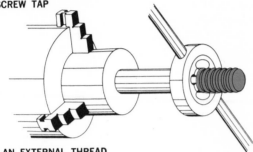

FIG. 2   CUTTING AN EXTERNAL THREAD
WITH A SCREW DIE

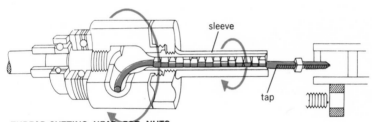

sleeve

tap

FIG. 3   THREAD-CUTTING HEAD FOR NUTS

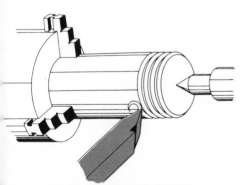

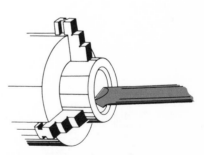

FIG. 5   CUTTING AN INTERNAL THREAD
WITH A SINGLE-POINT TOOL

FIG. 4   CUTTING AN EXTERNAL THREAD
WITH A SINGLE-POINT TOOL

169

THREAD MILLING

Screw threads, both external and internal, can also be cut efficiently and economically by milling. This is done on a milling machine, so-called thread-milling cutters being used for the purpose. These cutters may be of either the single or the multiribbed type, according to the kind of thread required and the design of the milling machine employed. A long screw thread of coarse pitch can suitably be cut by means of a disc-shaped single cutter (Fig. 1). The machine used for this work somewhat resembles a lathe, but instead of a saddle there is a carriage supporting a cutter head in which the cutter is mounted. The cutter is inclined to produce the correct helix angle of the thread. The feed (longitudinal motion) of the carriage and the rotation of the workpiece are interlinked by means of a lead screw and gearing so as to obtain the correct pitch of the thread being milled. The "long-thread milling" technique with a disc-shaped cutter can also be used for internal threading (Fig. 2) if the hole is of sufficiently large diameter to admit the cutter. In "short-thread milling" the tool is a multiribbed cutter (or multiple cutter) of the ring or shell type (Figs. 3 and 4) or of the taper-shank type (not illustrated). The ribs on the cutter have the shape of the screw-thread profile they have to cut. The cutter is usually as long as, or longer than, the required length of threading on the workpiece; it is fed radially toward the workpiece, and either the cutter or the workpiece is moved axially in synchronization with the slow rotary motion of the workpiece. Generally the latter performs only a little more than one revolution, the axial motion being only little more than one pitch. The axis of the cutter is usually parallel to the axis of the workpiece, but in some cases tilting may be necessary to produce the helix angle of the thread.

Another method of producing screw threads is by rolling under pressure. The part to be threaded is rotated and brought into contact with rollers that have the required profile and pitch of the thread. This is not a cutting method and involves no removal of metal, the thread being formed by plastic deformation. Not only is there a saving in metal, but the rolling operation causes cold working and thus improves the mechanical properties of the thread. The method is especially suitable for soft metals, such as aluminum, which are difficult to screw-cut with a smooth finish. It can be done on a lathe with the aid of a thread-rolling head (Fig. 6), which is equipped with three ribbed rollers that can move in and out radially. The rollers open out automatically at the end of the operation. A variant of this process consists in rolling the thread between grooved flat plates on a thread-rolling machine (Fig. 5).

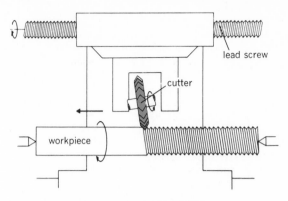

FIG. 1   LONG-THREAD MILLING (EXTERNAL)

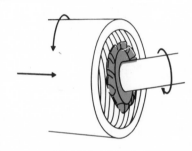

FIG. 2   LONG-THREAD MILLING (INTERNAL)

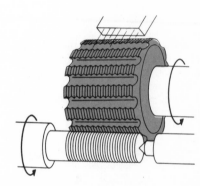

FIG. 3   SHORT-THREAD MILLING (EXTERNAL)

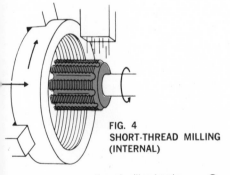

FIG. 4
SHORT-THREAD MILLING
(INTERNAL)

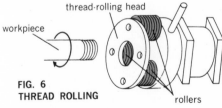

FIG. 5

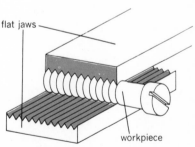

FIG. 6
THREAD ROLLING

171

GEARS

Toothed wheels whose teeth mesh with one another and which serve to transmit rotary motion or power from one shaft to another are called "gears." The smaller of a gear pair is more particularly called the "pinion" and the larger is the "gear." The term "gear wheel" is also used in the same general sense as "gear" or sometimes more specifically to denote a wheel comprising a toothed rim mounted on arms radiating from a boss. The rotation speeds of the shafts are inversely proportional to the numbers of teeth on their respective gears. A train of gears denotes a number of gears in mesh with one another.

Parallel shafts may be connected by spur gears, the simplest and commonest type, with teeth that are parallel to the axis of rotation (Fig. 2a). In the case of helical gears (Fig. 2b) the teeth are inclined in relation to the axis. This ensures smoother and quieter action and better load capacity, but there is the disadvantage that the teeth set up a side pressure which causes thrust on the bearings. To overcome this, double helical gears (or herringbone gears) may be used; these have teeth of V formation, so that lateral thrust is compensated. When two meshing gears both have external teeth, their shafts rotate in opposite directions (Fig. 1a); when one gear has external and the other has internal teeth, the shafts rotate in the same direction (Fig. 1b). This latter arrangement may be employed in cases where the axes of the respective shafts are very close together. Rack-and-pinion gearing (Fig. 1c) comprises a pinion with a straight toothed bar (the rack); this arrangement enables rotary motion to be converted into longitudinal motion, and vice versa. Bevel gears (Fig. 3) are employed in cases where the shafts form an angle with each other. If these shafts are at right angles, such gears are called miter gears. To obtain more efficient meshing, bevel gears may be provided with spiral teeth instead of straight teeth and are then known as spiral bevel gears. Hypoid gears are similar to spiral bevel gears, except that the axis of the pinion is offset from the gear axis—i.e., does not intersect it. In a case where shafts cross each other at a greater distance apart, crossed-axis helical gears may be used (Fig. 5). If large forces have to be transmitted, worm gearing (Fig. 4) may provide a suitable solution; one of the gears is called the worm and the other the worm wheel (or simply the "gear"). The worm is of helical shape, forming a continuous "tooth"; the worm wheel has independent teeth and is driven by the rotation of the worm with which it meshes.

Gears are usually made of metal and are formed by machining or molding. Spur gears may be made of cast iron, cast steel, forged steel, brass, special alloys, and other materials. To reduce noise, gear pinions are sometimes made of layers of rawhide or compressed paper. Plastics are widely employed as a material for gears used in small mechanisms.

(more)

172

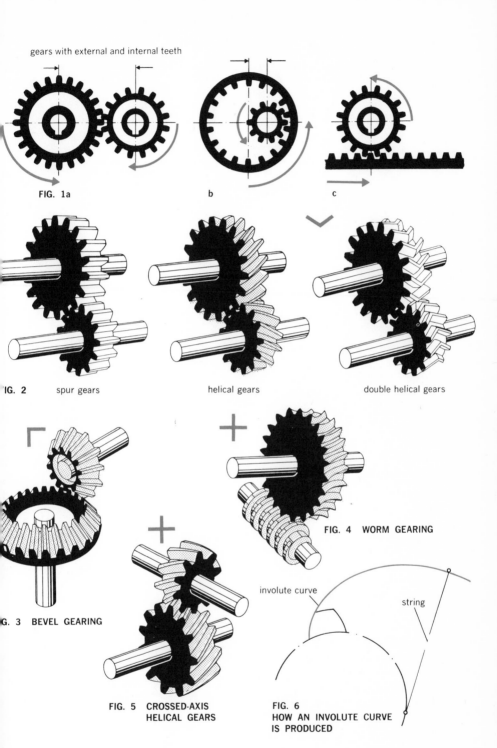

gears with external and internal teeth

FIG. 1a   b   c

FIG. 2   spur gears   helical gears   double helical gears

FIG. 4 WORM GEARING

FIG. 3 BEVEL GEARING

involute curve

string

FIG. 5 CROSSED-AXIS
HELICAL GEARS

FIG. 6
HOW AN INVOLUTE CURVE
IS PRODUCED

Gears in a weaving machine, Sulzer, Switzerland
Photo Roland Schneider, Len Sirman Press

Gears (continued)

Gear teeth must be correctly meshed together to ensure proper interlocking of the teeth. Straight-sided teeth (of trapezoidal profile) would have a jerky and noisy action. Smooth transmission of power can be achieved by suitably curving the sides of the teeth. Theoretically a great many gear-tooth profiles would be possible, but practical considerations of gear-cutting technique require shapes that are not too difficult and therefore uneconomical to produce. The shape usually adopted for the profile of each side of the tooth is an involute curve, this being the curve traced by a point on a taut string when it is unwrapped from a cylinder (Fig. 6, p. 173). Such a tooth is known as an involute tooth. On a gear of small diameter the sides of the teeth formed in this way show a pronounced curvature, but this becomes less pronounced on gears of larger diameter, and in the limiting case of the rack (Fig. 1c, p. 173) the involute is a straight line, so that the teeth are straight-sided in profile. The advantages of involute gear teeth are that they can be cut easily and accurately and that the center-to-center distance of meshing gears need not be exact.

Two gears that are in mesh can be conceived as a pair of imaginary friction rollers whose diameters correspond to the so-called pitch circles of the gears. The two pitch circles touch each other at the pitch point. The part of a gear tooth outside the pitch circle is called the addendum (h_k in Fig. 2, p. 177), and the part within is called the dedendum (h_1). The part of the side profile outside the pitch circle is the face; the part within is the flank. The circular pitch (t in Fig. 2) is the center-to-center distance (or the distance between corresponding points) between successive teeth, measured along the pitch circle. To ensure that the velocity ratio of a pair of gears remains constant, the profiles of their teeth must be so shaped that the common normal (NN in Fig. 1) passes through the contact point A of the sides of a pair of meshing teeth. In Fig. 1 the points 0_1 and 0_2 represent the centers of the two gears, while r_{01} and r_{02} are the respective pitch-circle radii, and C is the pitch point. In that diagram the vectors v_1 and v_2 representing the circumferential velocities of the gears have each been resolved into a velocity component along the common normal NN and a component along the common tangent TT. The components c_1 and c_2 along NN must be of equal magnitude, since the teeth are in mesh. On the basis of these kinematic relationships it can readily be shown that $n_1/n_2 = r_{02}/r_{01} = z_2/z_1$, where n_1 and n_2 are the rotational speeds of the two gears respectively, r_{01} and r_{02} are the radii of their pitch circles, and z_1 and z_2 are their respective numbers of teeth. The ratio n_1/n_2 is called the gear ratio (also known as the transmission ratio or speed ratio). The circular pitch t is equal to the pitch-circle circumference divided by the number of teeth—i.e., $t = 2\pi r_0/z$. The number of teeth in a gear divided by the diameter of the pitch circle is called the diametral pitch. The line of action (or pressure line) is normal to the involute curve of the tooth profile; the direction of pressure between the teeth in contact is along the line of action. The geometric and kinematic features of a pinion engaging with a rack (which is merely a gear wheel of infinite radius) are represented in Fig. 3. See also page 218.

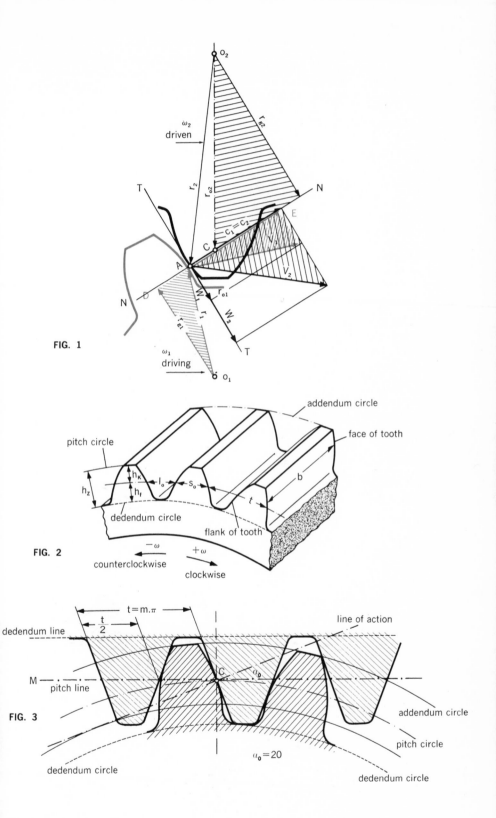

FIG. 1

ω₂ driven
ω₁ driving

FIG. 2

addendum circle
pitch circle
face of tooth
dedendum circle
flank of tooth

−ω counterclockwise
+ω clockwise

FIG. 3

$t = m.\pi$
$\frac{t}{2}$
dedendum line
line of action
M — pitch line
α_0
addendum circle
pitch circle
$\alpha_0 = 20$
dedendum circle
dedendum circle

GEAR CUTTING

Most metal gears for precision work are produced by machining—various cutting processes involving the removal of metal. A widely used method of cutting spur-gear teeth is by means of a rotary cutter whose shape corresponds to the required tooth space (a so-called formed cutter, Fig. 1). Mounted on a milling machine, the cutter takes successive cuts from the gear blank, which is rotated the correct distance after each cut to give the desired spacing of the teeth. This precisely controlled step-by-step rotation of the blank is called "indexing" and is performed by an indexing device, or dividing head, which is part of the equipment of the milling machine. Similar gear-cutting operations can also be performed on a suitably equipped lathe. Helical gears can likewise be produced by the formed-cutter technique: the gear blank must be set at the correct angle to the cutter, and the work table of the milling machine must be swiveled through the helix angle of the teeth being cut, so that the plane of the cutter becomes tangent to the helix.

For the quantity production of gears, the hobbing process (Fig. 2) is advantageous. The tool used is called a hob, a screw-shaped rotary cutter with gashes extending across the screw threads so as to form cutting edges. The hob is rotated and its teeth cut the blank. The tooth form of the hob is similar to that of the straight-sided teeth on a rack. Any involute gear will mesh with such teeth, so that one hob can be used to generate gears having any number of teeth which will mesh with one another. This is an advantage over the formed cutter, which in theory can produce only one particular tooth shape, so that a whole range of such cutters are needed for cutting different-sized gears. In spur-gear cutting, the teeth of the hob mesh with the gear teeth in the manner of a worm wheel. The motions performed by gear blank and hob are indicated in Figs. 2a and 2b. The blank is rotated at uniform speed and is geared to the spindle that rotates the hob, which is traversed slowly across the face of the gear blank in its axial direction (downwards in Fig. 2a). Since the hob teeth are disposed on a helix, the spindle of the hob is inclined at the helix angle of the hob thread. so that the tangent to this thread is parallel to the axis of the blank. Helical teeth also can be cut by hobbing (Fig. 3). In this case the indexing and feed gear system are so designed that the hob is appropriately advanced or retarded in order to obtain the correct helix angle of the gear. Alternatively, a so-called differential mechanism may be employed to increase or decrease the relative rotation of the hob and the blank to produce the helix angle.

(more)

178

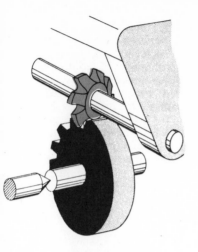

FIG. 1   GEAR CUTTING WITH
A FORMED CUTTER

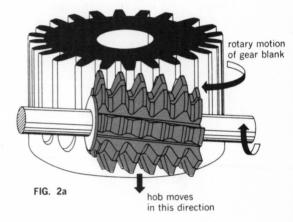

rotary motion
of gear blank

FIG. 2a

hob moves
in this direction

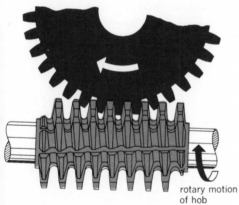

rotary motion
of hob

FIG. 2b

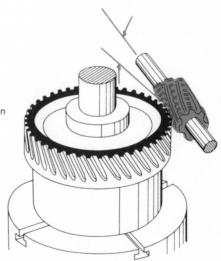

FIG. 3   HOBBING APPLIED TO
A HELICAL-GEAR CUTTING

179

Another method of cutting gear teeth in a blank is by slotting performed on the rotating table of a slotting machine (Fig. 1). The spaces between the teeth are cut by the action of a tool with an up-and-down motion. After each cut the blank is rotated an appropriate distance by the indexing mechanism, to obtain the required pitch of the teeth. This method of gear cutting is relatively seldom employed.

In the rack-cutter generating process, a rack-shaped cutter is employed whose teeth are provided with hardened cutting edges. The cutter moves to and fro across the blank, parallel to its axis, and is at the same time fed longitudinally, while the blank is rotated at appropriate speed (Fig. 2a). The teeth being formed on the blank are rolling in mesh with those on the cutter. As the cutter is of limited length, it cannot cut all the teeth of the gear in one continuous operation; a "step-back" motion is used to restart the cutting operation farther along the circumference of the blank when the teeth cut on the latter have moved out of engagement with those on the cutter. A helical gear can be produced by setting the cutter at an angle to the axis of the blank. Similar in principle is the pinion-cutter process, which can be used both for external (Fig. 2b) and for internal gears (Fig. 2c). In addition to this advantage, a favorable feature of this process is that the cutter rolls continuously, no "step-back" motion being necessary. There is, however, the disadvantage that the pinion cutter is more difficult to make than the rack cutter. The cutter performs its reciprocating cutting motion parallel to the axis of the blank (just as the rack cutter does); the gear teeth are generated by slow rotation of the cutter and the blank in synchronization, just as they would rotate if their pitch circles rolled together without slip.

Bevel gears can be produced with great precision on a bevel-gear planing machine (Fig. 4). The teeth of a bevel gear diminish in thickness and vary in the curvature of their sides from one end of the tooth to the other. To produce the correct tooth shape the machine employs two planing tools, each of which shapes one side of a tooth, while the machine imparts synchronized reciprocating and rotary motions to the tools and to the gear blank respectively.

To improve their precision and surface finish, the sides of gear teeth may be subjected to a grinding treatment. Grinding is also employed as a gear-generating process in its own right. A gear-tooth-grinding machine uses a grinding wheel which is shaped to correspond to the tooth space and which, while rotating, performs a reciprocating motion parallel to the axis of the gear being ground. The latter is indexed one tooth after each to-and-fro traverse of the wheel. In another and more frequently employed technique, the grinding tool consists of a pair of saucer-shaped grinding wheels (Fig. 3), whose faces correspond to the straight sides of a rack tooth. The "rack" is rolled in synchronization with the gear being ground, on the same principle as the motion performed by a rack cutter.

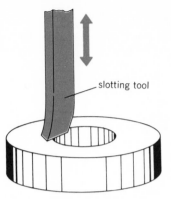

FIG. 1 GEAR CUTTING ON A
SLOTTING MACHINE

slotting tool

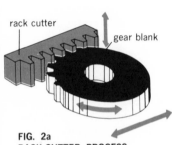

rack cutter

gear blank

FIG. 2a
RACK-CUTTER PROCESS

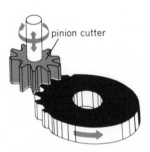

pinion cutter

FIG. 2b
PINION-CUTTER PROCESS
APPLIED TO EXTERNAL TEETH

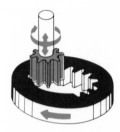

FIG. 2c
PINION-CUTTER PROCESS
APPLIED TO INTERNAL TEETH

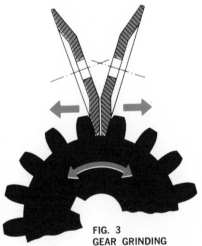

FIG. 3
GEAR GRINDING
WITH SAUCER-SHAPED
GRINDING WHEELS

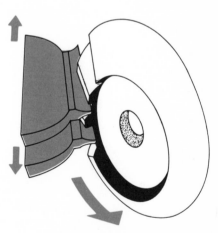

FIG. 4 BEVEL-GEAR PLANING

BALL AND ROLLER BEARINGS

Ball and roller bearings are collectively referred to as "antifriction bearings." A bearing of this type normally comprises two annular components known as races, the rolling elements (balls or rollers), and a cage for retaining the rolling elements in position. The races and other components are so designed as to achieve as far as possible pure rolling motion without additional sliding motion associated with friction. Under certain conditions one or both of the races may be omitted, in which case the rolling elements run directly in contact with the shaft and/or the housing in which it is mounted. Rollers are of various shapes: cylindrical, tapered, barrel-shaped, needle-shaped, etc. The function of the cage is to maintain the balls or rollers in their correct relative positions, so that they do not touch one another, and to hold them in one of the races when the bearing is dismantled. The cage also provides a certain amount of guidance for the rolling elements.

Antifriction bearings are characterized by low frictional losses. In particular, the starting friction is low, so that savings in driving power for machinery can be effected. Other features of these bearings are long service life, low lubricant consumption, hardly any wear, possibility of rapid fitting and dismantling, high degree of interchangeability. Antifriction bearings are normally supplied as units ready for installing. For commercially available types of bearing the external dimensions and the tolerances are internationally standardized. The internal dimensions (number and size of rolling elements, race diameter, etc.) are not standardized, though as a rule there are no significant differences between the bearings of a certain class and quality supplied by different manufacturers. Most antifriction bearings have a cylindrical bore, but in some cases a tapered bore is provided to enable the bearing to be fitted directly on to a tapered shaft.

Types of bearing: Differences in the functions and requirements to be fulfilled have led to the development of different kinds of antifriction bearings. The basic distinction, according to the shape of the rolling elements, is between ball bearings and roller bearings. Another important distinction is between radial bearings (designed to resist only or mainly radial loads) and thrust bearings (designed to resist thrust—i.e., loads acting in the axial direction of the shaft). Certain types of bearing can resist radial as well as axial loading. A single-thrust bearing resists thrust in one direction only; a double-thrust bearing resists thrust in both directions. To obtain greater mechanical strength without increasing the external diameter, double-row bearings instead of single-row bearings are used. A double-row bearing has two rows of balls or rollers side by side (Figs. 2, 3 and 6). So-called self-aligning bearings (Figs. 3 and 6) allow a certain amount of angular movement between shaft and housing, thus correcting any misalignment or deflection of the shaft.

(more)

182

FIG. 1   SINGLE-ROW GROOVED BALL BEARING

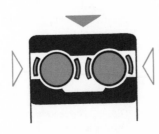

FIG. 2   DOUBLE-ROW ANGULAR CONTACT BEARING

FIG. 3   SELF-ALIGNING BALL BEARING   FIG. 4   CYLINDRICAL ROLLER BEARING

FIG. 5   NEEDLE ROLLER BEARING

Radial bearings: Single-row grooved ball bearings (Fig. 1) are most widely employed. They can take some thrust as well as considerable radial loading, even at fairly high speeds. Double-row bearings of this type are also used. Angular contact bearings (double-row type illustrated in Fig. 2) can resist larger amounts of thrust than grooved ball bearings. The term "magneto bearing" is applied to a single-thrust ball bearing with separately detachable outer and inner races, making for greater convenience of assembly. The self-aligning ball bearing (Fig. 3) has a spherical track in the outer race which enables it to compensate for misalignment. Such bearings have only a fairly limited load-carrying capacity. Cylindrical roller bearings (Fig. 4) have a much higher radial load-carrying capacity than ball bearings of equivalent size, but are generally not able to resist any considerable amount of thrust. In the bearing illustrated, the locating lips, or shoulders, are formed on the outer race. Needle roller bearings (Fig. 5) have relatively long rollers of small diameter. Their one advantage over normal cylindrical roller bearings is the radial saving in space; in other respects they are much less efficient. Needle roller bearings are used in low-speed heavily loaded positions. A double-row self-aligning roller bearing is illustrated in Fig. 6. This type of bearing can compensate for shaft misalignment and can resist thrust in both directions as well as considerable radial load. The taper roller bearing (Fig. 7) is suitable for any combination of thrust and radial load. The single-row type, as illustrated, can take thrust in one direction only, and as with angular contact ball bearings it is necessary to fit two bearings on each shaft if there is any possibility of two-way thrust. Barrel-shaped rollers are suitable for bearings subjected to heavy impact-type loading; such bearings are moreover self-aligning, but the thrust capacity is fairly low.

Thrust bearings: Ball thrust bearings (Fig. 8) can take thrust loads only and are used chiefly where a shaft revolving at not too high a speed requires rigid axial support. Angular contact thrust bearings are suitable for higher speeds. Self-aligning roller thrust bearings (Fig. 9) differ in performance from other types of thrust bearing in being able to resist radial loads as well as thrust, besides allowing angular movement between shaft and housing. Other forms of thrust bearing are the cylindrical roller thrust bearing, the needle roller thrust bearing, and the taper roller thrust bearing. These types of bearing are suitable only for fairly low speeds.

(more)

FIG. 6   DOUBLE-ROW SELF-ALIGNING ROLLER BEARING

FIG. 7   TAPER ROLLER BEARING

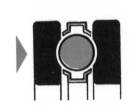 

FIG. 8   BALL THRUST BEARING

FIG. 9   SELF-ALIGNING ROLLER THRUST BEARING

185

Materials: High local stresses of varying magnitude occur in the rolling elements of antifriction bearings under the action of loading. For this reason very-high-grade steels of uniform texture and high resistance to wear are used in the manufacture of such bearings. In addition, they must be suitably machinable and hardenable. In Europe, low-alloy fully hardenable chromium steels are widely employed (chromium content ranging from 0.4 to 1.65%, depending on the purpose and size of the bearings). Case-hardening steels have hitherto not been much used there—in contrast with American practice, which makes fairly extensive use of these steels for antifriction bearings. Furthermore, for special applications other types of steel are employed, such as stainless steels, nonmagnetic steels and manganese-silicon steels. The cage does not participate in the transmission of forces, but may in certain circumstances be severely stressed by inertial forces, vibrations and impact effects. The choice of material for the cage is determined by considerations of strength and also of machinability and sliding capacity. The materials mainly used for the purpose are steel and brass. Sintered metals, cast iron, light alloys or plastics are also sometimes employed.

Manufacture (Fig. 10): The initial material for the manufacture of the ball or roller races are tubes, rods, rolled material and forged material. Small and medium-sized races are machined on single-spindle and multiple-spindle automatic lathes or on turret lathes, large races on turning and boring mills. After the turning operation comes heat treatment, in which the races are heated by gas or electricity to above 800° C in continuous furnaces or chamber furnaces, quenched in an oil or salt bath, and then tempered. The hardness attained in this way is in the range of 60 to 66 on the Rockwell scale. Then follows grinding of the sides and the internal and external faces, which are finished by polishing and honing.

Manufacture of the rolling elements (balls or rollers) starts from rod or wire. In a typical production process, pieces of wire are cut off in a press (a) and are then formed into balls or rollers by upsetting between dies (b). Large rollers are produced by machining (turning). The flash (fin of surplus material) formed in the pressing process is removed between rotating file discs (c). By means of grinding (d) and tumbling (e) the diameter is reduced, the specified roundness attained, and the surface finish improved. (Tumbling consists in rotation of the elements with an abrasive in a horizontal cylindrical container.) After hardening and tempering (f) come further polishing operations; then the rolling elements are given a high polish by further tumbling with a suitable polishing agent, and finally the elements are graded according to diameter (g).

Cages for antifriction bearings are made from deep-drawing steel strip or brass sheet or from tube material. Manufacture involves a series of press-tool operations (h) or, alternatively, various machining processes (i). The components are finally assembled into complete bearings (k). At all stages of manufacture appropriate checks for precision are maintained. The finally assembled bearings are tested for noiseless running (l), precision of bore, external dimension, clearance and play (m).

(more)

FIG. 10

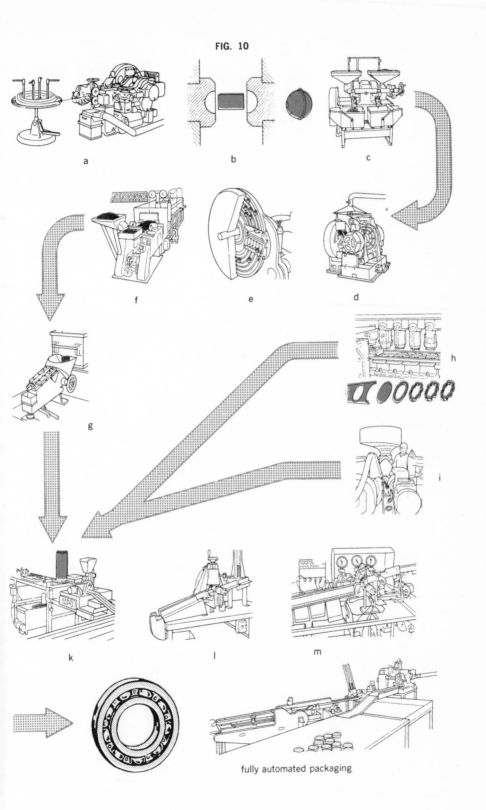

a

b

c

f

e

d

h

i

g

k

l

m

fully automated packaging

187

Ball and Roller Bearings (continued)

Applications (Figs. 11 to 13): Most of the bearings installed in modern machinery of all kinds, including motor vehicles, are antifriction bearings. These range from miniature bearings with bore diameters of less than 1 mm for fine precision-engineered apparatus to huge bearings with external diameters of 2 m and upwards and with load-carrying capacities in excess of 1000 tons. Speeds ranging from a few rpm to 300,000 rpm and upwards have to be provided for. For some purposes the requirements are not particularly stringent, whereas in other cases the bearings—e.g., those on certain parts of machine tools—must have very high true-running precision.

For reliable and lasting high performance of bearings under the conditions of use for which they are intended, certain requirements as to mounting and maintenance have to be fulfilled. One of these is the choice of the correct fit. The term "fit" with reference to antifriction bearings relates particularly to the diametral clearance —i.e., the total clearance between the rolling elements and the races, measured in the radial direction. The amount of end play may also be a significant criterion. Thrust bearings that have to resist axial loads in one or both directions will have to be additionally supported by shoulders on the shaft or by such devices as nuts, circlips (spring retaining rings), etc. Although a very tight fit of the bearing on the shaft and in the housing does provide the best support conditions for the races and the most efficient distribution of the loading over the rolling elements, this is not always practicable. A tight fit necessitates the application of relatively large forces in assembling the bearing on the shaft and within the housing. Small and not-too-tight-fitting bearings can be driven on to the shaft by means of light hammer blows, which should be applied to a special sleeve or bushing temporarily interposed between the hammer and the bearing. Also, it is bad practice to allow the assembly forces to be transmitted from one race to the other through the rolling elements. In the case of a tight fit on the shaft, the bearing may, for example, be heated in an oil bath to expand its bore before fitting.

Other important factors affecting bearing performance are lubrication and efficient sealing. Lubrication serves several purposes: reducing friction between the various parts of the bearing, providing protection against corrosion, excluding dirt (in the case of grease lubrication), and assisting the dissipation of heat (oil lubrication). Oil is a more reliable lubricant than grease and is essential where high speeds occur; grease is more convenient, however, and offers certain advantages. One of the commonest methods is oil-splash lubrication (e.g., in gearboxes: the rotation of the gears splashes oil on to the bearings). Other methods are oil-level lubrication (bearing partly immersed in oil), wick or drip-feed oil lubrication, oil circulating system (force feed by pump), and oil mist (for very high speeds: compressed air blows a fine spray of oil through the bearing). The service life of a bearing also depends on the efficiency of the sealing system, whose function is to prevent the entry of dirt, moisture, etc., and to retain the lubricant in the bearing. Sealing devices are of various kinds: grease grooves in the bore of the housing, felt washers (the most widely used sealing method with grease lubrication), leather or synthetic-rubber seals, labyrinth washers, etc.

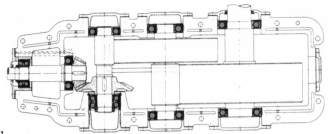

FIG. 11
BEVEL-AND-SPUR GEAR SYSTEM
WITH DOUBLE-ROW ANGULAR CONTACT
BEARINGS AND SINGLE-ROW GROOVED
BALL BEARINGS

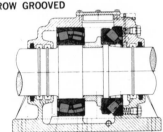

FIG. 12
HORIZONTAL WATER-TURBINE SHAFT
(HIGH AXIAL LOADING) WITH SELF-ALIGNING
ROLLER THRUST BEARING AND DOUBLE-ROW
SELF-ALIGNING ROLLER BEARING

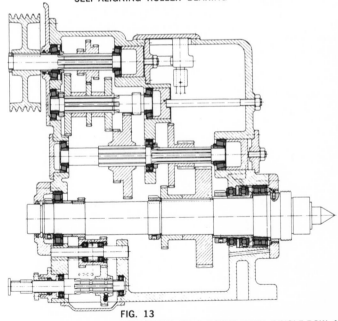

FIG. 13
HEADSTOCK OF A LATHE WITH SINGLE-ROW AND
DOUBLE-ROW CYLINDRICAL
ROLLER BEARINGS AND BALL THRUST BEARINGS

189

LATHE

A lathe is a machine for revolving a piece of material so as to enable a cutting tool to shape it into a component of circular cross section or to perform a screw-cutting operation. Lathes, which are among the most important machine tools, vary widely in design. What they have in common is that the workpiece is given a rotational motion and the material is cut away by a tool that is given an appropriate combination of linear (axial and radial) movements.

The most widely used type is the center lathe, also known as the engine lathe (Fig. 1), in which the work is held between centers or in a chuck. The rotational movement is imparted to the workpiece by the work spindle mounted in the head-stock (at the left-hand end of the lathe in Fig. 1). To enable long bars to be accom-modated, the work spindle may be of hollow construction. The end of this spindle is threaded to take various chucks (gripping devices for holding the work), as required. Alternatively, instead of a chuck, a center—a pointed steel attachment for mounting the work—may be fitted into a taper socket at the end of the work spindle. The required speed of rotation of the spindle, and therefore the cutting speed of the tool, is controlled by suitable selection of the transmission ratio of the main gear-box. Mounted on the guideways of the lathe bed is the saddle, or carriage, which carries the cutting tool and is constructed as a compound slide (Fig. 1): the saddle itself moves in the longitudinal direction of the lathe, whereas the cross slide can be moved only in the transverse direction. Mounted on the cross slide is the top slide, which in turn carries the tool post in which the tool is held. In its normal position the top slide can be moved longitudinally; it can, however, also be swiveled about a vertical axis and clamped in any position, so that conically tapered surfaces can be machined. The feed (advancing) and adjustment movements of the slides can be performed by means of crank handles on the saddle. Automatic control of the feed motion may be provided by means of the so-called feed shaft, which receives its rotational motion from the work spindle. The feed shaft is provided with a worm which rotates with this shaft, but can slide longitudinally in relation to it. When the longitudinal feed motion is started (position LF in Fig. 3), the worm rotates the worm wheel, which in turn rotates the gear Z_1 (mounted on the same shaft). Z_1 drives the gears Z_2, Z_3 and Z_4, which engages with the rack that moves the saddle longitudinally. When the cross-feed motion is engaged (position CF in Fig. 3), the gear Z_2—which can be swiveled—is brought into mesh with the gear Z_5 instead of with Z_3 and thus drives the shaft for moving the cross slide. The carriage can also be moved longitudinally by means of the lead screw, which is a long bar extending along the lathe and provided with a square screw thread. Two half nuts can be brought into engagement with the lead screw (Fig. 2), so that the rotation of the latter imparts a longitudinal motion to the saddle. The lead screw is intended essentially for screw cutting.

At the opposite end of the lathe bed from the headstock is the tailstock, which can move along the guideways and clamped in any desired position. The center sleeve in the tailstock can be moved in the longitudinal direction of the lathe by means of a handwheel and screw spindle and can thus be brought toward the workpiece. The sleeve is provided with a taper socket to take a center or a boring or reaming tool.

(more)

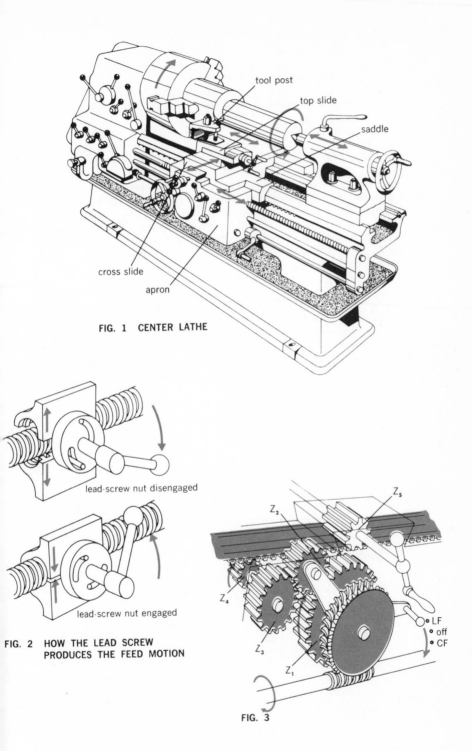

FIG. 1 CENTER LATHE

tool post

top slide

saddle

cross slide

apron

lead-screw nut disengaged

lead-screw nut engaged

FIG. 2 HOW THE LEAD SCREW
PRODUCES THE FEED MOTION

Z_5

Z_2

Z_4

Z_3

Z_1

LF
off
CF

FIG. 3

The most favorable cutting speed depends on the properties of the material and on the type of cutting tool employed. The speed can be varied by changing the rotational speed of the work spindle. Furthermore, to keep the cutting speed constant, the spindle speed must be increased when the tool moves inwards to cut at a smaller radius. The speed change can be effected by means of the gearbox controlling the work spindle.

With the belt drive (Fig. 1) and the gear drive (Fig. 2) the speeds of the two shafts are inversely proportional to the respective pulley or gear diameters (or inversely proportional to the number of gear teeth). The shafts of a pair of meshing gears rotate in opposite directions. When an intermediate gear is introduced, the transmission ratio remains unchanged, but now the two shafts have the same direction of rotation. The cone-pulley transmission system illustrated in Fig. 3 permits selection of any of four different speeds by shifting the belt from one pair of pulleys to the next. This type of transmission is now virtually obsolete. In the gearbox (Fig. 4) various pairs of gears are brought into mesh by shifting one of the two gears. As a rule, a whole range of gears is employed to provide a variety of speeds. For instance, if three gears, each with two possible combinations with other gears, are employed, a total of $2 \times 2 \times 2 = 8$ basic speeds will be available. Alternatively, the gears may be permanently in mesh and mounted loose on their respective shafts, but can be locked to the latter by means of multiple-disc clutches (see page 206). The outer element of the clutch forms an integral part of the gear and is provided on the inside with longitudinal grooves in which the outer discs can slide. When a coupling sleeve is actuated, the pack of discs is compressed and a frictional connection between the outer and inner discs is established, so that rotation motion is transmitted from one shaft to the other. These clutches are used for engaging and disengaging the main gearbox and also for engaging individual gear combinations to produce the desired transmission ratios.

(more)

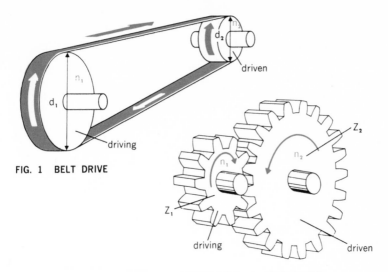

FIG. 1 BELT DRIVE

FIG. 2 GEAR DRIVE

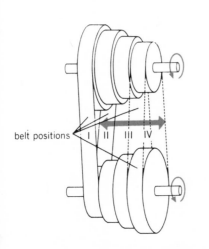

belt positions

FIG. 3 CONE-PULLEY SYSTEM

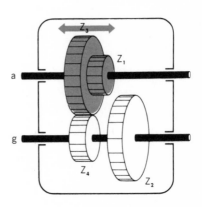

FIG. 4 CHANGE-SPEED GEARBOX

Adjustment of the speed of rotation to any desired value, so as to keep the cutting speed constant even when the cutting diameter continually varies, can be achieved by means of the PIV ("positive infinitely variable") drive (Fig. 1). This transmission system comprises a pair of radial-toothed conical pulleys on the driving shaft and on the driven shaft. A wide belt of special construction connects the two pairs of pulleys; it is provided with projecting elements which engage with the pulley teeth and thus provide a positive nonslip drive. Speed control is effected by the shifting of one pair of pulleys closer together and the other pair farther apart, and vice versa. In Fig. 1a the speed of the driven shaft is lower than that of the driving shaft; the speed of the former is progressively increased by the shifting of its two pulleys farther apart, while those on the driving shaft are brought closer together; thus in Fig. 1b the driven shaft rotates faster than the driving shaft.

Another type of variable-speed mechanical drive is shown in Fig. 2. The cone on the driven shaft can be shifted in the axial (arrowed) direction. Depending on its position, the contact diameter of the cone with the friction ring varies. The latter, which is driven by the cone, can perform a swiveling movement on the driven shaft, so that the friction surface is always in full contact with the driving cone. The transmission ratio can be varied by shifting the cone axially to the left or right. When the cone is moved inwards (to the right in Fig. 2), the speed of the driven shaft is increased, and vice versa. Fig. 3 illustrates a so-called fluid drive. Mounted on the left-hand shaft (the driving shaft) is the oil-pump rotor, rotated by an external power source (usually an electric motor). It rotates eccentrically in a movable casing. The space between the rotor and the casing is subdivided into compartments which increase and decrease in size in consequence of the rotation of the rotor, so that oil is alternately sucked into them and then discharged into the inlet of the oil motor, whose rotor is mounted on the right-hand shaft (the driven shaft). The motor is very similar in construction to the pump. The oil delivered by the pump causes the rotor of the motor to rotate. The greater the eccentricity of the pump rotor in relation to its casing, the higher the rate of delivery of the oil and the higher the rotational speed of the motor. When the rotor of the pump is shifted to the central position within its casing, delivery of oil ceases, so that the motor stops. When the pump rotor is shifted farther to the left (in Fig. 3), the direction of flow of the oil is reversed, and the motor therefore also reverses its direction of rotation. The tank merely serves as a container for a reserve supply of oil. Speed control is therefore effected by shifting the position of the pump rotor.

Infinitely variable speed control by electrical—as distinct from mechanical or hydraulic—means is usually effected by means of variable-speed direct-current motors.

(more)

194

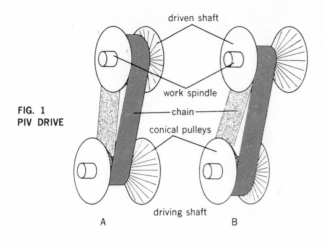

FIG. 1
PIV DRIVE

driven shaft

work spindle

chain

conical pulleys

driving shaft

A   B

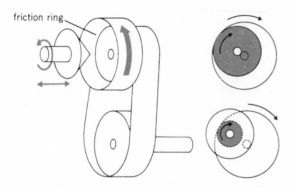

friction ring

FIG. 2   CONE-AND-FRICTION-RING
VARIABLE-SPEED DRIVE

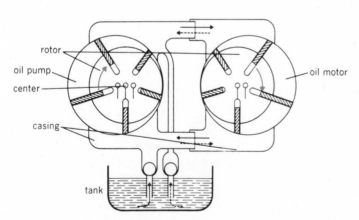

rotor

oil pump

center

casing

oil motor

tank

FIG. 3   FLUID-DRIVE OPERATING PRINCIPLE

Lathe (continued)

A wide variety of machining operations can be performed on a lathe, requiring appropriate control of the speed of the work spindle and also of the feed—i.e., the advance of the cutting tool (Fig. 1). For maximum efficiency it is necessary to adjust the feed correctly in relation to the size of the workpiece and the speed at which it rotates. For finishing cuts the speed is generally controlled by hand, but for roughing cuts and medium cuts an automatic feed is achieved by locking the saddle to the lead screw or to a separate feed shaft (if provided). This shaft is geared to the work spindle to give the appropriate traverse motion to the saddle. Fig. 2 shows a system of gears through which the feed shaft is driven by the work spindle. These gears can readily be exchanged to give various desired feed speeds. The reversing gear unit is shown in detail in Fig. 4. The lever can be moved up or down to engage the required direction of rotation. When it is up, the transmission from Z_1 to Z_4 is effected through Z_3 only; when it is down, the transmission is effected through Z_2 and Z_3, so that (as a result of the introduction of the additional gear Z_2) the direction of rotation of shaft II is reversed in relation to that of shaft I. The Norton gearbox (Fig. 3) comprises a tumbler gear which is mounted on a movable lever and can be brought into mesh with any one of a number of other gears, permitting rapid change in the speed of the feed shaft. Another type is the driving-key transmission, in which a number of gears of varying diameter are fixed to a shaft and are permanently in mesh with gears that are freely rotatable on a second shaft. By means of a movable driving key any one of the latter gears can be locked to this second shaft, so that this gear and its meshing partner transmit power. Sometimes the feed gear system on a lathe will comprise a driving-key system combined with a Norton gearbox and an additional sliding gear system similar to that for the main drive (Fig. 4, page 193). The number of possible feed speeds will then be equal to the product of the number of possibilities provided by each of these transmission systems.

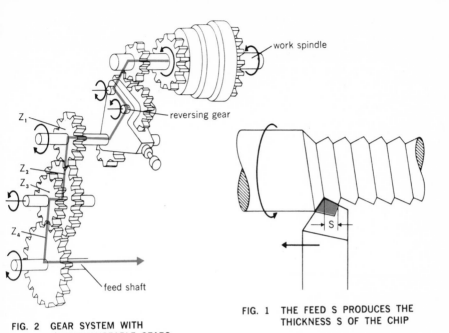

work spindle

reversing gear

Z_1

Z_2

Z_3

Z_4

feed shaft

FIG. 2 GEAR SYSTEM WITH
INTERCHANGEABLE GEARS

FIG. 1 THE FEED S PRODUCES THE
THICKNESS S OF THE CHIP

S

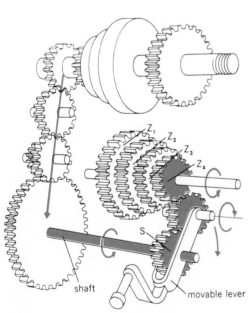

Z_1 Z_2 Z_3 Z_4

S

shaft

movable lever

FIG. 3 NORTON GEARBOX

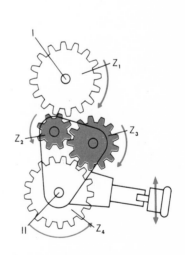

I

Z_1

Z_2 Z_3

II Z_4

FIG. 4 REVERSING GEAR (DETAIL)

MILLING MACHINE

Milling is a machining operation in which a workpiece is given the desired shape by the action of a rotating cutter while the workpiece performs linear movements. In its simplest form the milling cutter is a circular disc whose rim is provided with specially shaped teeth (cutting edges). Cutters are of many different kinds and shapes. The work is fed against the teeth of the cutter, while the feed motion is longitudinal, transverse or vertical, depending on the type of milling machine and the nature of the work. Milling machines are of the horizontal or the vertical type. A commonly employed horizontal machine is the knee type (Fig. 1). It comprises a massive column which contains the gearbox and spindle-drive motor and is provided with bearings for the spindle. The spindle speed can be varied by means of the gearbox, shown schematically in Fig. 2. Projecting from the front of the column is the knee, whose top surface carries the saddle. The latter in turn carries the work table, which slides in guideways. The motor providing the feed motions for the knee, saddle and work table is accommodated in the knee. The whole knee assembly can be raised or lowered by means of a crank handle or by power. The saddle can be traversed across the knee, and the work table can be moved to and fro in the guideways, by means of handwheels or by power drive. On some machines the work table can perform an automatic cycle of predetermined movements: e.g., a fast run to the cutting position, a change to slow feed motion during the actual cutting, and a quick return to the initial position on completion of the cut, after which the cycle is repeated. The milling cutter is mounted on a shaft called an arbor, whose extremity fits into a tapered socket in the driving spindle. The outer end of the arbor is supported on bearings mounted in the overarm. When the machine is taking a cut, the saddle is clamped to the knee, and the latter is clamped to the column. The knee-type horizontal milling machine illustrated in Fig. 1 is a so-called plain milling machine.

The universal milling machine, likewise of the knee type, is very similar to the plain milling machine, but has additional features, including more particularly a work table that can swivel in a horizontal plane (i.e., about a vertical pivot), so that it can move at angles other than 90 degrees to the spindle axis. A third type of horizontal milling machine is known as the manufacturing type (particularly the Lincoln type), which is characterized by having a work table that is fixed in height, the spindle being vertically adjustable, since it is mounted in a head that can be moved up or down the column of the machine. These machines are designed for heavy-duty milling. The work table slides on a bed that is supported directly on the foundation of the machine.

A vertical milling machine may be of the knee type and, apart from having a vertical spindle, is generally similar to the horizontal milling machine. The spindle is carried in a head that is vertically adjustable on the column, being provided with down feed by means of worm gearing.

198

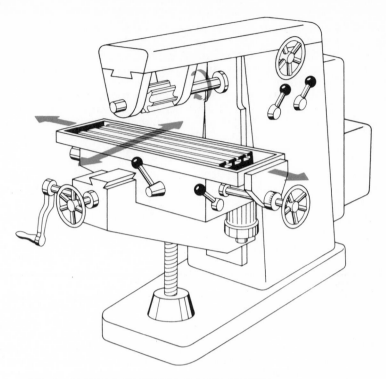

FIG. 1   KNEE-TYPE HORIZONTAL MILLING MACHINE

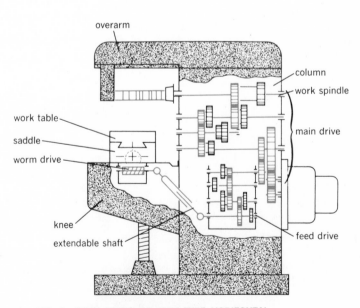

FIG. 2   MAIN PARTS OF KNEE-TYPE HORIZONTAL
MILLING MACHINE

199

COUPLINGS

A coupling is a device that connects two shafts end to end, while a clutch is a coupling provided with some form of sliding or other arrangement whereby the shafts can be connected and disconnected at will. Broadly speaking, couplings may be divided into rigid couplings and flexible couplings. The rigid type is used where accurate lineal alignment of the shafts is ensured. Where accurate alignment is not possible, a flexible coupling is used; it allows for a certain amount of misalignment, besides acting as a shock absorber for vibrations and jerks in torque transmission. The flanged coupling (Fig. 1), one of the simplest types, comprises two halves, each consisting of a flange mounted on the end of a shaft. The boss of each flange is keyed to its shaft, and the flanges are bolted together, thus connecting the two shafts. The split-type muff coupling (Fig. 2) is easier to install and remove because the two halves can be fitted around the aligned shaft ends and clamped by bolting. The muff is keyed to the shafts. A more elaborate form of construction is the serrated coupling (Fig. 3), comprising contact surfaces with interlocking teeth that are held meshed together by bolts. The jaw coupling (Fig. 4) consists of two flanged bosses with "jaws" projecting from their inner faces. This coupling allows longitudinal movement of the two shafts in relation to each other, so that it can compensate for thermal expansion or inaccuracies in assembly. If one of the halves is so mounted on its shaft that it can be slid into or out of engagement with the other half, the jaw coupling can serve as a clutch. The floating-center coupling (Fig. 5) may be used in a case where the two shafts are not accurately aligned and have a slight parallel shift in relation to each other. This coupling comprises two flanged halves and a center piece with lugs which engage with slots in the flanges. The lugs are set at right angles to each other and have a sliding fit in the slots, so that compensation for slight axial movements is provided. The toothed coupling illustrated in Fig. 6 allows a certain amount of parallel, angular and axial displacement between the two shafts. The two coupling bosses fitted on the shaft ends are provided with teeth which mesh with internal teeth in a coupling sleeve. The teeth have a "crowned" (convex) shape, thereby permitting some movement in all directions, including angular movement.

(more)

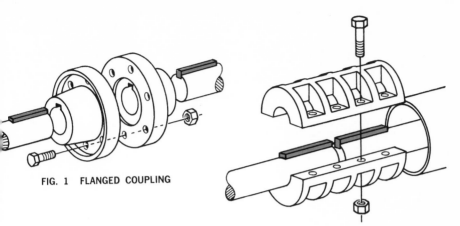

FIG. 1   FLANGED COUPLING

FIG. 2   SPLIT-TYPE MUFF COUPLING

FIG. 3   SERRATED COUPLING

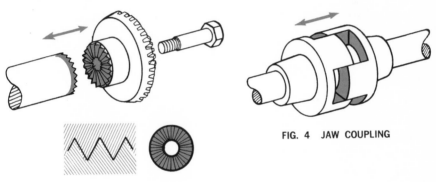

FIG. 4   JAW COUPLING

floating center

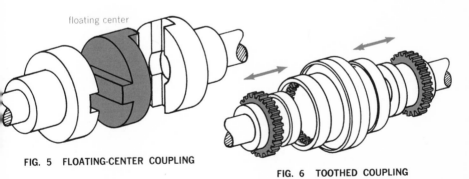

FIG. 5   FLOATING-CENTER COUPLING

FIG. 6   TOOTHED COUPLING

Couplings (continued)

A universal coupling (or cardan joint) is used for the connection of two shafts that are set at an angle to each other and whose angle can be varied while the shafts are rotating. An arrangement whereby two shafts are interconnected by an intermediate shaft with a universal coupling at each end is referred to as a universal shaft (Fig. 1). This principle is employed, for example, in propeller shafts of motor vehicles. The intermediate shaft is sometimes of telescopic construction to compensate for variations in length. The universal coupling may take a more elaborate form, permitting greater amounts of angular movement, as in Fig. 2, where each half of the coupling comprises two swivel pins which so engage with appropriate sockets in a ring that the pins of one half are set at 90 degrees in relation to those of the other half. Essentially the same principle is applied in the ball joint (Fig. 3): the ball is provided with four holes which engage with two pins on each half of the coupling. Consider two shafts, interconnected by a universal coupling, which are set at an angle β in relation to each other. If the driving shaft rotates at a uniform speed, the driven shaft will undergo speed fluctuations—i.e., it will be alternately accelerated and retarded according to a sinusoidal pattern (Fig. 4). These fluctuations will be accordingly greater as the angle β is larger. Such fluctuations can be eliminated by the interposition of an intermediate shaft and two universal couplings. If the two angles α (Fig. 5) are equal, so that the driving and the driven shaft are parallel to each other, these fluctuations will be canceled out. If the angles α and β (Fig. 6) are unequal, speed fluctuations will be transmitted to the driven shaft. In Fig. 6 the two universal couplings are moreover incorrectly mounted in that their respective pivot pins are not parallel to each other, as they ought to be to ensure uniform transmission of rotational motion from the driving to the driven shaft.

(more)

202

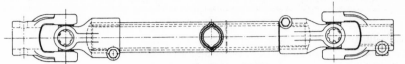

FIG. 1   UNIVERSAL SHAFT

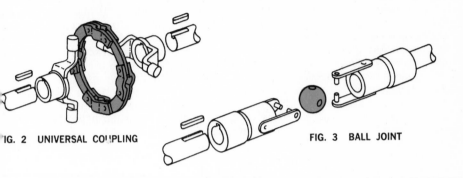

FIG. 2   UNIVERSAL COUPLING

FIG. 3   BALL JOINT

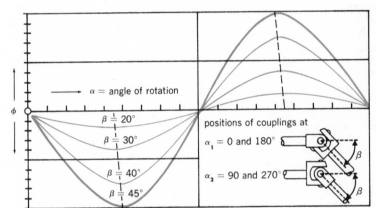

α = angle of rotation

$\beta \doteq 20°$

$\beta \doteq 30°$

$\beta \doteq 40°$

$\beta \doteq 45°$

positions of couplings at

$\alpha_1 = 0$ and $180°$

$\alpha_2 = 90$ and $270°$

β

β

**FIG. 4   LEAD AND LAG ANGLE ϕ OF ONE SHAFT
IN RELATION TO THE OTHER**

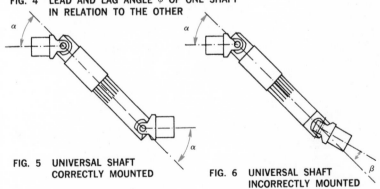

**FIG. 5   UNIVERSAL SHAFT
CORRECTLY MOUNTED**

**FIG. 6   UNIVERSAL SHAFT
INCORRECTLY MOUNTED**

Couplings (continued)

In a *flexible coupling* the connection between the two halves is formed by a "yielding" intermediate element which may consist of rubber, leather, steel springs or some other flexible material. This element allows small amounts of parallel and/or angular movement of the shafts in relation to each other, besides absorbing impact ("shock") due to irregularities in the motion of the driving shaft. Shock absorption may be achieved by storage of energy or by conversion of energy or both. Thus the coil-spring coupling (Fig. 1) stores the impact energy in its coil springs when one flange of the coupling undergoes rotation in relation to the other in consequence of a sudden variation in speed or torque. When the springs subsequently return to their original length, they transmit the temporarily stored-up impact energy to the driven shaft. Every resilient mechanism forms an oscillating system whose natural frequency of oscillation will depend on the spring characteristic and the oscillating masses. The extension or the shortening of the springs in the clutch, and thus the angle of relative rotation of the two clutch halves, is proportional to the magnitude of the torque applied (Fig. 3a). This oscillating system has a particular natural frequency, and if the coupling is rotated with an impact frequency corresponding to this natural frequency, the phenomenon known as resonance will occur, causing objectionable oscillations of large amplitude. As against a linear characteristic of the type represented in Fig. 3a, the steel-band coupling (Fig. 2) has a progressively curved characteristic (Fig. 3b): in this the angle of relative rotation is not proportional to the torque to be transmitted by the coupling. When the effective lever arm of the steel bands changes, the natural frequency of the coupling also changes, so that no resonance will occur. The area located under the characteristic line or curve in Fig. 3 (abc) represents a certain amount of energy, namely, the impact energy which is absorbed by the "yielding" system of the flexible coupling and subsequently given off by it. If the coupling, in addition to presenting a curved characteristic, also develops a so-called damping action (Fig. 3c), its recovery characteristic (the lower of the two curves) will differ from that of the characteristic for initial deformation. In general, the energy given off is less than the energy absorbed by the "yielding" system. The difference between these two energy amounts corresponds to the area between the curves; this "lost" energy may, for example, be converted into heat by internal friction in the coupling. The flexible coupling illustrated in Fig. 4 has a characteristic of this type because of the rubber bushings which enclose the bolts in one of the two halves. A similar effect is achieved by the arrangement shown in Fig. 5, where the two halves of the coupling are interconnected by a rubber "tire" which provides flexibility and shock-absorbing capacity. In the disc-type flexible coupling (Fig. 6), each of the two shafts is provided with a boss (called a "spider") having three radial arms set at 120 degrees in relation to one another. Between the two spiders is a flexible disc made of rubber and canvas bonded together. This disc has six equally spaced holes for bolting. The spider arms on each shaft are bolted to the disc, but at different positions from those on the other shaft. Thus "give" or "yield" of the disc will occur when power is transmitted.

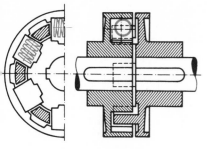

FIG. 1   COIL-SPRING COUPLING

FIG. 2   STEEL-BAND COUPLING

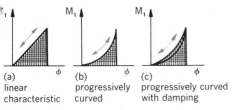

(a)
linear
characteristic

(b)
progressively
curved

(c)
progressively curved
with damping

FIG. 3   COUPLING CHARACTERISTICS

FIG. 4   FLEXIBLE BOLTED COUPLING

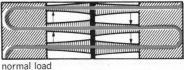

normal load

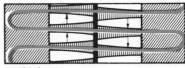

overload

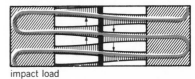

impact load

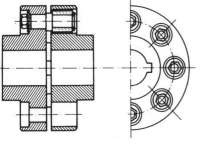

fabric ring to resist
centrifugal forces

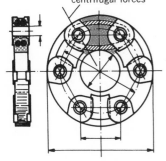

FIG. 6   DISC-TYPE FLEXIBLE COUPLING

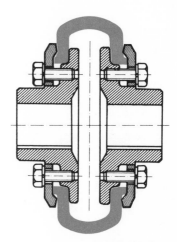

FIG. 5   PERIFLEX COUPLING

205

CLUTCHES

As p. 200 explained, a *clutch* is any coupling that enables shafts or other rotating parts to be connected or disconnected at will—i.e., without the removal or refitting of any components. In the claw clutch (Fig. 1) one half of the clutch can slide on its shaft, so that the claws can be engaged or disengaged. This type of clutch can be engaged only when the shafts are stationary or rotating at low speed. The geared clutch (Fig. 2) is widely employed in machine tools and motor vehicles. The two clutch bosses are each provided with external teeth which can mesh with a sleeve that has corresponding internal teeth and can be slid over both bosses so as to establish a positive connection between the shafts. To permit engagement of the clutch while the shafts are rotating, the sleeve and the shaft end to be coupled are respectively provided with friction surfaces which are brought into contact with each other and thus equalize the speed of the rotating parts before the teeth on the shaft and inside the sleeve are brought into mesh. Friction clutches transmit power through contact friction surfaces on the two halves to be connected. Various types of friction clutch are illustrated in Fig. 3. In the disc clutch (or plate clutch) and the cone clutch, the boss of the movable part slides in longitudinal grooves in the shaft on which it is mounted. The movements for engaging and disengaging the clutch are performed by the action of a lever whose forked ends fit into a circumferential recess in the boss of the clutch plate or cone. The internal-expanding shoe-type clutch comprises an outer shell attached to one shaft and two semicircular "shoes" which are mounted on arms attached to a sliding sleeve on the other shaft and which can be brought internally into contact with the shell. The forks of the clutch-operating lever engage with a recess on the sliding sleeve. A type of friction clutch widely used in machine tools and motor vehicles is the multiple-disc clutch (Fig. 4). It is based on the principle that a series of discs or plates alternately connected to the driving and the driven shaft will increase the power-transmitting capacity in proportion to the number of pairs of contact surfaces. In the form of clutch illustrated in Fig. 4 the boss mounted on the driving shaft is provided with external teeth with which the internal teeth on a series of thin steel plates engage. The outer shell of the clutch is mounted on the driven shaft and has internal teeth with which the external teeth of a second series of plates (alternating with those of the first series) likewise engage. When the clutch lever shifts a collar to the left, the plates are pressed together and thus transmit power by friction. Multiple-disc clutches in machine tools usually operate immersed in oil; those in motor vehicles are usually of the dry type. A magnetic clutch is a friction-disc clutch that is engaged by the energizing of a magnet coil, which attracts a set of steel friction discs and thus establishes the connection. A double-acting clutch based on this principle is illustrated in Fig. 5. When the coil "a" is energized, the discs "b" are compressed together by magnetic attraction, thereby connecting the gear "c" to the shaft "d." When the coil "e" is energized, the discs "f" are pressed together, so that now power is transmitted from the shaft "d" to the gear "g."

(more)

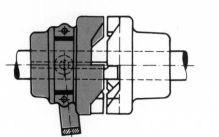

FIG. 1   CLAW CLUTCH

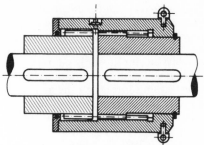

FIG. 2   GEARED CLUTCH

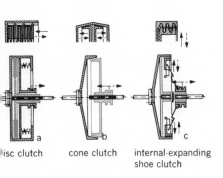

isc clutch   cone clutch   internal-expanding
                                              shoe clutch

FIG. 3   FRICTION CLUTCHES

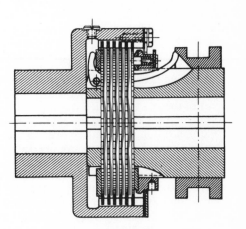

FIG. 4   MULTIPLE-DISC CLUTCH

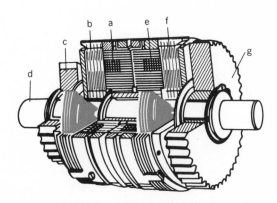

FIG. 5   MAGNETICALLY OPERATED MULTIPLE-DISC CLUTCH

Clutches (continued)

An *automatic clutch* is often installed between the driving shaft of a motor and the machinery it drives. It enables the shaft to reach a predetermined speed before engagement is effected and is especially useful in a case where the driven machinery requires a high starting torque. For such purposes a centrifugal clutch (Fig. 1) may suitably be employed. It comprises two or more "shoes" which, when the driving shaft on which they are mounted has reached a certain speed, overcome the pressure of restraining springs by the action of centrifugal force and move outwards to press against the inner surface of the rim mounted on the driven shaft. In this way the transmission of power to the driven shaft is gradually and automatically increased, so that smooth engagement is effected. The speed at which engagement takes place can be increased by fitting the clutch with more power-restraining springs, and vice versa. When the shafts are not rotating, the shoes are retracted and not in contact with the rim. Various other types of automatic clutch are likewise based on the centrifugal principle.

Freewheeling clutches drive in one direction only and permit free movement when the speed of the driven shaft exceeds that of the driving shaft. In the grip-roller type of freewheeling clutch (Fig. 2) each roller is gripped, i.e., jammed, in the wedge-shaped space as soon as the movement of the outer race in relation to the inner race causes the roller to move into the "shallower" part of this space. With clockwise rotation this occurs when the outer race tends to overtake the inner race; the two shafts then become locked together: i.e., the clutch is now engaged. When the outer race slows down and tends to lag behind the inner, the roller moves into the "deeper" part of the space in which it is housed. This disengages the clutch. In the slip clutch (Fig. 3), springs produce the contact pressure between the two clutch bosses and the interposed (longitudinally movable) friction plate provided with friction linings on both its faces. The friction developed at these faces will depend on the contact pressure exerted by the springs. If the pressure is low, the friction will also be low, so that slip in the clutch will occur at a low value of the torque. By means of a screw it is possible to increase the spring pressure and therefore the friction, so that the clutch will be able to transmit a greater torque without slipping. The torque can thus be adjusted to a predetermined value, and the clutch can serve as a safety device against overloading of the driven machinery. A simpler safety device for this purpose is the shear-bolt coupling (Fig. 4). It comprises two flanges connected by bolts that are designed to fail in shear (i.e., to "break off") when the torque exceeds a predetermined value.

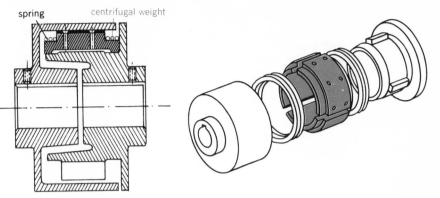

spring   centrifugal weight

FIG. 1   CENTRIFUGAL CLUTCH

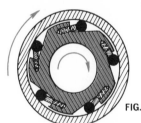

	when rotated	
	clockwise	counterclockwise
clutch is engaged	when outer race tends to overtake inner race	when inner race tends to overtake outer race
clutch is disengaged	when inner race overtakes outer race	when outer race overtakes inner race

FIG. 2   GRIP-ROLLER
FREEWHEELING CLUTCH

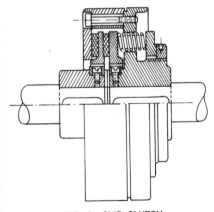

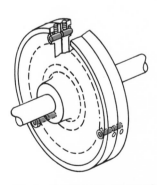

FIG. 4   SHEAR-BOLT COUPLING

FIG. 3   SLIP CLUTCH

MECHANICAL POWER TRANSMISSION

Devices for the mechanical transmission of power, or "mechanisms," constitute the basic units from which all kinds of machinery are built up. They are devices whereby certain actions can be exercised when certain motions are performed. Every mechanism consists of individual elements whose movements in relation to one another are "positive": i.e., the motion of one element produces an accurately determinable and definable motion of every individual point of the other elements of that mechanism. Numerous combinations and modifications are possible, but six basic types of mechanism are to be distinguished:

1. Screw mechanism (Fig. 1): When the screw spindle is rotated, the element attached to the nut will move in the longitudinal direction of the screw. (Examples: vise, cross slide of a lathe, work table of a milling machine). Conversely, if the nut is rotatably mounted in the frame of the mechanism and driven, the screw spindle will move longitudinally.

2. Linkage or crank mechanism (Fig. 2): The characteristic element is the crank, which is rotatably mounted on the frame and is usually so designed that it can perform complete revolutions. Its motion is transmitted through the coupler (or connecting rod) to the lever (or rocker arm), likewise rotatably mounted, but not performing complete revolutions. Alternatively, instead of being connected to a lever, the coupler may be attached to a sliding element—e.g., a piston in a steam engine or internal-combustion engine.

3. Gear mechanism (Fig. 3): This type of mechanism transmits rotary motion from one shaft to another, usually in conjunction with a change in rotational speed and torque. In a gear mechanism of the usual type the transmission is effected by the meshing of gear teeth, but in the friction-gear mechanism this positive drive is replaced by frictional contact of wheels or rollers.

4. Pulley mechanism (Fig. 4): Connection between the pulleys on their respective shafts is effected by flexible elements (belts, ropes, etc.).

5. Cam mechanism (Fig. 5): A cam plate mounted on a frame is driven and thus moves a lever or slider which thus performs a desired predetermined motion depending on the shape of the cam (example: valve control mechanism in an internal-combustion engine).

6. Ratchet mechanism (Fig. 6): This serves to arrest a motion or to produce an intermittent rotation in the driven element. The pawl allows the ratchet wheel to rotate in one direction only, preventing rotation in the opposite direction by engaging with the specially shaped teeth on the wheel.

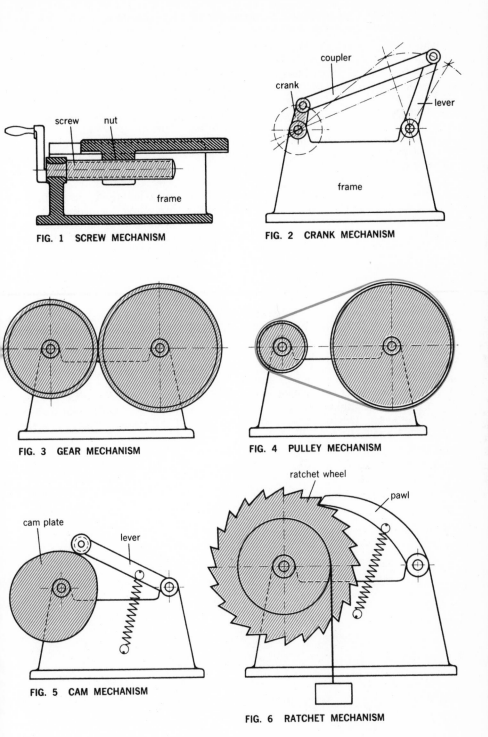

FIG. 1   SCREW MECHANISM

FIG. 2   CRANK MECHANISM

FIG. 3   GEAR MECHANISM

FIG. 4   PULLEY MECHANISM

FIG. 5   CAM MECHANISM

FIG. 6   RATCHET MECHANISM

LINKAGES

The term "linkage" is applicable to any mechanism that is a combination of links or bars which are connected by pins, sliders, etc. The basic system of a crank mechanism is the four-bar linkage (or quadric-crank mechanism, Fig. 1), comprising four links connected by pin joints which form pivots. The dimensions the individual links are given, and which of the four links is made the stationary "frame," determine whether particular links will perform complete revolutions or merely oscillatory (to-and-fro rocking) movements. For example, if the bottom link in Fig. 1 is stationary and thus constitutes the frame of the mechanism, the shorter of the two links attached to it can rotate through 360 degrees (and is accordingly termed the "crank"), whereas the other link attached to the frame (and connected to the crank by the fourth link, termed the "coupler") can only oscillate about its pivot and is accordingly referred to as the "lever" (or rocker arm). The amplitude of the lever will be accordingly smaller as the crank is shorter. On the basis of this principle, it is possible to construct a mechanism in which the length of the crank can be varied while it is in motion. As shown in Fig. 2, the lever may be connected to a ratchet wheel and pawl, so that the driven shaft (on which the ratchet wheel is mounted) rotates intermittently in one direction only. By varying of the length of the crank (by means of the slot), the amplitude of the lever can be varied from almost zero to a maximum, when the point A of the coupler is at the lower or at the upper end of the slot respectively.

If the shortest link of a four-bar linkage is held stationary (Fig. 3), the resulting mechanism is called a drag-link mechanism. Here both of the links (crank and lever) attached to the stationary frame can perform complete revolutions. When the left-hand crank rotates at constant speed, the right-hand crank (originally the "lever") rotates at varying speed. A special case is the parallel linkage, in which the frame and coupler are of equal length and the two cranks are likewise of equal length (Fig. 4). If the two cranks rotate in opposite directions, the mechanism is known as an antiparallel linkage (Fig. 5). The drafting machine (Fig. 6) comprises two parallel linkages which provide parallel motion of the straight edges. The same principle is applied to the toolbox illustrated in Fig. 7.

(more)

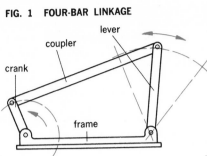

FIG. 1 FOUR-BAR LINKAGE

lever

coupler

crank

frame

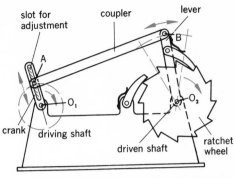

slot for adjustment

coupler

lever

A

B

O₁

crank

driving shaft

driven shaft

ratchet wheel

O₂

FIG. 2 COMBINED LEVER-AND-RATCHET MECHANISM WITH INFINITELY VARIABLE DRIVE

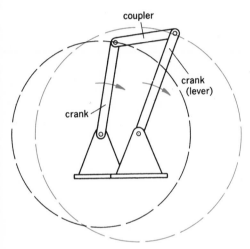

coupler

crank (lever)

crank

FIG. 3 DRAG-LINK MECHANISM

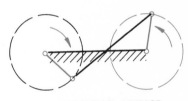

FIG. 4 PARALLEL LINKAGE

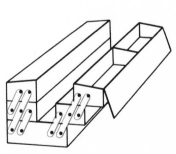

FIG. 5 ANTIPARALLEL LINKAGE

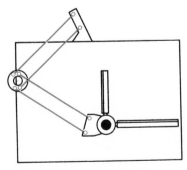

FIG. 6 DRAFTING MACHINE

FIG. 7 TOOL BOX

The *pantograph* (Fig. 8a) utilizes a parallel linkage for the proportional enlargement or reduction in scale of a given drawing. The points B and C of this mechanism trace figures that are similar in shape but differ in scale. The linear dimensions of the two figures are proportional to the respective distances of the points B and C to the pivot A. For example, if the distance CA is four times the distance BA, and if B is made to trace the outlines of a drawing, then a pencil at C will reproduce this drawing at four times the original size, and vice versa. A multiple pantograph is shown in Fig. 8b. Here all the points located on the horizontal line—i.e., B, C, C_1 and C_2—will trace similar figures of varying size, depending on the respective distances from those points to the pivot at A. The familiar device known as "lazy tongs," used for such purposes as lamp or telephone supports, consists of an assembly of parallel linkages. Fig. 9 shows a typical application of a four-bar linkage for producing a to-and-fro swinging motion of a fan.

An interesting feature of the beam-and-crank mechanism (Fig. 10) is that whereas all points of the crank and lever trace only circular paths, points on or associated with the coupler trace paths that may have a wide variety of shapes, depending on where these points are located. This principle may be utilized for obtaining motions conforming to paths of particular shape. If the trace of a point C on the coupler AB in the mechanism illustrated in Fig. 11 locally conforms to a circular curve with radius r, it is possible to connect at C a link CM, of length r, which will produce a temporary standstill of the oscillating lever attached to it. So long as the point C travels along the circular curved portion of the trace, the link CM will rotate only about the point M, without causing displacement of this point.

(more)

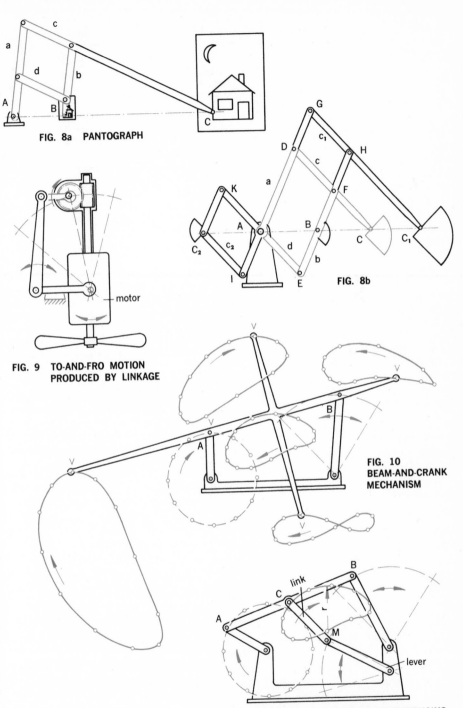

FIG. 8a PANTOGRAPH

FIG. 8b

FIG. 9 TO-AND-FRO MOTION PRODUCED BY LINKAGE

FIG. 10 BEAM-AND-CRANK MECHANISM

FIG. 11 BEAM-AND-CRANK MECHANISM FOR PRODUCING TEMPORARY STANDSTILL OF OSCILLATING LEVER

215

Linkages (continued)

One or more of the pin joints (pivots) of a four-bar linkage may be replaced by a "slider"—i.e., a pivoted element that can perform a guided linear motion in a slideway. The mechanism thus obtained is called a slider-crank linkage (Fig. 1). In this form it is used for the crankshaft, connecting rod, piston and cylinder of an internal-combustion engine or air compressor. The stroke performed by the slider is equal to twice the length of the crank if the center line of the slideway passes through the crank pivot. In the eccentric crank mechanism (Fig. 2) the stroke is less than twice the crank length. The farthest points reached by the slider in the course of its to-and-fro motion are called the "dead centers." The crank angles α_1 and α_2 between the two dead-center positions in the eccentric crank mechanism are not equal; the return movement of the slider is therefore faster than the forward movement. In the case of the oscillating crank mechanism (Fig. 3) the crank end is pivotally attached to a slider which moves up and down in a slot in an oscillating bar which in turn moves a horizontal rod to and fro. For the direction of crank rotation indicated in Fig. 3 the movement of the slotted bar to the left is associated with a larger crank angle than the movement to the right. Thus the horizontally moving rod (which may, for example, actuate the work table of a machine tool) will perform a slow forward movement and a rapid return movement. If the length of the crank is greater than the distance designated as "frame length" in Fig. 3, the slotted bar will perform a rotational instead of an oscillatory movement. A combination of a rotating and an oscillating slotted bar (Fig. 4) is often used for obtaining the work-table motion on machine tools in order to ensure as far as possible a constant low speed for the forward movement (feed) and a rapid return.

Fig. 5 shows a cross-shaped bar assembly with slot-and-crank drive. The distance traveled by the cross, measured from its middle position, is proportional to the sine of the angle α or the cosine of the angle β. This characteristic of the mechanism is utilized for certain purposes, such as the production of sinusoidal cam drives. The device known as the elliptic trammel (Fig. 6), which is used for drawing ellipses, comprises two slideways at right angles to each other. A crank is pivotally connected to a slider in each slideway. All points on the crank will trace elliptical curves; only the center point on the crank (midway between A and B) traces a circle. When an ellipse is traced by a point C located beyond B, the length BC will be equal to the semiminor axis and AB will be equal to the difference between the semimajor and semiminor axes of the ellipse. If the point that traces the ellipse (e.g., the point D) is located between A and B, the length AD will be equal to the one semiaxis (in this case the semiminor axis), and AB will be equal to the sum of the two semiaxes of the ellipse.

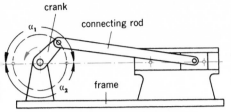

FIG. 1   SLIDER-CRANK MECHANISM

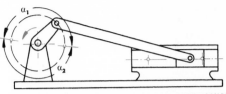

FIG. 2   ECCENTRIC SLIDER-CRANK MECHANISM

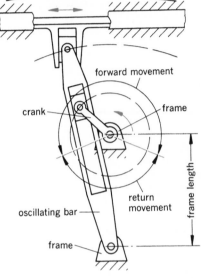

FIG. 3   OSCILLATING CRANK MECHANISM

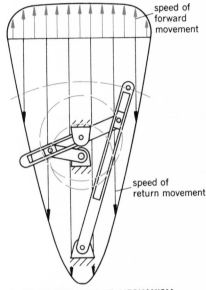

FIG. 4   WORK-TABLE DRIVE MECHANISM (COMBINATION OF ROTATING AND OSCILLATING SLOTTED BAR)

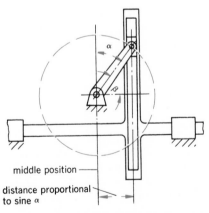

FIG. 5   SLOT-AND-CRANK-DRIVE MECHANISM

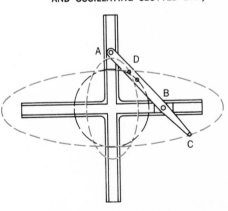

FIG. 6   ELLIPTIC TRAMMEL

217

GEAR MECHANISM

Gears transmit rotary motion from one shaft to another through meshing perimetral teeth on wheels mounted on the shafts. Usually the transmission of motion is associated with a change in torque. It is effected without slip and with a high degree of mechanical efficiency. The simplest gear mechanism comprises two meshing gears (toothed wheels) mounted in a fixed cage or frame (Fig. 1). Since the two gears intermesh, they must rotate with the same circumferential velocity. This means that the smaller gear (usually referred to as the "pinion") has to rotate at a higher angular velocity, i.e., has to perform more revolutions per minute, than the larger. The rotational speeds of the gears are inversely proportional to their respective diameters or their respective numbers of teeth. Since the force exerted by two teeth in contact must be of equal magnitude for both (action is equal to reaction: $F = F_R$), the torque acting on the larger gear ($= F \times R$) must be of greater magnitude than that acting on the smaller gear ($= F \times r$). The ratio of the speed of the driving shaft to that of the driven shaft is called the gear ratio or transmission ratio.

If, instead of the cage, one of the gears is held stationary and the other gear is driven, the cage will perform a rotary motion; a planetary gear system is thus obtained (Fig. 2), comprising the sun wheel, the planet wheel (as a rule there are two or more planet wheels), the cage, and the internally toothed annulus which meshes with the panel wheel, while the latter meshes with the sun wheel. In Fig. 2 the sun wheel is conceived as being stationary, while the annulus drives the planet wheel. Alternatively, any one of the three elements—sun wheel, planet wheel, cage—may be assigned the role of the stationary element and any of the two others of this trio may be driven. Thus six different possibilities of transmission are available, as well as the possibility of locking the sun wheel and the planet wheels, so that direct drive is obtained. Examples of planetary gear systems are given on pp. 184–185 and pp. 218–219 of Volume II.

In general, gear systems are named after the shape of the gears or the arrangement of their teeth (see page 172 et seq.). Shafts whose center lines cross but do not intersect are connected by spiral gears (Fig. 3). In the worm gear (Fig. 4) the basic shape of the worm is a cylinder or a globoid, while that of the worm wheel is a globoid. A globoid is a body of revolution that is generated by the rotation of a circular arc about any axis.

Change-speed gears permit the selection of various transmission ratios. The simplest method of doing this is by the removal and replacement of gear wheels of different sizes. Greater ease and convenience are provided by a change-speed gearbox, such as is used on motor vehicles and certain machine tools. Such gearboxes permit the selection of various transmission ratios between driving shaft and driven shaft by appropriate operation of a lever. The speed changes are obtained by the action of sliding pinions that are moved into or out of mesh with gear wheels. A type of transmission that provides as many ratios as there are gear pairs and that takes up little space is the draw-key transmission (Fig. 5). Whenever the draw key is shifted, one of the gears that are mounted loose on shaft II is locked to the shaft, so that the gear pair concerned then transmits power. This type of gear is used as feed gearing on machine tools (see page 196). A reversing gear serves to reverse the direction of rotation. In the bevel-gear device of this kind (Fig. 6) shaft I is the driving shaft, on which an engaging element with claws is slidably mounted. When this element is shifted to the left, the bevel gear C and therefore the driven shaft II is driven through the agency of the bevel gear A; when the engaging element is slid to the right, the drive is effected through the agency of the bevel gear B instead of A, so that now the shaft II rotates in the opposite direction.

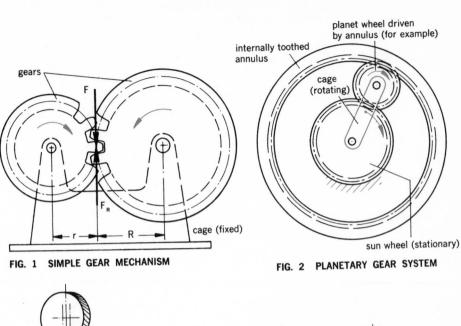

gears

F

F_R

r

R

cage (fixed)

FIG. 1 SIMPLE GEAR MECHANISM

internally toothed annulus

planet wheel driven by annulus (for example)

cage (rotating)

sun wheel (stationary)

FIG. 2 PLANETARY GEAR SYSTEM

elevation

plan

FIG. 3 SPIRAL GEARS

FIG. 4 WORM AND WORM WHEEL

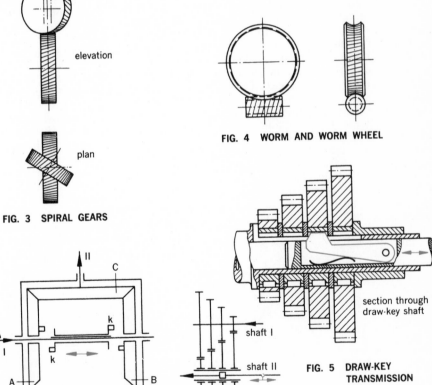

II

C

k

k

I

A

B

FIG. 6 REVERSING BEVEL-GEAR TRANSMISSION

shaft I

shaft II

schematic diagram

section through draw-key shaft

FIG. 5 DRAW-KEY TRANSMISSION

FRICTION DRIVES

In a friction-drive mechanism the friction elements are usually cylindrical, conically tapered or globoid wheels which are pressed together so firmly that the frictional force developed at the point or line of contact transmits power. The power that can be transmitted in this way will depend on the magnitude of the contact pressure and the coefficient of friction of the surfaces in contact. In every friction drive a small amount of slip develops between the friction elements: i.e., at the point of contact the driven wheel always has a slightly lower circumferential velocity than the driving wheel. The drive is therefore not a fully positive one. Such forms of drive have the advantage that the effective radius can be varied quite simply by a shifting of the point of contact of the friction wheels toward or away from the axis of rotation, so that "infinitely variable" control over the transmission ratio is obtained.

In the simplest form of friction-wheel drive, cylindrically shaped wheels roll against each other. The resilience of the (often rubber-covered) wheels, spring pressure or weights produces the necessary contact pressure and thus develops the friction through which power is transmitted. Just as with toothed gears, the transmission ratio is determined by the ratio of the respective radii, while the rotational speeds of the two wheels (rpm) are inversely proportional to their radii. (Examples: record-player drive, tape-recorder drive.) Every powered traction wheel of a road vehicle or rail-mounted vehicle is in effect a friction drive. The contact pressure due to the weight of the vehicle enables the wheel to develop friction and thus "get a grip" on the road or rail surface. This combination is comparable to a rack and pinion, the wheel being the "pinion" and the road or rail the "rack." Fig. 1 shows a friction drive that is similar in construction to a planetary gear (see page 218) and is of the type used for the tuning mechanism on some radio receivers. The balls correspond to the planet wheels; they roll on the inner shaft, which corresponds to the sun wheel. When the fine-adjustment knob mounted on the inner shaft is rotated, the "cage" formed by the hollow shaft (on which the large coarse-adjustment knob giving direct drive is mounted) will rotate at a lower speed and thus make possible precision tuning.

A friction drive for infinitely variable speed control comprising two conically tapered friction elements and an intermediate ring is illustrated in Fig. 2. When the ring is in the right-hand position (shown in black), the upper shaft will rotate faster than the lower shaft, which is the driving shaft, because in this position the driving radius R is larger than the driven radius r. When the ring is shifted to the left-hand position (shown in red), the driving radius r will be smaller than the driven radius R, so that now the upper shaft will rotate more slowly than the lower shaft. Fig. 3 shows a friction drive comprising a large flat wheel and a small friction wheel which can be slid to different positions on the driving shaft on which it is mounted. The small wheel can thus engage with the large wheel at any desired radius of the latter, so that the speed of the driven shaft can be varied.

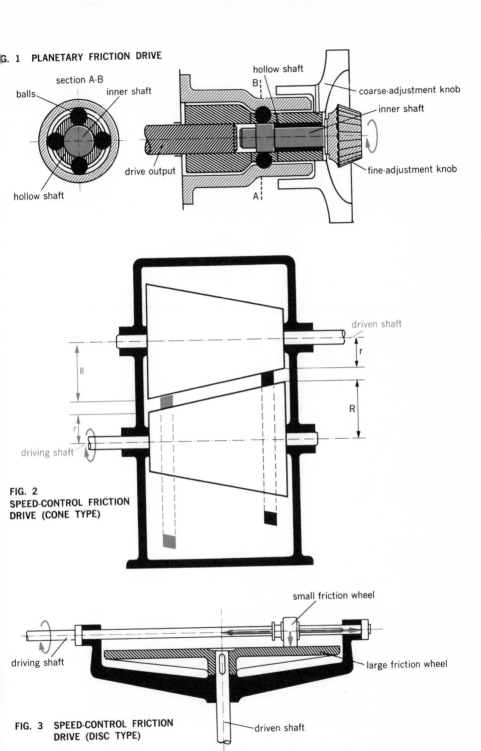

FIG. 1 PLANETARY FRICTION DRIVE

section A-B

balls
inner shaft
hollow shaft
drive output
hollow shaft

hollow shaft
B
coarse-adjustment knob
inner shaft
fine-adjustment knob
A

driven shaft
r
R
R
r
driving shaft

FIG. 2
SPEED-CONTROL FRICTION
DRIVE (CONE TYPE)

small friction wheel
driving shaft
large friction wheel
driven shaft

FIG. 3   SPEED-CONTROL FRICTION
DRIVE (DISC TYPE)

221

PULLEY DRIVES

The simplest form of pulley drive is the "fixed pulley" (Fig. 1), where the force Z needed to raise the load Q is equal to the latter. In the arrangement shown in Fig. 2 the load is suspended from the pulley; the (upward) force needed to raise the pulley with the load suspended from it is now only half the magnitude of the load (assuming the pulley itself to be weightless). Pulleys employed as lifting tackle are described on pp. 264-265 of Vol. I.

The flexible connecting elements used in pulley drive systems are ropes, belts, wires, chains, etc., made of a variety of materials (rubber, leather, textile fabrics, metal, etc.). These elements can take only tensile loading. Power transmission is effected through the action of friction between the flexible elements and the pulleys around which they pass. In some cases, however, a positive drive is obtained by means of chains whose links engage with the teeth on special toothed wheels called sprockets (example: bicycle or motorcycle chain drive).

Transmission of rotational motion between shafts at any distance apart can be effected through a belt drive. The necessary contact pressure between the belt and the pulleys is ensured by appropriate tightening of the belt. This may be achieved by means of a tensioning roller or pulley. By the use of a belt of V-shaped cross section (V-belt) the contact pressure can be increased and the power transmission thus made more efficient. In the pulley drive illustrated in Fig. 3 each pulley consists of two halves which can be moved farther apart or closer together. The effective radius of the pulleys and therefore the transmission ratio can be varied at will. In the PIV (positive infinitely variable) gear based on this principle the pulley halves are provided with radial grooves which engage with projections on a special belt, so that positive nonslip drive is achieved (see also page 194). Fig. 4 shows a pulley drive that provides a simple solution of the problem of shifting the position of the driven shaft in relation to that of the driving shaft while the shafts are rotating. In Fig. 5 a pulley drive system is used for producing symmetrical motion of two parts in relation to each other (e.g., for opening and closing of curtains, sliding doors, etc.). When the left-hand door leaf is moved to the left, the belt or rope that is attached to it and passes around the right-hand pulley causes the right-hand leaf to move an equal distance to the right, and vice versa. Fig. 6 shows a pulley drive utilized in a high-lift truck. When the driving shaft is rotated clockwise, the large pulley winds up the rope, thus shortening it, so that the platforms are raised. They are lowered by counterclockwise rotation of the shaft. The raising and lowering of a fire ladder is based on the same principle (Fig. 7).

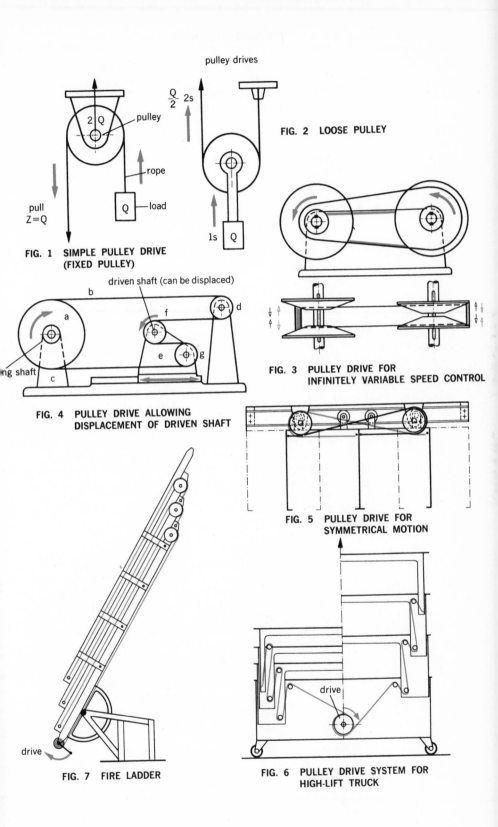

pulley drives

FIG. 1 SIMPLE PULLEY DRIVE
(FIXED PULLEY)

FIG. 2 LOOSE PULLEY

FIG. 3 PULLEY DRIVE FOR
INFINITELY VARIABLE SPEED CONTROL

FIG. 4 PULLEY DRIVE ALLOWING
DISPLACEMENT OF DRIVEN SHAFT

FIG. 5 PULLEY DRIVE FOR
SYMMETRICAL MOTION

FIG. 7 FIRE LADDER

FIG. 6 PULLEY DRIVE SYSTEM FOR
HIGH-LIFT TRUCK

223

CAM MECHANISM

A cam is a specially shaped component that serves to guide the motion of a component called a follower. The cam may have a linear or a rotary motion. Like the crank mechanism, the cam mechanism serves to convert a given input motion (usually a uniform motion) into a desired output motion of particular form. With a crank mechanism it is not always possible to produce a motion whose path is of the desired shape, whereas a suitably designed cam mechanism will make possible practically any shape or pattern of motion. A great advantage of the cam principle is that it is quite conveniently possible to introduce pauses of any desired length into the motion. This advantage is widely utilized in machinery of all kinds, such as packaging machines and many others. With cams it is possible to perform simple oscillatory or sliding movements as well as precisely controlled movements of elaborate shape (e.g., guiding a milling cutter along a curved outline of any desired shape).

Every cam mechanism (Figs. 1, 2 and 3) essentially comprises three parts: the frame or base (a), on which the cam (b) is mounted, and the follower (c) whose motion is controlled by the cam, which is given a linear (Fig. 1) or a rotary (Figs. 2 and 3) motion. As a rule, the follower is held in contact with the cam by a spring or a guiding groove or some other appropriate device.

A typical example of a cam mechanism is the valve gear of an internal-combustion engine (Fig. 4). The rotating cam has an approximately pear-shaped profile comprising two circular curves joined by two straight lines which are tangential to those curves. The follower consists of a roller tappet which is moved up and down by the cam and imparts this motion to the rod that controls the opening and closing of the valve. The center of the roller traces a curve of similar shape to the cam profile (equidistant curve). In Fig. 5 the stroke, the speed and the acceleration of the roller tappet have been plotted against the angle of rotation of a cam of the type shown in Fig. 4. At a certain angle of rotation the acceleration undergoes a sudden change in value, which imparts a jerk to the tappet. This occurs every time the radius of curvature of the cam profile changes abruptly (e.g., transition from circular curve to tangent, and vice versa). Conversely, it is possible to start from a certain acceleration curve that comprises no abrupt changes (red curve in Fig. 5) and design a cam so shaped as to produce this "gentle" acceleration, free of jerks.

Fig. 6 shows a cam mechanism whose two paths can so move a milling cutter in two mutually perpendicular directions that a cut conforming to a specific predetermined shape (in this case the letters "HB") can be produced. The two cam paths are determined as follows: The trace is subdivided into a number of approximately equal portions (22 in the present example). Then the distances that the cutter has to move in the horizontal and vertical directions, respectively, to reach this point from the initial position 0, are plotted in two diagrams for all the points (0 to 22). Then the circumference of the cam disc is also divided into 22 equal parts. The distances from the respective cam paths for horizontal and vertical cutter movements to a certain reference radius on the disc are then marked out in radial directions. From 19 to 22 the cutter must moreover be lifted off the work, since this constitutes the return motion to the starting point.

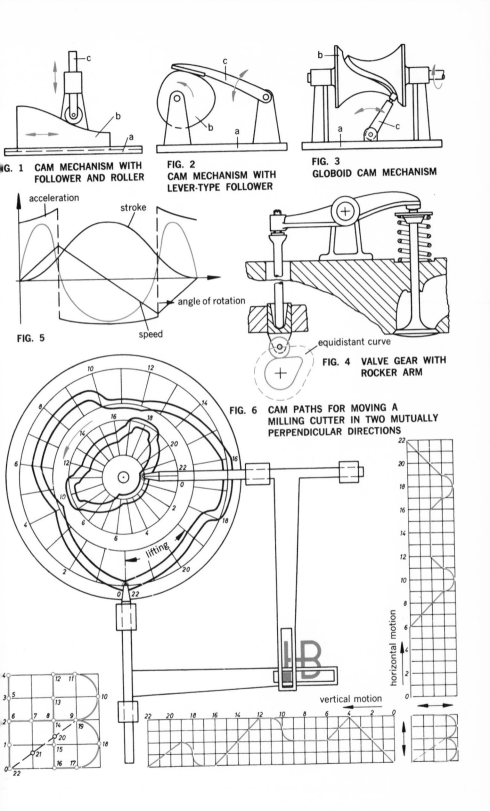

FIG. 1 CAM MECHANISM WITH FOLLOWER AND ROLLER

FIG. 2 CAM MECHANISM WITH LEVER-TYPE FOLLOWER

FIG. 3 GLOBOID CAM MECHANISM

FIG. 5

acceleration
stroke
angle of rotation
speed

FIG. 4 VALVE GEAR WITH ROCKER ARM

equidistant curve

FIG. 6 CAM PATHS FOR MOVING A MILLING CUTTER IN TWO MUTUALLY PERPENDICULAR DIRECTIONS

lifting

horizontal motion

vertical motion

LOCKING AND ARRESTING MECHANISMS

A ratchet mechanism is usually employed as a means of arresting a motion and producing intermittent action of a force so that it develops its action at particular instants. The ratchet bar A in Fig. 1 is provided with teeth with which the pawl B engages. The pawl, which is controlled by a spring, is pivotably mounted in a frame C in which the ratchet bar is also mounted in a slideway. The pawl is thus able to arrest the motion of the ratchet bar when the latter is thrust to the right and can, for example, periodically release it, so that the bar moves in successive jerks. In the grip-roller locking device (Fig. 2a) the bar A can move in relation to the cage C. When A moves to the right, the roller (or ball) jams and thus locks the two parts immovably together. When A moves to the left, the roller is released. Fig. 2b shows a locking or clamping device for a belt or strap working a roller blind or some such device. In the friction brake (Fig. 3), counterclockwise rotation of the wheel causes friction to build up as a result of the thrust exerted by the brake block on its pivoted angle lever, so that the wheel is braked; no braking action is developed when the wheel rotates in the clockwise direction. An ordinary lock is also essentially a device of this general type. In the catch lock (Fig. 4) the sliding element A is slid forward in the guide C and is locked by means of the catch B. The latter is released when it is lifted by the key, so that A can then be slid back.

The grip brake (Fig. 5) that acts as a safety device for elevators (passenger lifts) in the event of cable fracture is a locking mechanism of this class. When the rope exerts an upward pull, the gripping jaws are released, so that the grip brake as a whole can be moved in relation to the fixed guide rod. If the cable breaks, the powerful spring will push the slide down, causing the pivoted angle lever to thrust the brake blocks with considerable force against the rod.

A ratchet-wheel mechanism is used to produce intermittent motion, as already stated. The mechanism illustrated in Fig. 6 is equipped with two pawls. The upper pawl is operated by an eccentric drive, and its successive thrusts cause the ratchet wheel to rotate counterclockwise in an intermittent motion. The lower pawl prevents clockwise rotation of the ratchet wheel while the driving pawl is performing its return motion. The Maltese cross mechanism used, for instance, in motion-picture equipment also belongs to this class of devices (see Vol. I, pp. 216–217). The star-wheel mechanism (Fig. 7) operates on the same principle. The large driving wheel drives the small driven wheel only as long as the drive pins on the former engage with the teeth of the latter. As there are (in this particular case) eight pins and eight teeth, the small wheel will always perform one complete revolution as long as there is engagement. A mechanism of this type is used in most counting devices: e.g., the mileage counter in a motor vehicle.

(more)

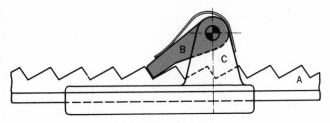

FIG. 1   RATCHET BAR AND PAWL

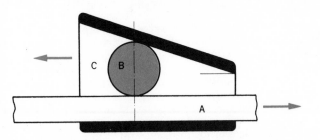

FIG. 2a   GRIP-ROLLER LOCKING MECHANISM

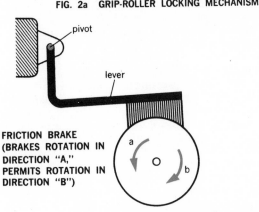

3   FRICTION BRAKE
(BRAKES ROTATION IN
DIRECTION "A,"
PERMITS ROTATION IN
DIRECTION "B")

FIG. 2b   GRIP-ROLLER LOCKING
DEVICE FOR A BELT

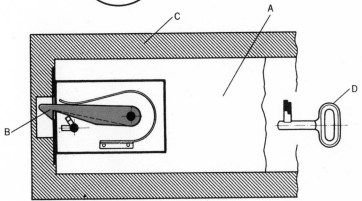

FIG. 4   CATCH LOCK

227

The operating principle of the mileage counter is as follows: The hollow cylindrical roller on which the ten numerals representing the units are indicated is provided internally with one drive pin. Every time the figure 9 appears in the small "window" on the instrument panel and the roller has therefore performed a complete revolution (but only then and at no other time) this pin engages with a small wheel to advance the roller on which the "tens" are marked to the next figure (e.g., from 0 to 1); at the same time, the figure 0 appears in the window of the first roller (the "units" roller). When the 9 again appears on this roller, the "tens" roller is again rotated on to the next figure, so that it now shows the figure 2 in the window, and so on. A star-wheel drive of this kind (with only one drive pin) is provided between each successive pair of rollers and brings about the change from, for instance, 0089 to 0090 or from 0999 to 1000.

The striker-cocking mechanism in a rifle (Fig. 8) keeps the energy locked in the compressed spring F. When the trigger D is pulled to the right, it first compresses the spring F even more. Then, as a result of the inclined guiding surface at B, the locking pin B is slid downwards so that the striker A can fly to the right, propelled by the force of the spring F. In the drop-weight device (Fig. 9), which is used for certain mechanical testing purposes, the potential energy stored in the weight A in its raised position is released when the lever B is swung to the right, thereby disengaging the catch. When the weight is raised again, the pin attached to it automatically re-engages with the catch. The mechanism illustrated in Fig. 10 is called an escapement. It enables a force to be released and develop its action intermittently on the same principle as the ratchet-wheel-and-pawl mechanism already discussed. The escapement is more particularly a feature of clockwork drives. Mounted on the shaft, which is driven in the clockwise direction by a spring or a weight, is the so-called escape wheel, which is in fact a ratchet wheel. When the lever H is released, the spring pulls the pawl B_1 into engagement with the escape wheel and prevents its rotation. When the lever H is pushed down (by pressing the button), B_1 is disengaged, so that the wheel can now rotate; but by the time it has rotated a distance corresponding to half a tooth spacing, it is arrested by the pawl B_2, which has meanwhile come into engagement with it. When the button is released, the wheel can rotate once more, but again only half a tooth spacing, because now the spring pulls the pawl B_1 into engagement, as before. So every time the button is pressed, it allows the escape wheel to perform a movement corresponding to twice a half tooth spacing. Fig. 10 is intended merely to illustrate the principle of the escapement. In a clock or watch the periodic motion of the pawls (called "pallets" in horology) is controlled by a timing device such as a pendulum (shown schematically in red in Fig. 10) or a balance wheel. The reaction impulse of the escape wheel acting through the pallets upon the pendulum or the balance wheel maintains the motion. See also Vol. I, pp. 242–243.

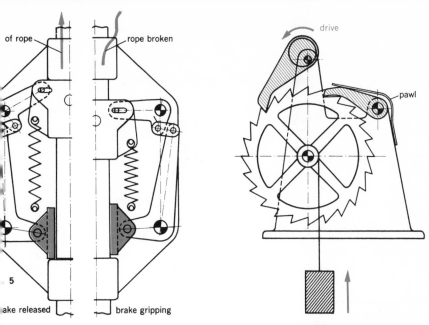

FIG. 6   RATCHET-WHEEL MECHANISM

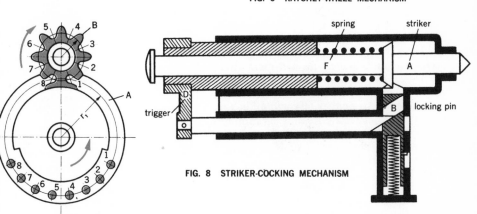

FIG. 7   STAR-WHEEL MECHANISM

FIG. 8   STRIKER-COCKING MECHANISM

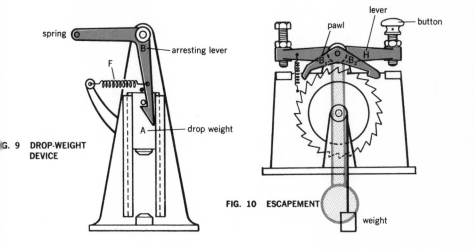

FIG. 9   DROP-WEIGHT DEVICE

FIG. 10   ESCAPEMENT

In its widest sense the term "gun" can include any kind of firearm from a pocket pistol to a heavy siege gun, but in the present article it will be used more particularly in the sense of "cannon"—i.e., an artillery weapon of relatively large bore and fired from a carriage or a fixed mount.

Guns are of many different sizes and types, according to the purposes for which they are intended. Broadly, they can be divided into flat-trajectory guns with long barrels (Fig. 1) and high-angle guns with relatively short barrels (mortars, howitzers) (Fig. 2). Guns for action against targets on the ground (Figs. 3 and 4) differ in many ways from antiaircraft guns (Fig. 5). Land-based guns are in some respects fundamentally different from naval guns installed on ships (Figs. 6 and 7).

The function of a gun barrel is to enable the projectile to reach a suitably high initial velocity in a very short time by utilizing the energy released by ignition of the propellant charge and to give the projectile the direction which, in combination with its velocity, will carry it to the target. To obtain a high initial velocity, a long barrel is necessary. Irrespective of the caliber, or bore, of the gun, the muzzle velocity —i.e., the velocity of the projectile on emerging from the muzzle of the gun—tends toward a maximum which cannot be further increased even by the use of a large propellant charge (Fig. 8).

The rear end of the barrel is closed by a device which may be in the form of a sliding block (breech block) or a screw. In front of the closing device is a chamber which receives the propellant charge. There is tapered transition from the chamber to the barrel proper. The interior of the latter is provided with spiral grooves (rifling), which impart a spinning motion to the projectile. The pitch of the rifling is expressed as a multiple of the bore; for instance, the pitch may be forty times the bore, meaning that the projectile performs one revolution about its longitudinal axis over a distance equal to forty times the bore of the barrel.

When a gun is loaded, the soft-metal driving band at the back end of the projectile (see page 238) is pressed into the rifling grooves and thus centers the projectile in the barrel. When the gun is fired, the firing pin strikes the primer and this ignites the charge, which may either be enclosed in a cartridge case or be entirely separate from the projectile (separate-loading ammunition, usually for guns of large bore). The explosive powder burns extremely rapidly and develops a very high gas pressure in the chamber—of the order of 45,000 lb./in.^{2} (3000 atm.) and upwards. As soon as the gas pressure exceeds the pressure with which the driving band is gripped in the rifling, the projectile is set in motion, so that the space behind increases in volume and the gas expands. After the initial pressure buildup in the chamber there is therefore a drop in pressure as the projectile makes its way along the barrel (Fig. 9). At the instant when it leaves the muzzle, the gas still has a high pressure, which causes the report when it escapes into the atmosphere. The maximum pressure developed by the propellant can be measured by means of a device called a crusher cylinder (Fig. 10). With the aid of a quartz crystal utilizing the piezoelectric effect, in combination with an oscillograph, it is possible to plot the variation of the gas pressure as a function of time.

(more)

FIG. 1   FLAT-TRAJECTORY GUN

FIG. 2   HIGH-ANGLE GUN

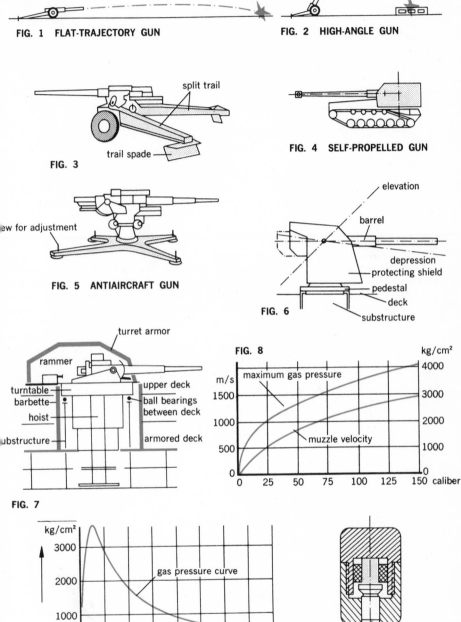

split trail

trail spade

FIG. 3

FIG. 4   SELF-PROPELLED GUN

ew for adjustment

FIG. 5   ANTIAIRCRAFT GUN

elevation

barrel

depression

protecting shield

pedestal

deck

FIG. 6

substructure

turret armor

rammer

turntable

barbette

hoist

ubstructure

upper deck

ball bearings
between deck

armored deck

FIG. 7

FIG. 8

kg/cm²

m/s

maximum gas pressure

4000

3000

2000

1000

0

1500

1000

500

0

muzzle velocity

0   25   50   75   100   125   150   caliber

kg/cm²

3000

2000

1000

0

gas pressure curve

FIG. 9

distance traveled by
projectile

FIG. 10

The gas pressure developed when the gun is fired produces high stresses, particularly in the interior of the barrel (Fig. 11). For this reason, monobloc ("one piece") barrels are now used only for guns of fairly small caliber. Medium- and large-caliber guns have barrels of composite construction, built up from several layers. In heavy guns the outer layers are shrunk on to the inner ones. As a result the innermost layer of the tube is in a state of precompression when the gun is not in action, while the layers around it are in tension (Fig. 12). When the charge in the chamber is fired, the gas pressure first overcomes the precompression and momentarily causes tensile stresses to develop in this innermost layer, though these tensile stresses are now much lower than they would be if there had been no initial precompression.

As already stated, in heavy guns the closing device at the rear end of the barrel may take the form of a screw mechanism or a horizontally sliding block (Fig. 13); a vertically sliding breech block (Fig. 14) is used for light and medium guns. In the firing position the breech block must be locked against the force of the exploding charge. In addition to suitable means for moving the block, the breech mechanism comprises the firing pin and the extracting system for removing the spent cartridge case when the breech is opened after the gun has been fired.

In every gun of the conventional type dealt with here the expulsion of the projectile is accompanied by a recoil movement of the barrel. Hydraulic braking cylinders are usually employed to arrest this movement. A piston rod attached to the barrel pulls the piston back when the barrel recoils, so that hydraulic fluid behind the piston is forced through narrow passages into the space in front of the piston, thereby producing a braking effect. By appropriate design of the braking system it is possible to keep the resistance developed by the piston approximately constant over its entire length of travel (Fig. 15).

To return the gun to its firing position after recoil, a special recuperator (or counterrecoil) mechanism is provided. In a light gun this may take the form of recuperator springs (Fig. 16), while medium and heavy guns are generally equipped with pneumatic recuperators (Fig. 17). To save weight, the braking cylinder and recuperator are often combined. Another device for reducing the forces acting upon the gun mount is the muzzle brake. It may be fitted to the muzzle of the gun barrel.

(more)

232

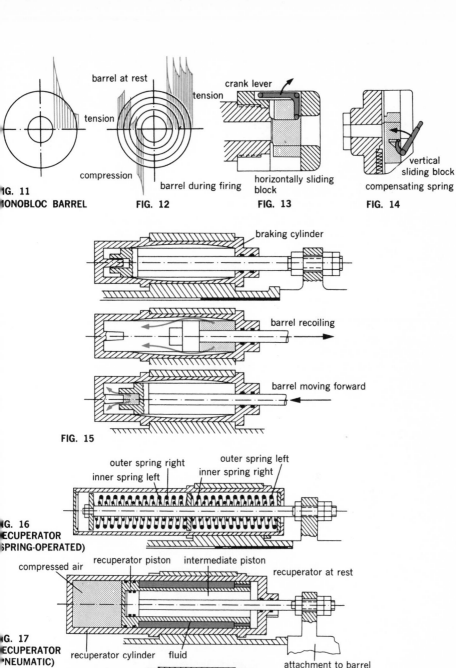

barrel at rest

tension

tension

compression

barrel during firing

FIG. 11
MONOBLOC BARREL

FIG. 12

crank lever

horizontally sliding block

FIG. 13

vertical sliding block

compensating spring

FIG. 14

braking cylinder

barrel recoiling

barrel moving forward

FIG. 15

outer spring right

inner spring left

outer spring left

inner spring right

FIG. 16
RECUPERATOR
(SPRING-OPERATED)

compressed air

recuperator piston

intermediate piston

recuperator at rest

FIG. 17
RECUPERATOR
(PNEUMATIC)

recuperator cylinder   fluid

attachment to barrel

barrel has recoiled

233

and its function is to deflect part of the propellant gases sideways or to the rear (Fig. 18). A properly designed muzzle brake can absorb 50–60% of the recoil, permitting the use of a lighter gun mount. On the other hand, the gun barrel is more severely stressed at the muzzle in consequence of this brake and there is more lateral air-pressure buildup (Fig. 19), which may be objectionable to the gun's crew.

As a rule, the gun mount has two axes of rotation, for aiming the barrel (Fig. 20). The latter can be swung about a vertical axis (this movement being called traversing or training) and also about a horizontal axis (this movement is called elevating). Mounts for ships' guns which have to be aimed at high angles of elevation for anti-aircraft defense may have a third axis of rotation to compensate for the rolling motion of the ship (Fig. 21).

The gun proper is mounted in a cradle attached to the top carriage of the mount. The top carriage rotates about a vertical axis for traversing the gun, while the cradle has trunnions which form the horizontal axis about which the gun can be rotated in elevation.

One of the main requirements with regard to the mount is that it provide adequate stability when the gun is fired. Stability can be improved by varying the recoil length. With low angles of elevation a long recoil with a small braking force is employed, whereas with high angles a shorter recoil with a larger braking force is more suitable. The variable recoil of the gun barrel is obtained by appropriate varying of the cross-sectional area of the flow passages for the hydraulic fluid in the braking cylinder with the angle of elevation.

The range of traversing and elevating movements that can be performed by the aiming mechanism depends on the type and purpose of the gun concerned. Thus a field gun generally has only a limited range of traversing movement, whereas an antiaircraft gun can be swung around in all directions and be elevated to high angles. The simplest aiming mechanism is manually operated by means of a handwheel and gearing (Figs. 22 and 23). This kind of mechanism is not, however, suitable for dealing with fast-moving targets. For such purposes mechanized operation, with a wide range of control adjustment, is employed: e.g., electrohydraulic drive systems, which have the advantage that they are relatively simple to control and are particularly suitable for remote control of guns from a fire-direction center. In this way a battery of several guns can be jointly aimed and fired—e.g., at fast aircraft. Heavy naval guns may have electrically powered traversing gear (Ward-Leonard control system) and hydraulic elevating gear (Fig. 24). The operating speed of the hydraulic cylinder is varied by means of valves which control the flow rate of the hydraulic fluid (oil or a mixture of glycerine and water). The two piston areas F and f are so dimensioned that the force acting upon the piston rod is of equal magnitude in both directions. Only the flow of fluid acting upon the larger piston area F is controlled; the force thus developed is counteracted by the force on the other side of the piston. Depending on the relative magnitude of these forces, the piston moves in the cylinder and varies the elevation of the gun. Turret-mounted naval guns are usually equipped with a hoist system for bringing the shells up into the turret from the shell room. With separate-loading ammunition, a second system for hoisting the cordite propellant charges from the magazine is provided. A modern warship's guns are controlled from a control tower where information about the enemy's range, speed, course and heading is fed into a computer, which processes the information and in turn passes aiming instructions to the gun turrets. Each turret rotates on rollers and is operated hydraulically.

For aiming the gun at a directly visible target, some form of sighting device is required. Such devices range from simple front and rear sights, like those on an ordinary rifle, to complex "fire-control systems" for large guns. The sighting device may move with the gun barrel (Fig. 25) or may be separate from the gun-elevating

(more)

234

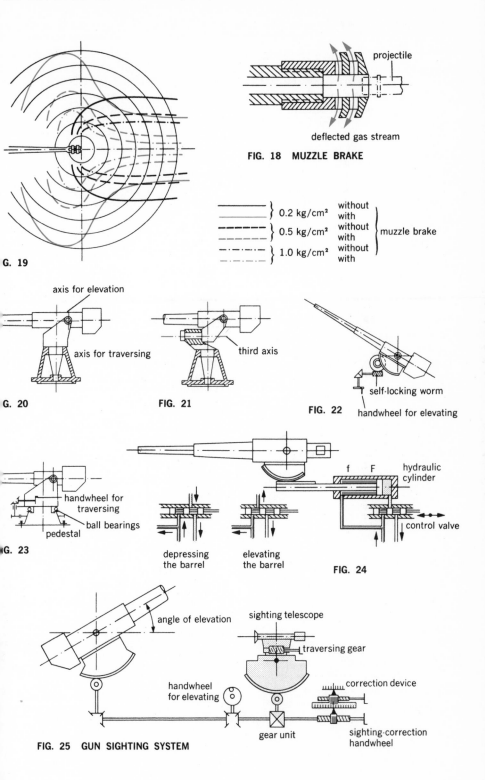

projectile

deflected gas stream

FIG. 18   MUZZLE BRAKE

────── }	0.2 kg/cm²	without / with
── ── ── }	0.5 kg/cm²	without / with } muzzle brake
─·─·─·─ }	1.0 kg/cm²	without / with

G. 19

axis for elevation

axis for traversing

G. 20

third axis

FIG. 21

self-locking worm

FIG. 22   handwheel for elevating

handwheel for traversing

ball bearings

pedestal

G. 23

depressing the barrel

elevating the barrel

f   F   hydraulic cylinder

control valve

FIG. 24

angle of elevation

sighting telescope

traversing gear

handwheel for elevating

correction device

gear unit

sighting-correction handwheel

FIG. 25   GUN SIGHTING SYSTEM

235

mechanism (Fig. 26). Precise prediction of the details of the trajectory of the projectile is based on ballistic calculations. The results of such calculations are embodied in a firing table, summarizing the trajectory information needed for correctly aiming the gun to hit the target. In the simplest case, the table will comprise a list of angles of elevation corresponding to various ranges. The elevation data for aiming the gun may be plotted in graph form, as in Fig. 27. This graph gives the so-called tangent elevation values for various ranges. The tangent elevation is the angle between the direction in which the gun is actually aimed and the line of sight—i.e., the straight line joining gun and target.

A projectile fired from a gun is subject to a number of different forces. In the first place, there is the force exerted by gravity. There are also forces due to the rotation of the earth, including more particularly the centrifugal force. Then there are the aerodynamic forces, which are produced by the resistance of the air. The most important of these is called drag, which acts along the axis of the projectile. Stability of the projectile in flight is ensured by the spinning motion imparted to it by the rifling.

To obtain a practically serviceable firing table, various corrections must be applied to the standard trajectories. Corrections must be made for meteorological conditions (temperature, wind, etc.; see also page 238), the decrease in muzzle velocity as the barrel wears, and other factors. The firing table may be incorporated into a machine called a director, into which observations of the target position are fed and which computes the projectile-release conditions. A radar sighting device, a director and a power-aimed gun (or a battery of guns) provide a fully automatic system for antiaircraft defense (Fig. 28). Manual adjustment of the gun's aim against such fast-moving targets as modern aircraft is impracticable, and for this reason the high-speed computerized control provided by a director system is essential.

236

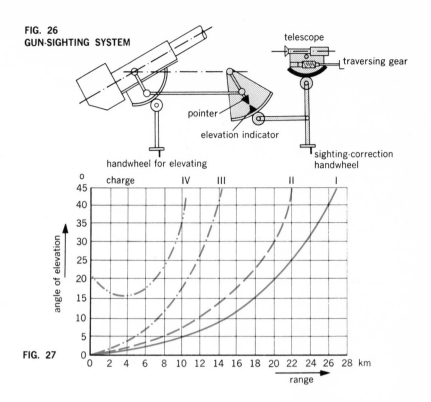

FIG. 26
GUN-SIGHTING SYSTEM

telescope

traversing gear

pointer

elevation indicator

handwheel for elevating

sighting-correction
handwheel

FIG. 27

charge   IV   III   II   I

angle of elevation

range

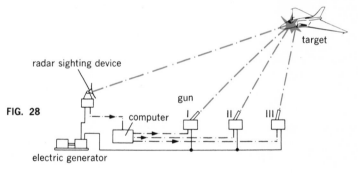

target

radar sighting device

FIG. 28

gun

computer

electric generator

237

PROJECTILES

The external shape of a projectile fired from a gun is so designed as to enable it to achieve a favorable ballistic trajectory. A typical projectile has a tapered point which is called the ogive and which is joined to a cylindrical portion (Fig. 1). The ogive usually contains a fuse for detonating the bursting charge of the shell (in certain types of shell, however, the fuse is located at the base instead of at the nose). At the transition from the ogive to the cylindrical part is an accurately machined band called the bourrelet. It serves to center and guide the projectile in the gun barrel. The driving band (or rotating band) is a ring of softer metal which engages with the rifling grooves and forms a seal to the gas pressure developed by the propellant. With fixed and semifixed ammunition the propellant charge is contained in a cartridge case which is attached to the base of the shell—e.g., by being crimped so as to engage with a groove. Within the cartridge case is the primer, a metal tube containing the primary explosive which detonates the main propellant.

When the gun is fired, the driving band engages with the rifling and causes the projectile to spin about its longitudinal axis. This spinning motion stabilizes the projectile in flight and keeps it aligned—i.e., with its nose always pointing forward. The projectile in flight is subject to the action of gravity and to the air resistance it encounters. The magnitude of this resistance is largely dependent on the velocity of the projectile. The density and temperature of the air and the velocity of the wind (if any) are important factors which affect the trajectory. A 28-cm (11-in.) shell fired with an initial velocity of 900 m/sec. (3000 ft./sec.) at an elevation of 45 degrees would attain a range of about 80 km (50 miles) in a vacuum, but under actual atmospheric conditions the range is less than half this distance (Fig. 2).

Artillery ammunition is of various kinds, depending on the purpose (type of target) at which it is fired. The high-explosive shell (Fig. 3), with a sensitive fuse in the nose, is used mainly against unarmored targets. The shell wall is relatively thin, enclosing a large bursting charge, whose weight corresponds to between 7 and 10% of the total weight of the projectile. The effect of such a shell is due mainly to the blast and the splinters from the shattered shell wall. The effect of a shell can be determined by measurement of the number and penetrating power of the splinters formed. This is done on a special testing site provided with walls of a certain thickness arranged at various radial distances from the center of the explosion (Fig. 4). After the shell has been exploded, these walls are examined to ascertain the number of splinters that have struck them and the proportion of splinters that have penetrated them. The usual explosive filling for high-explosive shells has long been either TNT or amatol. In recent years various new explosives have been developed for use in artillery ammunition.

Tracer ammunition (Figs. 5a and 5b) is fired at a rapid rate from automatic weapons. It permits the course of the projectiles to be observed and corrected as necessary. The "tracer" is a cartridge of pyrotechnic composition at the base of the shell and is visible both in daylight and at night.

(more)

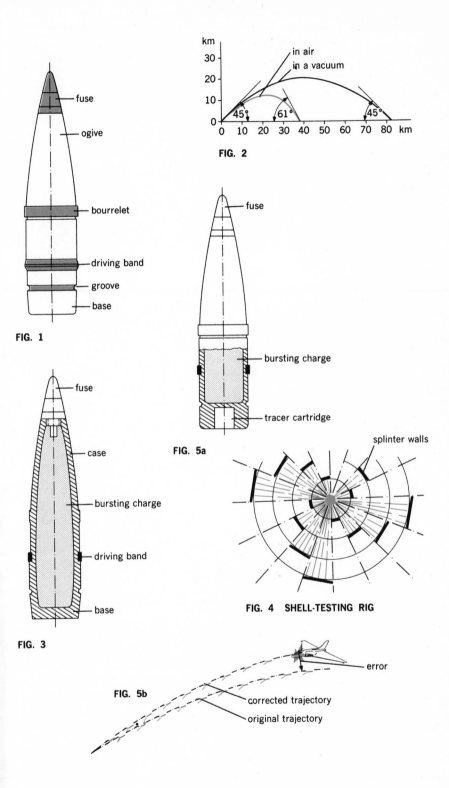

FIG. 1

fuse
ogive
bourrelet
driving band
groove
base

FIG. 2

km
30
20
10
0

in air
in a vacuum

45°   61°   45°

0 10 20 30 40 50 60 70 80 km

FIG. 5a

fuse
bursting charge
tracer cartridge

FIG. 3

fuse
case
bursting charge
driving band
base

FIG. 4   SHELL-TESTING RIG

splinter walls

FIG. 5b

error
corrected trajectory
original trajectory

239

Projectiles (continued)

The high-explosive shell shown in Fig. 6 has its fuse at the base instead of at the nose and is used mainly against lightly armored targets. The wall of the shell is somewhat thicker than that of the ordinary high-explosive shell, while the bursting charge is about 6–7% of the weight of the shell. The fuse is screwed into the base plug, which in turn is screwed into the base of the shell. The penetrating power of such a shell depends on the caliber, the velocity and the angle of impact; it is not so great as that of an armor-piercing shell. In Fig. 7 the curves present a comparison of the penetrating power of armor-piercing shells and high-explosive shells with base fuses.

The armor-piercing shell (Fig. 8) is employed against heavily armored targets. It has a relatively thick wall and a small bursting charge (about 2% of the weight of the projectile). It is provided with an armor-piercing nose and sometimes a thin-walled windshield to improve the ballistic properties, as in Fig. 8, where the hardened nose moreover has a cap of softer metal which flattens out on impact with the target and thus forms a kind of guiding pad for the hard armor-piercing nose. In this type of shell the fuse is always located at the base.

Artillery ammunition of various kinds used for producing light for illuminating enemy positions or for signaling is collectively referred to as "pyrotechnics." The illuminating shell (Figs. 9a and 9b) contains an illuminant (sometimes called the "candle"), which may consist of magnesium or aluminum powder in combination with an oxidizing material. Attached to the candle is a parachute which opens when an expelling charge, detonated by a time fuse, forces it out of the shell.

Most mortar ammunition differs from other artillery ammunition in that it is fired from smooth-bore weapons. The projectile employed is fin-stabilized, not spin-stabilized. Fig. 10 shows a typical teardrop-shaped mortar projectile, with a fuse in the nose and metal fins in the tail. It is dropped, tail first, into the muzzle of the mortar; when the ignition charge strikes the firing pin, the propellant in the tail of the projectile is ignited. To increase its range, the projectile may contain a booster propellant charge (as in Fig. 10) which provides "rocket propulsion." In general, projectiles fired from mortars are characterized by low muzzle velocity, high trajectory and short range.

To obtain very high muzzle velocities, projectiles whose caliber is less than that of the gun barrel may be employed (Fig. 11). For firing, the projectile is inserted into a special propelling base which fits the barrel of the gun and which drops off shortly after the projectile emerges from the muzzle of the gun. Because of its smaller size, the projectile receives a more powerful acceleration from the gas pressure than would a shell of normal size. By this means it is possible to attain muzzle velocities of 1600 m/sec. (5300 ft./sec.) and upwards, whereas approximately 1200 m/sec. (4000 ft./sec.) is the maximum for normal projectiles.

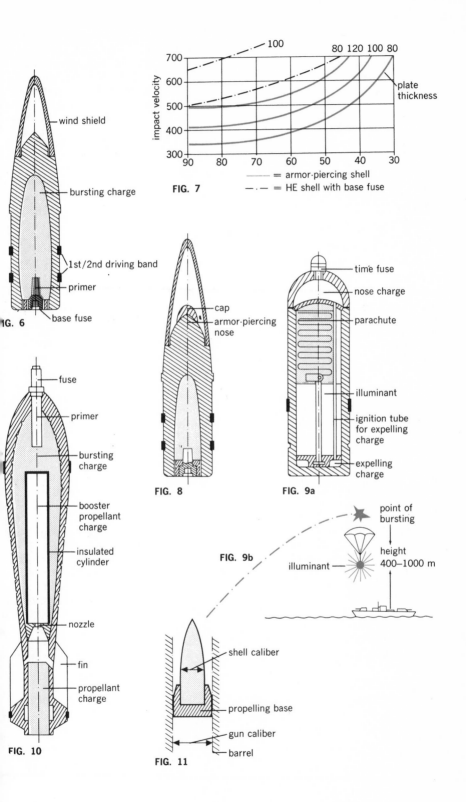

FIG. 6
wind shield
bursting charge
1st/2nd driving band
primer
base fuse

FIG. 7
impact velocity
700
600
500
400
300
90 80 70 60 50 40 30
100
80 120 100 80
plate thickness
——— = armor-piercing shell
—·—· = HE shell with base fuse

FIG. 8
cap
armor-piercing nose
bursting charge

FIG. 9a
time fuse
nose charge
parachute
illuminant
ignition tube for expelling charge
expelling charge

FIG. 9b
point of bursting
height 400–1000 m
illuminant

FIG. 10
fuse
primer
bursting charge
booster propellant charge
insulated cylinder
nozzle
fin
propellant charge

FIG. 11
shell caliber
propelling base
gun caliber
barrel

241

FUSES

A "fuse" is a device for detonating the explosive charge in a shell, missile, mine or bomb. This article is concerned more particularly with fuses employed in artillery shells. According to the position of the fuse in the projectile, a distinction can be made between the nose fuse (or point fuse) and the base fuse. With regard to the mode of functioning, a fuse may be an impact fuse (with or without delayed action), a time fuse or a proximity fuse. Fuses should be safe to handle and store and be safe against accidental detonation due to jolting or shaking. In addition, a fuse should be "bore-safe"—i.e., it should not be able to function until the shell has traveled some considerable distance from the gun muzzle. This precaution is necessary to protect the gun's crew against premature explosion of the shell.

The impact fuse, without delay action and installed in the nose of the shell, is used mainly against unarmored targets such as aircraft, boats and small vessels which present sufficient resistance to actuate the highly sensitive fuse. Delayed-action impact fuses are used against targets into which the shells are required to penetrate before they explode. In general, the time lag is only a few hundredths of a second. Fig. 1 shows a typical impact fuse.

Base fuses are used in shells employed against lightly armored targets and also in armor-piercing shells, the latter being used for attacking heavily armored targets. In both cases the fuses function with a delayed action, so as to give the shell time to penetrate before exploding.

Time fuses are of two types, the powder-train type and the mechanical (clockwork) type. They are used in cases in which it is required that the shell explode after a certain precise length of time—i.e., at a particular point of the trajectory in the proximity of the target; for example, an antiaircraft shell is set to burst at a predetermined altitude. Setting the fuse to the required time is done in a special device just before the shell is loaded into the breech of the gun for firing. Certain types of shell are fitted with a fuse that detonates on impact and also embodies a self-destroying time fuse. The latter causes the shell to explode while still in the air if it has missed the target; this arrangement obviates the danger that the unexploded shell will plunge back to earth, where it could harm one's own personnel. When the functions of an impact fuse and a time fuse are embodied in one device, it is called a combination fuse.

A proximity fuse (Fig. 2) causes the shell to explode when it passes within a specific distance of the target. This result is achieved by means of electronic devices carried in the shell. A well-known example is the VT fuse developed in World War II. It contains a miniature radio transmitter and also a miniature receiver. The transmitter sends out a continuous signal, and when this signal is reflected back by a solid object, the fuse detonates the explosive charge.

The impact fuse illustrated in Fig. 1 comprises a device to make it "bore-safe." When the projectile is fired from a rifled gun, a number of rotations of the shell about its longitudinal axis are needed to "arm" the fuse—i.e., to release the striker so that it can pierce the detonating cap when the shell hits the target. This "arming" is effected by centrifugal action by which a number of blades or other elements are retracted and the striker thus released.

(more)

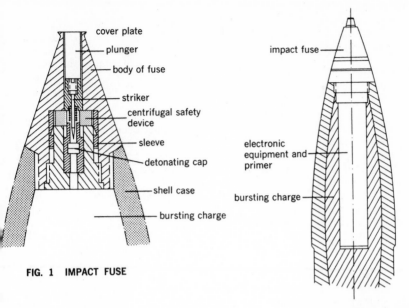

FIG. 1 IMPACT FUSE

FIG. 2 PROXIMITY FUSE

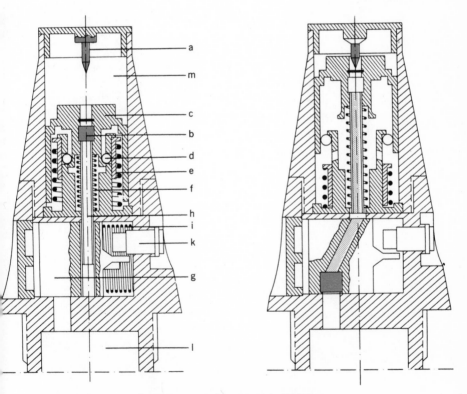

FIG. 3 IMPACT FUSE FOR SMOOTH-BORE GUN,
BEFORE AND AFTER HITTING TARGET

A highly sensitive impact fuse with self-destroying time action for rifled guns is illustrated in Figs. 4a–4d. When the projectile is fired, it acquires such a high spinning speed that the steel balls *a* are forced outwards by centrifugal action and cause the sliding element *c* to move forward toward the nose of the shell, against the restraining force of the spring *b*. As a result, the two pins *d* are released and are then able to move outwards against the pressure of the annular spring *e*. When this happens, the sliding element *f* is released, which now likewise moves radially outwards and thereby brings the detonating cap *h* into alignment with the striker *g*. The fuse is now "armed"—i.e., ready to function; when the impact occurs, the striker pierces the cap, which ignites the priming charge, and this in turn detonates the bursting charge. Self-destruction occurs when the spin of the projectile has slowed down to such an extent that the counteracting force developed by the spring *b* is stronger than the centrifugal force acting on the balls *a*. The balls are thus forced back into the sliding element *c*. The action of the spring *b* now thrusts the striker into the cap, so that the shell explodes.

Fig. 3 illustrates the functioning of a highly sensitive impact fuse for smooth-bore guns which is convertible from instant to delayed action. The fixed striker *a* is attached to the front cover of the fuse. The detonating cap *b* is located in a piston *c*, which is held in its lower position by the balls *d*, which in turn are retained by the collar *e*. The spring *f* forces the piston *c*, braked by the air cushion *m*, on to the striker *a*. In the bottom part of the fuse is the device for interrupting the ignition passage, if desired, and interposing the delayed-action element. The cylinder *g* is maintained in the safe position by the tube *h* attached to the piston *c*; the passage from the cap to the priming charge is now interrupted. When this tube is withdrawn, the cylinder *g* rotates (under the action of the spring *i*) through the angle permitted by the setting knob *k*. Thus the ignition flash issuing from the cap is conducted to the priming either direct or, alternatively, through the interposed delayed-action element. When the projectile is fired, the longitudinal acceleration causes the collar *e* to slide back and release the balls *d*. Consequently, the piston *c* can be slowly slid forward by the spring *f* to such an extent that the striker touches but does not as yet pierce the thin cover plate over the cap. At the same time, the tube *h* is withdrawn from the cylinder and the latter is rotated through its preset angle (as determined by the setting given to the knob *k* before the shell is fired). The fuse is now armed for functioning on impact, when the striker is forced through the thin plate and into the detonating cap.

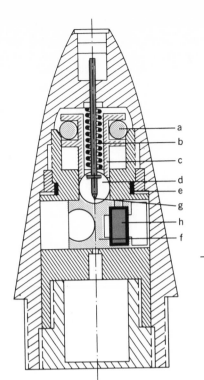

a
b
c
d
e
g
h
f

FIG. 4a FUSE SAFE

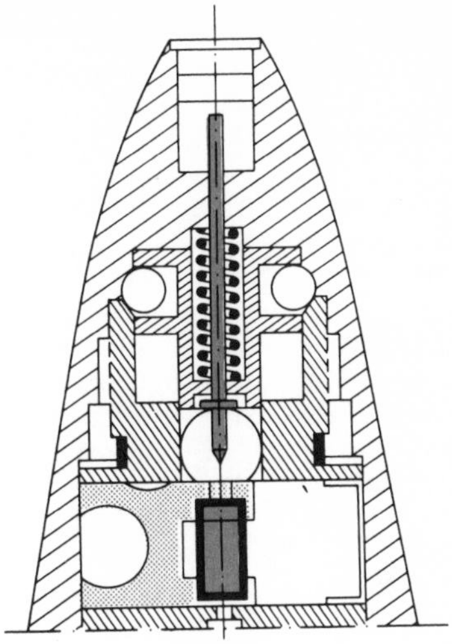

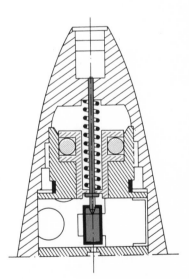

FIG. 4b FUSE ARMED

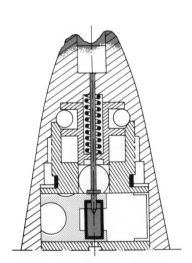

FIG. 4c STRIKER PIERCES CAP
ON IMPACT

FIG. 4d SELF-DESTROYING ACTION

245

MINES

Land mines, which were developed particularly in World War II, are buried just below the surface of the ground. They are of two main types: antitank mines and antipersonnel mines. A land mine consists of a container (made of metal, plastic or some other material) with an explosive charge, a fuse and a detonator. Fuses are mostly of the type operated by the weight of a vehicle or a man.

Naval mines are of two main types: moored mines (used in depths of water up to about 1300 ft.) and ground mines (resting on the bottom down to about 130 ft.). Moored mines are laid by vessels or by aircraft; Fig. 1 shows a contact mine of this type. The casing of the mine is usually spherical and contains the explosive charge with the detonator and firing mechanism. The mine is provided with an arming device which makes it operational only after it has been deposited from the mine-laying craft and which also disarms the mine if it breaks loose from its mooring. The mine, attached to its anchor, is thrown into the sea. At first this assembly floats. An auxiliary weight connected to a rope whose length is equal to the desired depth of the anchored mine below the surface of the sea is released and the mine is automatically detached from the anchor (to which it remains connected by the mooring cable, however). The anchor is flooded with water, so that it sinks, unwinding the mooring cable as it descends. As soon as the auxiliary weight, suspended below the anchor, touches the bottom, the rope of the auxiliary weight slackens. This causes the unwinding of the mooring cable to stop and the cable to be locked at the length it has then attained. The anchor continues to descend, pulling the mine down with it. Thus when the anchor reaches the bottom, the mine will be floating at the desired depth, attached to its cable. The pull on the cable now arms the mine by closing an electrical contact. Alternatively, the mine may be provided with a hydrostatic arming device which reacts to a predetermined depth of water.

The mine explodes when a vessel strikes one of the contact horns. This causes an electric current to actuate the firing mechanism, which in turn sends a strong current from a battery through the detonator. One type of contact horn contains an acid-filled glass tube which fractures, allowing the acid to enter a zinc-carbon electric cell which then produces a current to energize the firing mechanism (Fig. 2a). In another type (Fig. 2b), contact is established by a spring-loaded contact piece, so that current from a battery can flow. These and other detonating systems are illustrated schematically in Fig. 3. The four in the top row are for contact mines. In the third diagram of that row is shown a system in which the impact causes sea water to enter an electric cell and thus generate the energizing current. In the hydrostatic detonating system (fourth diagram) the pressure of sea water admitted to the interior of the mine when the contact horn is struck causes the energizing circuit to be completed. The systems illustrated in the bottom row relate to so-called influence mines—i.e., mines that are actuated not by contact but by the proximity of a ship. Ground mines are always of this kind. The magnetic mine is actuated by the change in the earth's magnetic field, producing, when a steel vessel passes within a certain distance, a deflection of a magnetic needle. Actuation of the pressure mine is brought about by the change in water pressure under a vessel in relatively shallow water. The mine contains a chamber divided into two parts, with one side of the chamber open to the sea; the deflection of the diaphragm establishes electrical contact. The acoustic mine is actuated by the sound of the ship's engines or propellers, which is picked up by sensitive microphones. The last diagram in the bottom row illustrates a detonating system for a controlled mine detonated from an observation station on land.

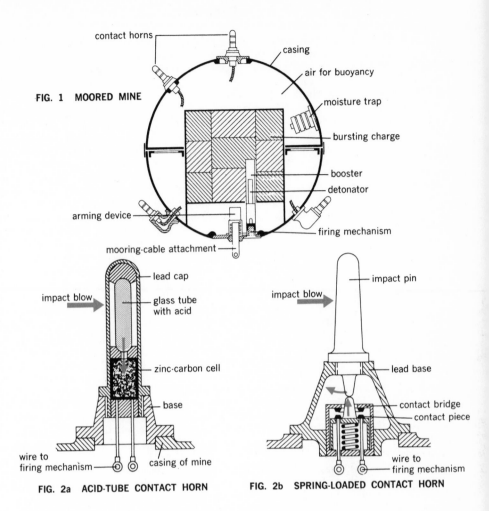

FIG. 1 MOORED MINE

contact horns — casing — air for buoyancy — moisture trap — bursting charge — booster — detonator — firing mechanism — arming device — mooring-cable attachment

lead cap — glass tube with acid — zinc-carbon cell — base — impact blow — wire to firing mechanism — casing of mine

impact pin — impact blow — lead base — contact bridge — contact piece — wire to firing mechanism

FIG. 2a ACID-TUBE CONTACT HORN   FIG. 2b SPRING-LOADED CONTACT HORN

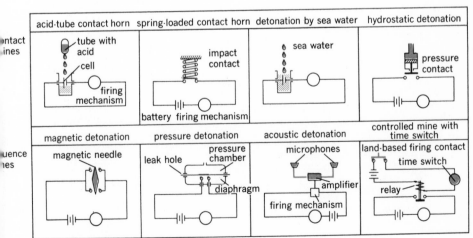

acid-tube contact horn	spring-loaded contact horn	detonation by sea water	hydrostatic detonation

contact lines — tube with acid — cell — firing mechanism — impact contact — battery firing mechanism — sea water — pressure contact

magnetic detonation	pressure detonation	acoustic detonation	controlled mine with time switch

uence nes — magnetic needle — leak hole — pressure chamber — diaphragm — microphones — amplifier — firing mechanism — land-based firing contact — time switch — relay

FIG. 3 MINE-DETONATING SYSTEMS

TORPEDOES

A torpedo is a self-propelled underwater missile with its own guidance system. In some cases it is provided with homing equipment enabling it to seek out its target. It is fitted with an exploder which detonates the explosive charge in the warhead when it strikes the target or comes close to it. Fig. 1 shows a typical torpedo of the ordinary kind employed against surface craft. With a diameter of 53 cm (21 in.) and a length of 7 m (23 ft.), it weighs about $1\frac{1}{2}$ tons, roughly one-fifth of which is taken up by the explosive charge. Torpedoes used against submarines are shorter and lighter.

The typical torpedo comprises the main sections shown in Fig. 1: the warhead, the air-flask section (or battery compartment in an electrically powered torpedo), the afterbody (comprising the "engine room" and the compartment containing the regulating equipment), and the tail. The warhead carries the exploder mechanism and contains the explosive charge. The homing mechanism, if any, is accommodated in a detachable nose section. The air-flask section of the torpedo contains compressed air, water and fuel. The afterbody contains the gyroscope, the depth-regulating mechanism, the combustion chamber (in which the fuel is burned and the water turned into steam), and the turbine or reciprocating engine (powered by the air and steam mixture) which drives the propellers (mounted on coaxial shafts and rotating in opposite directions). The tail section also contains the tail blades and rudders.

Surface ships may launch torpedoes from tubes which can be aimed in the desired direction (Fig. 3). Alternatively, the torpedo may be launched sideways from a special launching frame (Fig. 2), a method used on small craft. Submarines and also some surface vessels are provided with launching tubes built into the hull. Above-water torpedo tubes are fired by a charge of black powder or by compressed air. The latter propellant is always used for underwater tubes. Alternatively, a submerged tube is sometimes of the type that can be flooded, so that the torpedo emerges under its own power. Torpedoes may also be launched from aircraft flying at relatively low altitudes.

A fairly recent development is the rocket-propelled torpedo for use against submarines. This may take the form of an Asroc (antisubmarine rocket) for use from surface ships (Fig. 4) or a Subroc (submarine rocket) fired from the torpedo tube of a submarine; it emerges from the water, travels some considerable distance through the atmosphere, and then reenters the water on approaching its submerged target (Fig. 5). With these devices, the torpedo propulsion mechanism is automatically switched on when the torpedo enters, or reenters, the water. This mechanism is preset before launching: i.e., it is fed the data of the enemy's position (distance, course, speed).

(more)

248

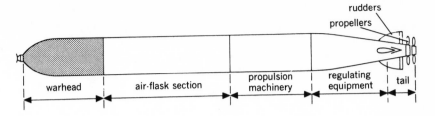

FIG. 1   MAIN PARTS OF A TORPEDO

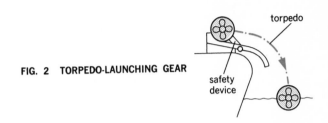

FIG. 2   TORPEDO-LAUNCHING GEAR

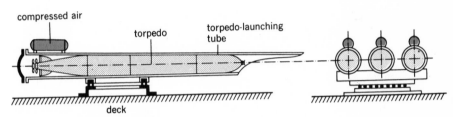

FIG. 3   TRIPLE LAUNCHING TUBES

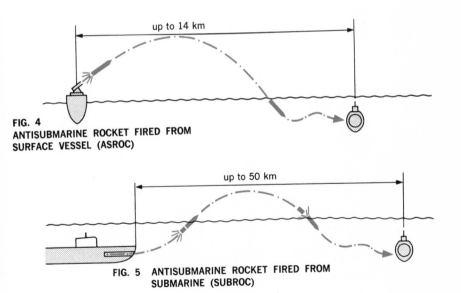

FIG. 4
ANTISUBMARINE ROCKET FIRED FROM
SURFACE VESSEL (ASROC)

FIG. 5   ANTISUBMARINE ROCKET FIRED FROM
SUBMARINE (SUBROC)

Torpedoes are driven by multicylinder reciprocating engines, turbines or battery-powered electric motors. The propulsive agent may be compressed air, a mixture of compressed air and steam, electricity, etc. Fuels may be oil, alcohol, hydrogen peroxide, etc.

With compressed air and steam drive (Fig. 6a), air is supplied from a flask (a) through a pressure-reducing valve which is preset to enable the torpedo to develop its appropriate speed. Oil, atomized by the compressed air, is burned in the combustion chamber (b), into which water is sprayed so that steam is generated. The resulting mixture of air and steam is fed to the four-cylinder radial-type engine (Fig. 6b). After expansion, the exhaust gas is expelled, leaving a wake of bubbles. The telltale wake is absent in the electrically propelled torpedo, which has the further advantage that it does not lose weight during the run (as a steam torpedo does, since it burns up its fuel).

Depth control is effected by hydrostatic pressure and is preset to give a depth at which the torpedo will be most effective against its target. Lateral guidance is controlled by a gyroscope (driven by electricity or compressed air), by which the torpedo can be made to travel in a predetermined linear course or a curved path (Figs. 7a and 7b).

The conventional torpedo fired in a straight line is effective only if the target does not vary its course and speed during the torpedo's run. An increased chance of scoring a hit is obtained by the firing of two or more torpedoes simultaneously in a fanwise pattern (Figs. 8a, 8b, 8c). Another method is to program the torpedo to follow a zigzag (Fig. 10) or a spiral path, so that it will repeatedly cross the target's path. For this purpose the torpedo is equipped with a cam mechanism which actuates the steering mechanism. Another means of increasing the accuracy is provided by the wire-guided torpedo (Fig. 9), which is connected to the attacking vessel by an electric wire through which control signals are fed to keep the torpedo on a collision course with the target despite evasive action of the latter. A further advance in this direction is the homing torpedo, which is provided with a special device, mounted in the nose, which may consist of a sensitive acoustic receiver that picks up sounds emitted by the enemy vessel and controls the torpedo's steering equipment accordingly (passive acoustic torpedo). Alternatively, the device itself may generate a sound signal and home on the echo reflected from the target (active acoustic torpedo). Modern antisubmarine torpedoes are almost invariably of the homing kind.

Exploder mechanisms are of various types. Detonation may be caused by physical impact with the target, by acoustic influence (noise of enemy vessel's engines or propellers), by magnetic influence (change of magnetic field in the vicinity of the target), or by optical influence (the shadow of the enemy vessel when the torpedo passes under it). After launching, a torpedo must run for some distance before it becomes "armed"—i.e., ready to explode. Also, it must be fitted with a device that will automatically sink it when it completes its run without having hit the target. These precautions are necessary to minimize risk to the attacker's own ships.

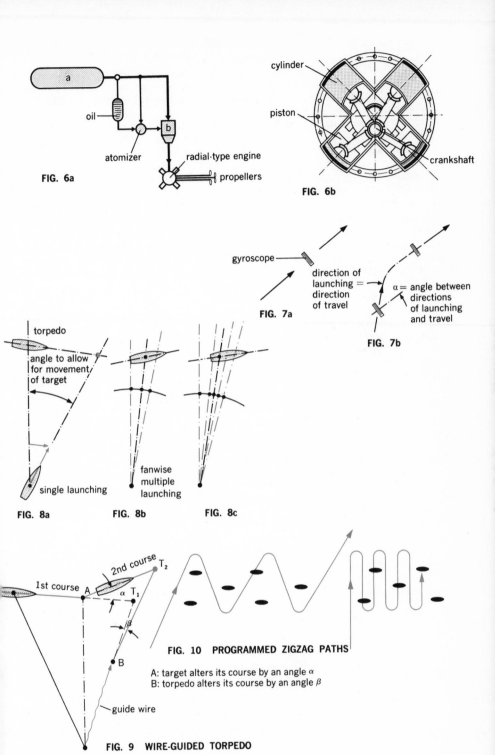

FIG. 6a

FIG. 6b

cylinder

piston

crankshaft

oil

atomizer

radial-type engine

propellers

a

b

gyroscope

direction of
launching =
direction
of travel

FIG. 7a

α = angle between
directions
of launching
and travel

FIG. 7b

torpedo

angle to allow
for movement
of target

single launching

FIG. 8a

fanwise
multiple
launching

FIG. 8b

FIG. 8c

1st course

2nd course

A

α T₁

β

B

guide wire

FIG. 10 PROGRAMMED ZIGZAG PATHS

A: target alters its course by an angle α
B: torpedo alters its course by an angle β

FIG. 9 WIRE-GUIDED TORPEDO

TANKS

Tanks are self-propelled armored combat vehicles designed to perform various functions in modern land warfare. There are a number of different types of tanks and comparable vehicles, so that sharp distinctions are not always possible.

The general-purpose heavy or medium tank (Figs. 1 and 2) is heavily armored and heavily armed, with its main armament usually mounted in a turret having a wide range of traverse. It is generally a full-track vehicle. The howitzer-carrying tank (Fig. 3) is a more specialized vehicle, equipped with a high-angle gun for action against targets concealed behind defense works. Assault tanks (Figs. 4 and 5) are used mainly to attack enemy armored vehicles and carry artillery or rocket armament suitable for the purpose. Antiaircraft gun carriers (Figs. 6 and 7) are relatively light tanks equipped with rapid-firing guns capable of high angles of elevation and possessing a high degree of maneuverability against fast-moving aircraft. Scout tanks are fast, lightly armored, highly mobile vehicles. They may be of the full-track type or be half-track or (Fig. 8) wheeled vehicles (scout cars). Armored machine-gun carriers and personnel carriers (Figs. 9 and 10) are lightly armored vehicles used for various supporting duties, often in combination with infantry. These too may be full-track, half-track or wheeled vehicles. Self-propelled guns and mobile rocket launchers are not really tanks, but artillery; they usually lack complete armor protection (Figs. 11, 12, 13). In addition to those mentioned, there are various special-purpose types of armored vehicle, such as bridge-laying tanks (Fig. 14).

From the operational standpoint, a tank must fulfill some exacting general requirements. It should have sufficient engine power to negotiate slopes of at least 30 degrees on rough terrain (Fig. 15). There must be adequate climbing capacity to overcome vertical obstacles within the limits imposed by the overall design (Fig. 16). Also, the vehicle must be able to cross ditches, trenches and the like (Fig. 17). In this respect the full-track vehicle is superior to the half-track or the wheeled vehicle. Another important requirement is the fording capacity, or water-crossing ability (Fig. 18). Amphibious tanks are so designed that they can cross deep water, floating and propelled by their own power (Fig. 19). Some tanks can be fitted with collapsible screens and thus be converted to amphibious operation. Propulsion is effected by propeller or water jet. Heavy tanks which cannot be given the necessary buoyancy to float on the water may be equipped to cross water obstacles by traveling along the bottom, air for the engine and crew being supplied through a tube mounted on the tank (Fig. 20).

(more)

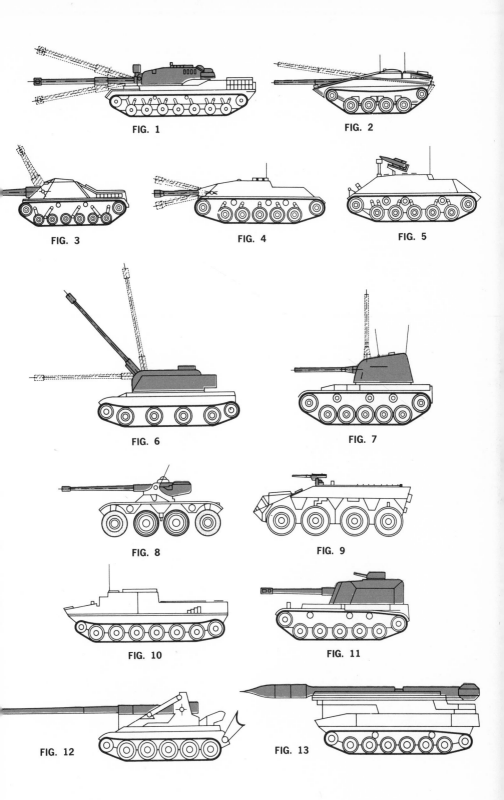

FIG. 1

FIG. 2

FIG. 3

FIG. 4

FIG. 5

FIG. 6

FIG. 7

FIG. 8

FIG. 9

FIG. 10

FIG. 11

FIG. 12

FIG. 13

The hull (Fig. 21) constitutes the basic structural element, the chassis, of the tank. It carries the power unit and transmission, the running gear and suspension, and the armament. It also has the function of protecting the crew. It is constructed of steel armor plates and cast steel and is so designed in shape and armoring as to provide the best possible protection against projectiles fired against it. Thus, the surfaces of the hull are sloped to increase the likelihood that projectiles will glance off. The whole silhouette of the tank should be squat and low so as to present a target that is as difficult as possible to hit. Especially the frontal armor must be strong and sloped well back. Complete protection of the crew by heavy armor is not, however, compatible with adequate mobility and maneuverability of the tank. The designer will always have to effect a compromise between weight and mechanical performance. In general, the weight of the armor corresponds to at least a third of the total weight. The hulls of amphibious tanks and fording tanks must of course be of watertight construction.

The power unit is almost invariably an internal-combustion engine, usually of the diesel type. Multifuel engines which can run on other fuels besides diesel oil are sometimes used, offering obvious advantages from the standpoint of supply in the field. The engine is normally installed in the rear of the hull (Fig. 22).

Wheeled armored vehicles are steered in the same way as ordinary road vehicles (front-wheel or all-wheel steering). The steering of tracked vehicles is effected by stopping the track on one side or by controlled variation of the track speeds (Fig. 23). In the clutch-and-brake steering gear (Fig. 24), the engine power output is transmitted through the shaft a and the bevel gears b to the clutch shaft c, on which the primary components of the friction clutches d are mounted. Each of the two driven shafts e carries the fixed secondary component of the clutch d, the track brake f and the track drive wheel g, which drives the crawler tracks. When the vehicle is traveling straight ahead, both clutches d are engaged, and the shafts e rotate at the same speed. When the driver wishes to make a left turn, for example, the left-hand clutch d is gradually disengaged, so that the speed of the left-hand driven shaft e decreases and the left-hand track is therefore slowed down in relation to the right-hand track. When the clutch d is completely disengaged, the shaft e stops rotating; the vehicle then swivels about the stationary track and thus describes its minimum turning circle. The effect of the clutches can be intensified by the two track brakes f, by which the shafts e can be additionally slowed down or indeed completely locked. The driving shafts for the change-speed gearbox and steering gear pass through the sides of the hull and are connected to side gear units (Fig. 25). The latter transmit the power to the track drive wheels through planetary gear systems.

(more)

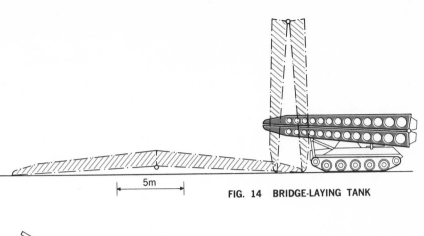

FIG. 14   BRIDGE-LAYING TANK

5m

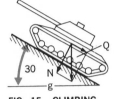

FIG. 15   CLIMBING

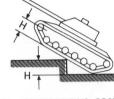

FIG. 16   SURMOUNTING OBSTACLES

FIG. 17   CROSSING DITCHES

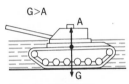

FIG. 18   FORDING

G>A

A

G

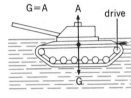

G=A

A

drive

G

FIG. 19   FLOATING

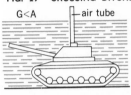

G<A

air tube

FIG. 20   SUBMERGENCE

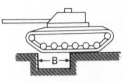

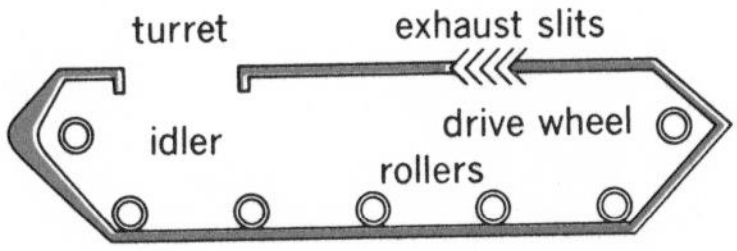

FIG. 21   LONGITUDINAL SECTION
THROUGH HULL OF TANK

turret   exhaust slits

idler   drive wheel
rollers

FIG. 22
DRIVE
MACHINERY

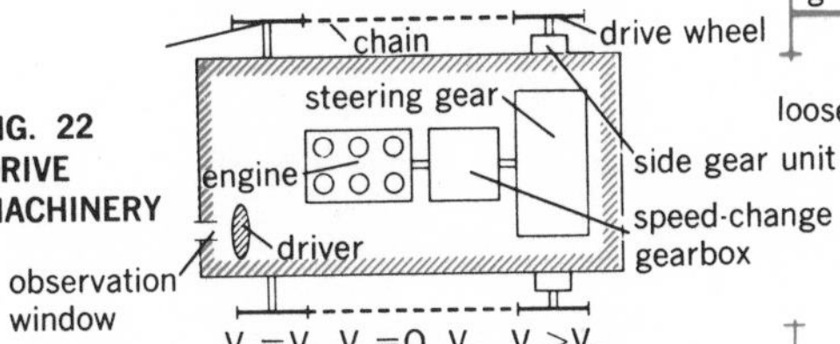

chain   drive wheel
steering gear
side gear unit
engine
driver
observation
window
speed-change
gearbox

FIG. 23
STEERING
SYSTEM

$V_1=V_2$ $V_1=0$ V_2 $V_1>V_2$

straight travel

left track stopped,
right track moving

left track faster
than right track

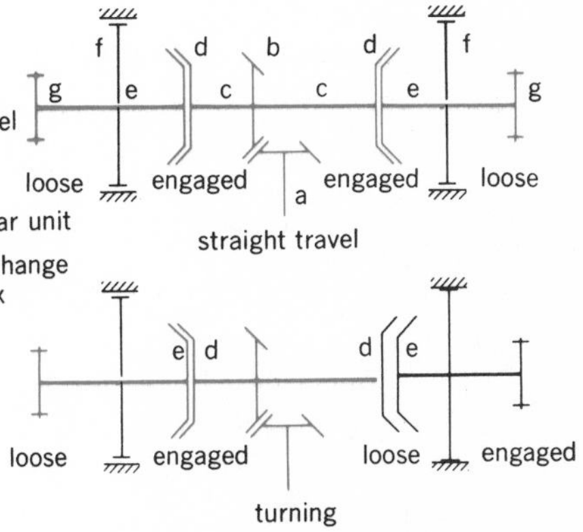

f   d   b   d   f
g e   c   c   e g
loose   engaged   a   engaged   loose

straight travel

e d   d e
loose   engaged   loose   engaged

turning

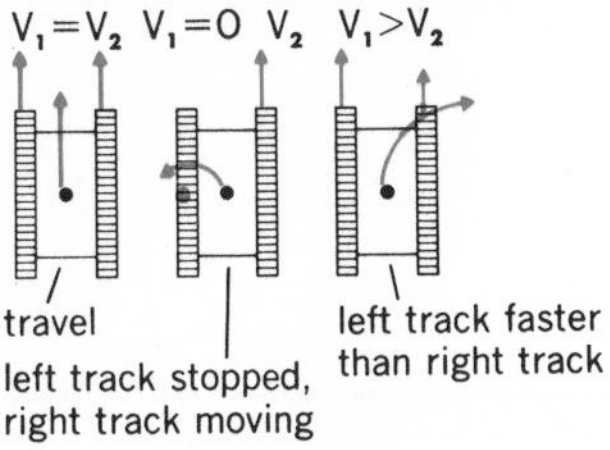

FIG. 24   CLUTCH-AND-BRAKE
STEERING GEAR

257

The running gear of the tank has to transmit the weight of the vehicle, the recoil forces developed by the gun, and the engine power for propulsion. All these forces have to be suitably transmitted to the ground. The running gear comprises the crawler tracks, the track drive wheels, the track rollers with their suspension system, the supporting rollers, and the take-up idlers with their track-tensioning devices (Fig. 26). The individual links composing the crawler tracks are joined to one another by pivoted connections (Fig. 27). To reduce noise when traveling on roads, they are often provided with detachable rubber coverings. The track drive wheels may be located either at the front or at the rear (Figs. 26 and 29). Each drive wheel is provided with teeth which engage with recesses in the track links. The track rollers may be disposed one behind the other or in a staggered arrangement (Fig. 29). They have sprung suspension mountings in the hull of the tank, for which torsion-bar suspension is now particularly favored (Fig. 30).

The main armament installed in tanks varies according to the purpose for which it is intended. Action against enemy tanks requires long-barreled guns firing projectiles of high muzzle velocity and great penetrating power. As the range at which the enemy is engaged is usually not very great, the guns need not be elevated to high angles. Instead of conventional guns, recoilless guns may be fitted. A weapon of this kind is often equipped with a retractable mount; this can be raised for firing the gun, which is loaded, aimed and fired from within the tank (Fig. 31). Concealed targets have to be attacked with relatively short-barreled high-angle guns (howitzers) firing projectiles of low muzzle velocity. The guns constituting the main armament of tanks usually have calibers between 7 cm and 12 cm, but calibers up to 20.3 cm are employed for self-propelled guns and howitzers. In addition to the main armament, tanks usually carry light secondary armament (machine guns or small-caliber artillery) for use against aircraft, unarmored vehicles or personnel. Antiaircraft gun carriers are usually equipped with turret-mounted multibarreled guns capable of a rapid rate of fire; the turrets may be entirely closed or be open on top (Figs. 6 and 7). These guns can be traversed and elevated smoothly and quickly.

The main gun of a tank may be mounted in a revolving turret (Fig. 32) or it may be mounted in the hull itself, in which case only a limited traverse is possible (Figs. 33 and 34). Sometimes no independent traverse motion of the gun is possible at all, or indeed the gun may be rigidly fixed to the hull and thus incapable of independent traversing or elevation. Traversing must then be effected by aiming the whole tank at the target, while elevation is effected by means of the hydropneumatic suspension system.

(more)

258

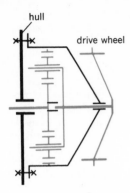

FIG. 25   SIDE GEAR UNIT

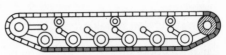

FIG. 26   CRAWLER TRACK WITH DRIVE WHEEL
AT REAR AND SUPPORTING ROLLERS

FIG. 28   CRAWLER TRACK WITH DRIVE WHEEL
AT REAR, NO SUPPORTING ROLLERS

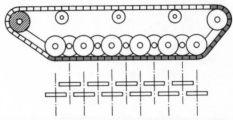

FIG. 29   CRAWLER TRACK WITH DRIVE WHEEL
IN FRONT AND STAGGERED ARRANGEMENT
OF TRACK ROLLERS

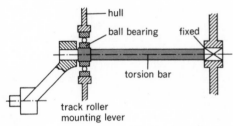

FIG. 30

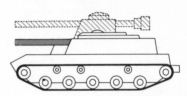

FIG. 31   TANK WITH RECOILLESS GUN
ON RETRACTABLE MOUNT

FIG. 27
CRAWLER TRACK

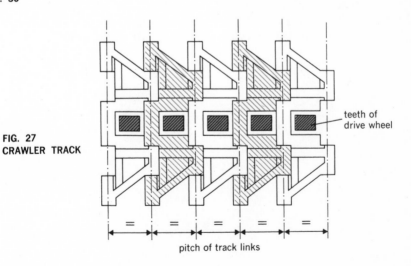

teeth of
drive wheel

pitch of track links

When traveling on rough ground, a tank performs irregular angular movements (rolling and pitching) about its longitudinal and its transverse axis. Such conditions would make it impossible to use the main armament effectively. A means of stabilizing the gun and maintaining its aim is provided by the gyroscope, a device that strives to maintain the position of its axis of rotation unchanged (see Vol. II, page 180). Employed in combination with a mechanical sighting device that can compensate sufficiently quickly for changes in the vehicle's position, it is thus possible to obtain a fire-control system that will enable the gun to be used effectively even when the going is rough (Fig. 35). Fig. 36 is a simplified schematic diagram of such a stabilizing system for the elevation of the gun barrel. Attached to the barrel, which can pivot on a horizontal axis, is a gyroscope that responds to variations in position in the vertical plane. The control signal emitted by the gyroscope is amplified and passed to the electromagnet coils of the mechanically interlinked control valves. These valves continuously control the flow of hydraulic fluid, which comes from the gear pump and is admitted to both sides of the piston of the working cylinder, whose piston movements elevate or depress the gun barrel. The flow is controlled in such a manner that the barrel is constantly maintained in the same position in the vertical plane. Greater accuracy of stabilization is achieved by the use of gyroscopes that measure and respond with corrective action to the angular velocity of the pitching motion of the tank. Lateral stabilization, for rolling motion, is achieved on the same principle, except that for this purpose a rotary machine (hydraulic or electric motor) is used instead of a hydraulic cylinder.

A modern tank is fitted with a variety of auxiliary equipment. To give the crew a good field of vision, various windows and observation slits are provided, together with optical devices such as telescopes, periscopes, etc. For dusk and nighttime operation, searchlights and infrared steering and sighting devices may be provided. These devices are of the kind that either detects infrared rays emitted by the target (e.g., heat from the engine of an enemy vehicle) or picks up the reflection of infrared rays directed on to the target by an infrared projector mounted on the tank itself. Steering devices based on infrared rays provide a range of vision of some 200 or 300 yards, while infrared gunsights may range up to about 2000 yards. The actual effective range of these devices is considerably affected by weather conditions. Because of disturbing reflections from the ground and natural obstacles, radar is generally unsuitable for use in tanks. Communication between one tank and another and between tanks and their base command post is provided by radio.

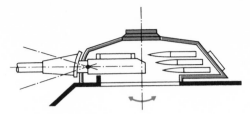

FIG. 32   TURRET

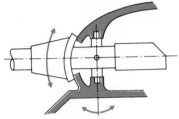

FIG. 33   GUN MOUNTED FOR
TRAVERSING AND ELEVATION

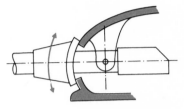

FIG. 34   GUN MOUNTED FOR
ELEVATION ONLY

FIG. 35   TANK WITH STABILIZING SYSTEM FOR GUN

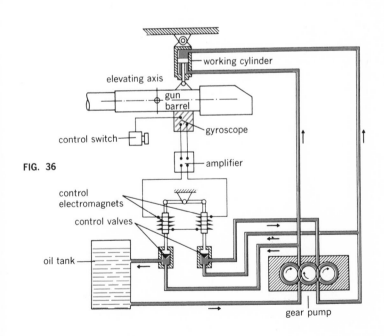

working cylinder

elevating axis

gun barrel

control switch

gyroscope

amplifier

FIG. 36

control electromagnets

control valves

oil tank

gear pump

261

ROAD INTERSECTIONS AND JUNCTIONS

The term "intersection" is used in a general sense to denote all types of connection between similar or dissimilar roads. "Junction" is sometimes also used in a general sense—for example, "cloverleaf intersection" and "cloverleaf junction" are synonymous—but is often used more particularly with reference to a single connection of one road with another (T junction) or a meeting point of three roads (Y junction). A road that has priority of traffic movement over that of other roads at a junction or intersection is called the "major road"; a "minor road" (or "subsidiary road") has a lesser traffic value than a major road. These are relative terms in the sense that even the minor road at a particular intersection may carry a considerable volume of traffic.

Properly designed intersections which ensure a smooth and brisk traffic flow in conjunction with good safety conditions are obviously very important features in the overall design of an efficient road system. A distinction is made between intersections of roads that are all located at the same level (grade intersections) and intersections where one or more roads are routed over or under one or more other roads by means of bridges or tunnels (grade-separated, or multilevel, intersections). The latter category obviously offers advantages in terms of smooth traffic flow and safety because of the segregation of vehicles traveling in different directions and the reduction or elimination of the number of points where different traffic streams have to cross one another. On the other hand, the bridges (overpasses, or flyovers) and tunnels (underpasses) make grade-separated intersections much more expensive, so that they are usually employed only on important roads for fast traffic (in particular, expressways).

Figs. 1 and 2 show the basic traffic streams at a four-way intersection and a T junction respectively. The design of important intersections is based on traffic surveys which provide information on the anticipated traffic flows. The slowing down and obstruction of the general flow of traffic on the intersecting roads in consequence of "weaving" movements of vehicles wishing to turn right or left at the intersection reduces the traffic-handling capacity of the roads and increases the accident hazard. The reduction in capacity is determined to a large extent by the delay arising from the time that vehicles on the minor road have to wait for suitable gaps in the main traffic stream and by the reduction of speed of the main-stream vehicles that is necessitated by the entry ("weaving in") or crossing of vehicles from the minor road. The loss of capacity due to vehicles leaving the main stream ("weaving out") in order to turn into the minor road is less serious. It largely depends on the difference in speed between the traffic streams that are thus disengaging themselves from each other.

(more)

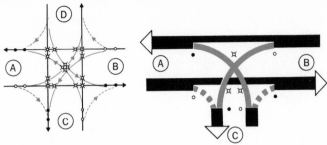

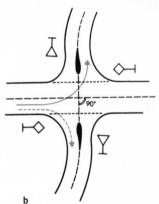

FIG. 1   → = TRAFFIC GOING STRAIGHT AHEAD

        ✧ = CROSSING POINT

        → = LEFT-TURNING TRAFFIC

        ···▶ = RIGHT-TURNING TRAFFIC

FIG. 2   ● = WEAVING-IN POINT

        ○ = WEAVING-OUT POINT

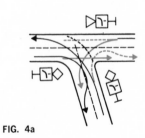

FIG. 3a

b

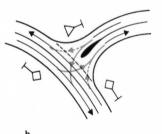

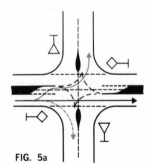

FIG. 4a

b

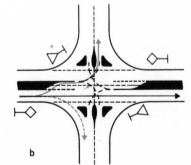

FIG. 5a

b

263

   Some general principles governing the design and layout of road intersections will now be considered. The main traffic streams should be routed along the most direct possible paths; the subsidiary streams should be routed as far as possible at right angles to the main streams. The use of signs and signals that stop the flow of traffic should be avoided to the degree compatible with safety. The most serious disturbing factor is the left-turning vehicle.* If this drawback cannot be obviated altogether by an appropriate layout providing suitable segregation of traffic streams, the aim should be to enable left-turning traffic to extricate itself as easily and smoothly as possible from the main stream by the provision of a special traffic lane and an appropriate layout of the intersection. The main stream of traffic traveling in the opposite direction should be crossed by left-turning traffic as nearly at right angles as possible. In situations where large flows of traffic intersect, it becomes necessary to provide signals (traffic lights, etc.). If the total delay times for traffic at such intersections become excessive, and if linked control of the traffic lights at a number of adjacent intersections (coordinated control system) fails to solve the problem, then the grade-separated intersection becomes a necessity. In such solutions the left-turning traffic is routed either indirectly through a 270-degree loop or semi-indirectly via individual ramps, so that the movements of this traffic are thus reduced to basic weaving-in (merging) and weaving-out (disengaging) movements. Grade-separated intersections are a standard feature of modern expressways and other important highways for motor traffic.
   The disturbing effect of right-turning vehicles on the general flow of traffic is relatively slight and can be minimized by appropriate routing with the aid of triangular islands and special traffic lanes (acceleration and deceleration lanes).
   Some examples of layouts for intersections will now be briefly discussed.
   Fig. 3a shows a simple intersection of two roads not at right angles to each other. Though commonly employed, this is an unsatisfactory solution in cases where appreciable flows of traffic occur, inasmuch as the points of encounter (potential points of collision) between vehicles moving in different directions are scattered all over the area of the intersection, the curbs fail to provide sufficient guidance, and the roads cross each other obliquely. The efficiency is poor, since only low vehicular speeds can be tolerated. This type of intersection is at best acceptable for residential roads. In Fig. 3b an improvement has been achieved in that the main stream of traffic (i.e., on the major road) has been given preferential treatment by suitable constructional arrangements. The turning movements have been more precisely defined by means of teardrop-shaped islands in the minor road, right-angled intersection of major and minor road, large-radius curb alignments, and traffic lane markings by which points of encounter are more definitely located. This layout is suitable for medium traffic flows and may be used in conjunction with control signals.

(more)

*The text and illustrations are based on the assumption that traffic normally travels on the right-hand side of the road. In countries where left-hand driving is the rule, as in Great Britain, the problem of course arises from right-turning vehicles.

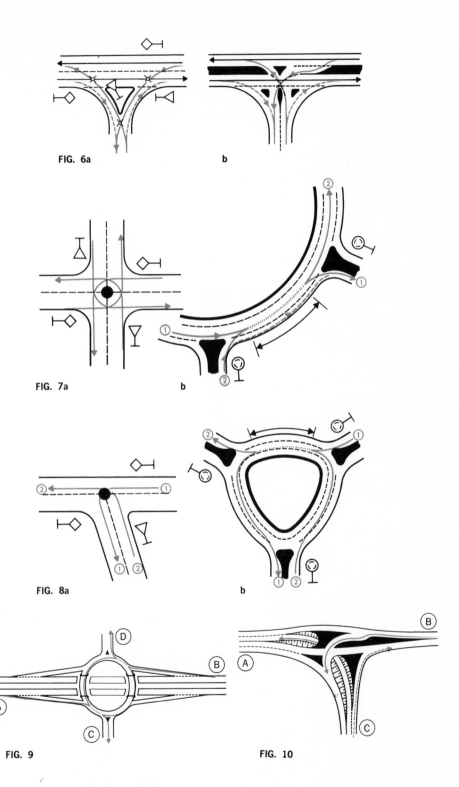

FIG. 6a   b

FIG. 7a   b

FIG. 8a   b

FIG. 9   FIG. 10

The simple T junction in Fig. 4a is unsatisfactory for much the same reasons as those relating to Fig. 3a. It is sometimes possible to improve this type of junction into the layout illustrated in Fig. 4b, which is more particularly characterized by the fact that the minor road now joins the major road at right angles.

The intersections in Fig. 5 are developments of the simple intersection. In Fig. 5a the left-turning traffic is detached from the main stream well before the actual intersection. A more advanced solution of this type is illustrated in Fig. 5b: here all the traffic streams have been assigned their own lanes at the intersection; acceleration and deceleration lanes may additionally be provided. Control signals for traffic approaching the intersection are usually unnecessary with this type of intersection, which is suitable for major urban thoroughfares and heavily trafficked rural highways.

Fig. 6 represents developments of the T junction, likewise characterized by segregation of traffic streams on separate lanes provided for them. The layout illustrated in Fig. 6a, embodying a relatively large triangular island, used to be the standard solution for certain secondary T junctions on German highways. However, it is now recognized that it incorporates danger spots where traffic streams cross one another obliquely and has accordingly been abandoned. In the layout in Fig. 6b the points where the streams cross are concentrated before the teardrop-shaped island, providing more favorable conditions of intersection.

Fig. 7a shows an obsolete form of intersection which is in effect a small traffic circle, or roundabout, in which the central "rotary island" is more an obstacle than an aid to traffic. The layout illustrated in Fig. 7b reduces all crossing of traffic streams to entering and exiting movements and transition from one lane to another. This arrangement requires long weaving distances and a layout in which the traffic streams cross obliquely. It is adopted at intersections where more than four roads, carrying approximately equal volumes of traffic, converge. Under favorable conditions this type of traffic circle has a high traffic capacity. Signals controlling access to the traffic circle are at variance with the principle and are also undesirable in that they reduce the capacity of the circle.

Fig. 8a is an obsolete junction layout with the same general drawbacks as the intersection in Fig. 7a. The layout shown in Fig. 8b represents a modern solution with a high traffic capacity. The large central island ensures smooth, continuous traffic flow.

(more)

266

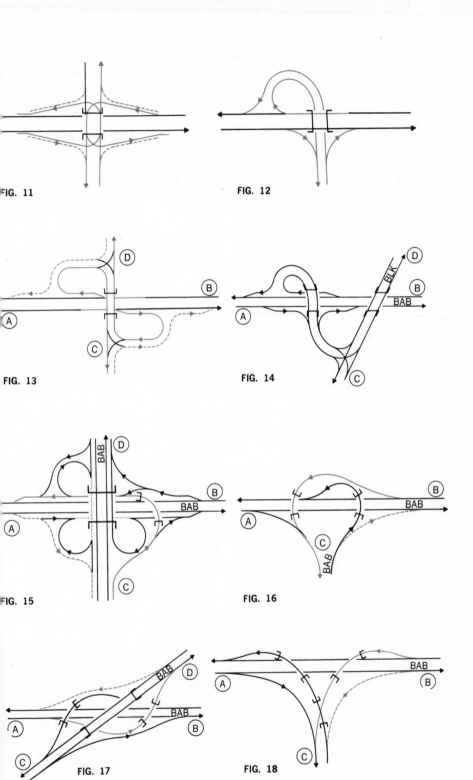

FIG. 11

FIG. 12

FIG. 13

FIG. 14

FIG. 15

FIG. 16

FIG. 17

FIG. 18

267

Fig. 9 shows a familiar form of grade-separated (or multilevel) intersection. In this case the traffic streams A–B and B–A are routed under or over the minor road, which is connected to the major road by means of a traffic circle and ramps (slip roads). This is a good solution for an interchange where access between a street (the minor road) and an expressway in a built-up area has to be provided.

Fig. 10 is a grade-separated junction in which the large volumes of left-turning traffic have been routed at different levels. Fig. 12 is a somewhat different grade-separated layout for a junction. A type of intersection that originated and is still widely used in Holland (and elsewhere) is shown schematically in Fig. 11, while Fig. 13 is a so-called semicloverleaf intersection in which the main streams A–D and B–C are kept entirely free of grade intersections. In this latter layout the major road (A–B) is usually an expressway and routed under the minor road (C–D). The solution illustrated in Fig. 14 is a different type of grade-separated intersection between a major road (A–B) and a minor road (C–D): there is only one junction of the link road with the minor road, as compared with two such junctions in Fig. 13; against this, the layout in Fig. 14 involves the construction of two overpasses and moreover has a smaller traffic capacity than the semicloverleaf intersection.

Fig. 15 illustrates what could be termed a three-quarter cloverleaf intersection between two roads of equal importance—e.g., two highways. All traffic turning out of the main stream is routed on to parallel service lanes. Fig. 16 is a grade-separated junction between two highways. The through road (A–B) is routed over or under the link roads. An oblique intersection of two highways is illustrated in Fig. 17. This is an efficient solution, but relatively expensive because it necessitates three overpasses. Fig. 18 is another grade-separated junction. It achieves the same result as the junction in Fig. 16, but presents smoother traffic-flow conditions; it is also more expensive in that it has three overpasses instead of two.

Figs. 19 and 20 are perspective drawings of intersections of the types illustrated schematically in Figs. 13 and 18. In the cloverleaf type of intersection, turning traffic has to make considerable detours. The space occupied by a cloverleaf is so great that the adoption of this form of intersection is seldom practicable in built-up areas. A traffic circle, though minimizing detours, imposes speed restraint on the flow of both direct and turning traffic. A grade-separated layout of the kind illustrated in Fig. 19, which is suitable for built-up areas, permits free flow of through traffic, while exercising no more restraint on turning traffic than would be imposed by a normal traffic circle. Generally speaking, the layouts in Figs. 11–18 are typical of main roads in open country or relatively sparsely populated areas.

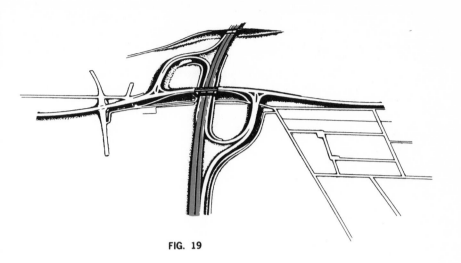

FIG. 19

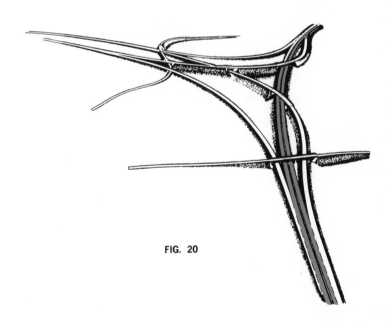

FIG. 20

Before the engine of a standard-shift car is started, the gear lever should be shifted to the neutral position (Fig. 2b) to disconnect the engine from the drive shaft. Now the ignition key is inserted into the ignition switch. When the key is turned to the right (clockwise), the steering-wheel lock (an antitheft device fitted to some cars) is first released, so that the wheel can be freely rotated. Turning the key farther to the right switches on the ignition. The ignition coil and distributor are now energized (cf. Vol. II, page 206). The charging control light and oil-pressure control light in the combined instrument assembly should light up (Fig. 1). When the key is turned still farther to the right, against the spring pressure that is then encountered, the starter (cf. Vol. II, page 200) is energized, so that the engine is rotated. As soon as the engine has started, the key should be released, so that it springs back to the normal "driving" position. The key must not be held in the "starting" position while the engine is running, as this would soon damage the starter. For starting a cold engine the choke, if the car has a manual choke, should be pulled out before the ignition is switched on. The function of the choke is to supply the engine with a very rich gasoline-and-air mixture (cf. Vol. II, page 204) to facilitate starting. Most modern cars have an automatic choke.

When the engine is running and has reached a certain speed of rotation, the charging control light and oil-pressure control light go out. The choke should be pushed in as soon as possible, as the rich starting mixture contains too much fuel, which washes away the film of lubricating oil on the cylinder walls.

Depressing of the clutch pedal (Fig. 1) causes the mechanical connection between engine and gearbox to be interrupted (cf. Vol. II, page 210). To enable the vehicle to move off, the gear lever, which at first was in neutral, is shifted to "first gear" and the hand brake is released. Then the clutch pedal is slowly allowed to rise so as to achieve smooth engagement of the clutch. The vehicle is now in motion. When the accelerator pedal is depressed, the throttle opens wider, thereby supplying more air to the carburetor and thus increasing the supply of the fuel-and-air mixture to the engine (cf. Vol. II, page 202). As a result, the engine speed increases and the vehicle goes faster.

The drive shaft (or cardan shaft) connects the gearbox to the differential gear of the rear axle (cf. Vol. II, page 224). The gearbox and differential gear have resilient rubber mountings, so that they can perform a certain amount of independent movement. For this reason the drive shaft which connects them is designed as a universal shaft (see page 202). A rigidly connected shaft would render the damping action of the rubber mountings ineffective; besides, the shaft would soon be destroyed

(more)

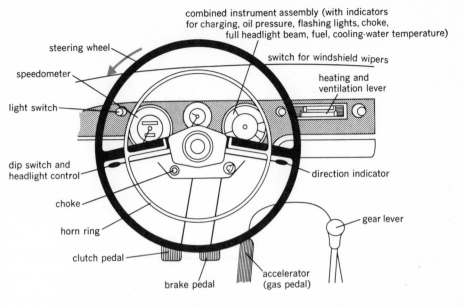

combined instrument assembly (with indicators for charging, oil pressure, flashing lights, choke, full headlight beam, fuel, cooling-water temperature)

steering wheel

switch for windshield wipers

speedometer

heating and ventilation lever

light switch

dip switch and headlight control

direction indicator

choke

gear lever

horn ring

clutch pedal

brake pedal

accelerator (gas pedal)

FIG. 1

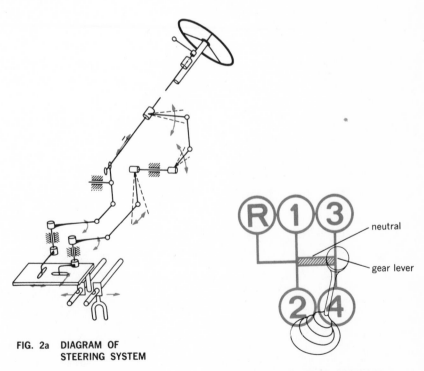

FIG. 2a DIAGRAM OF STEERING SYSTEM

neutral

gear lever

FIG. 2b GEAR-LEVER POSITIONS

271

Car production line. General Motors, Bienne, Switzerland
Photo Roland Schneider, Len Sirman Press

The two rear wheels are driven by the differential gear through their respectiv half-shafts, which are likewise universal shafts. In the suspension illustrated in Fig. the independently sprung rear wheels are attached to swinging arms which pivc about a point adjacent to the rear-axle housing. Another widely used type of susper sion is the rigid axle. In this system the differential gear, the two half-shafts, and th wheel bearings are all accommodated in one sheet-steel casing, which is connecte to the chassis through two springs (usually leaf springs disposed longitudinally one on each side of the vehicle. When a wheel encounters an irregularity, the sprin on that side is compressed and the whole axis tilts. The oscillations of the springs ar damped by shock absorbers (see Vol. II, pp. 226–232).

The front-axle assembly (Fig. 2a) of the vehicle illustrated in Fig. 1 comprises lower control arm, which transmits the lateral and longitudinal forces, and McPherson suspension unit, which consists of a two-tube telescopic shock absorbe the outer tube of which carries a seat for the coil spring. At its upper end the pisto rod of the shock absorber is attached to the body of the car. This form of fron axle suspension is now widely used in passenger cars.

When the steering wheel is turned to the left (Fig. 2a), the steering gear is actuate by the steering column (cf. Vol. II, page 234). This causes the drop arm (Fig. 2b) t swivel inwards. The track rod connects the steering drop arm with the axle-contro arm. As a result, the outer tube of the telescopic shock absorber—to which the fron wheel is attached—rotates in the direction indicated by the red arrow in Fig. 2a The vehicle accordingly makes a left turn. When the steering wheel is turned to th right, the two front wheels are correspondingly swiveled to the right.

The motorist signifies his intention of turning left or right by means of the sel canceling flashing direction indicators (cf. Vol. II, page 244). Braking of the vehicl is normally done by means of the foot brake, the braking action varying with th force exercised by the foot on the brake pedal. The brakes are hydraulically actuate (cf. Vol. II, page 236). The front wheels may have disc brakes and the rear wheel have drum brakes. When the vehicle is stationary, it can be held immovable b application of the hand brake. The hand-brake lever is connected to the two rear wheel brakes and presses the brake shoes against the drums. Because of the mech anical—as opposed to hydraulic—transmission of the force, the effectiveness of th hand brake is relatively poor. However, this brake is essentially no more than ¿ parking brake and its action should be sufficient to prevent the vehicle from rolling down a slope.

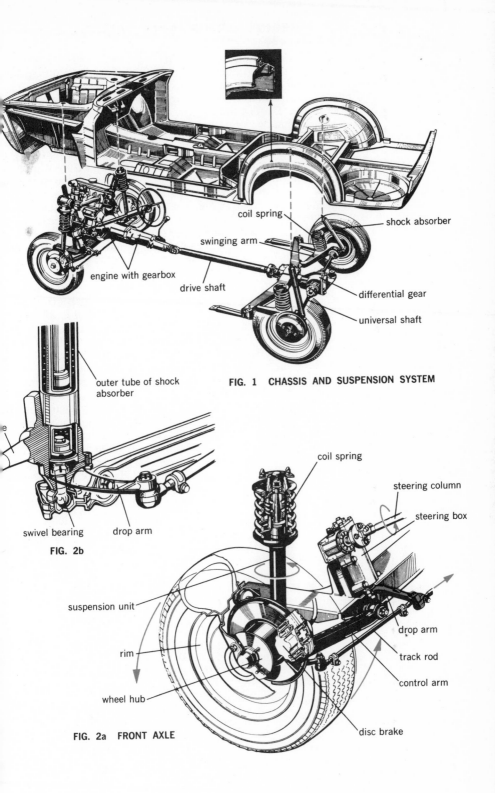

coil spring

shock absorber

swinging arm

engine with gearbox

drive shaft

differential gear

universal shaft

FIG. 1 CHASSIS AND SUSPENSION SYSTEM

outer tube of shock absorber

swivel bearing

drop arm

FIG. 2b

coil spring

steering column

steering box

suspension unit

drop arm

rim

track rod

control arm

wheel hub

disc brake

FIG. 2a FRONT AXLE

In a gasoline-driven internal-combustion engine (cf. Vol. II, page 188) the gasolin
and-air mixture which enters the cylinder during the suction (or intake) stroke
first fills a volume equal to $V_Z + V_B$, where V_Z represents the piston-swept workin
volume of the cylinder (= piston area × piston stroke) and V_B represents the volun
of the combustion chamber. During the compression stroke which then follow
the mixture is forced into a smaller space by the rising piston. When the latter ha
reached its highest point, referred to as "top dead center" (TDC), the mixture ha
been compressed into the relatively small volume V_B (right-hand drawing in Fig. 1
This compression of the mixture is associated with a rise in temperature which, in
spark-ignition engine, must not, however, be so high as to cause spontaneou
ignition. The compressed mixture is ignited by a spark from the spark plug and burr
in a fraction of a second—i.e., explodes. The heat released on combustion furthe
raises the temperature of the gas, which therefore strives to expand. As the pisto
is momentarily stationary at top dead center, the pressure of the imprisoned ga
greatly increases (firing pressure). In the then following power stroke, this hig
pressure thrusts the piston down to "bottom dead center" (BDC). The space occupie
by the gas thus increases, so that the gas pressure correspondingly decreases. If th
pressure is plotted against the piston stroke in a graph, the diagram shown in Fig.
(page 279) is obtained. The line AB is so positioned in relation to the horizontal lin
representing atmospheric pressure (1 atm) that, with the vertical lines at TDC an
BDC, it forms a rectangle whose area is equal to that enclosed between the curv
and the three last-mentioned lines. The distance from the base line at 1 atm to th
line AB represents the "mean effective pressure" for the power stroke (p_{m3} in Fig. 2

If a similar diagram representing pressure plotted against stroke is drawn for th
intake stroke, compression stroke and exhaust stroke, a continuous diagram fo
the four-stroke engine is obtained (Fig. 3). For performing the intake and compressio
of the mixture (strokes 1 and 2) and for the expulsion of the burned gas from th
cylinder (stroke 4) the engine has to supply a certain amount of energy correspondin
to the areas shaded in red in Fig. 3. This energy is deducted from the energy delivere
by the power stroke (stroke 3), corresponding to the area shaded in black. In it
more usual form this diagram—known as the indicator diagram (or cylinder
pressure diagram)—for the four-stroke engine is represented in Fig. 4. If the mear
effective pressure, as defined above, is determined for each of the four strokes, the
"indicated mean effective pressure" can be determined:

$$p_{mi} = p_{m3} - (p_{m1} + p_{m2} + p_{m4})$$

The pressure p_{mi} acting on the piston area produces a force which is transmitted to
the crankshaft by the connecting rod and develops a torque—i.e., a turning momen
about the axis of the crankshaft. The magnitude of this torque is determined by the
indicated mean effective pressure p_{mi}, the piston area F_k, and the crank radius *
(which is equal to half the stroke: i.e., $r = \frac{1}{2} s$; see Fig. 1). The total torque M_d

(more)

FIG. 1   WORKING VOLUME AND COMBUSTION CHAMBER
OF A CYLINDER

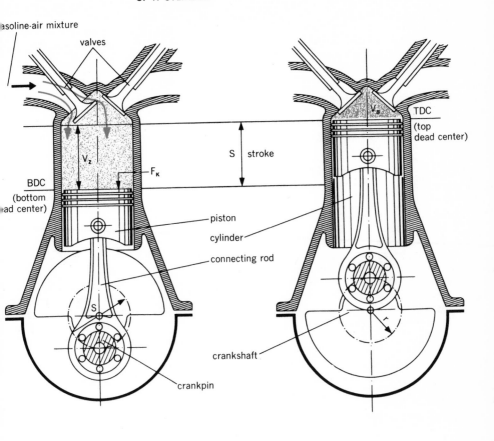

developed at the crankshaft is of course also dependent on the number of cylinders i
Hence:

(1) $M_d = k_1 \cdot p_{mi} \cdot F_k \cdot s \cdot i$

where k_1 denotes a constant. The product of F_k and s represents the swept volume of the individual cylinder; multiplied by i (the number of cylinders) it gives the total cubic capacity (or cylinder capacity) V_H of the engine. The torque can thus be expressed in terms of the indicated mean effective pressure and the total cubic capacity:

(2) $M_d = k_1 \cdot p_{mi} \cdot V_H$

The power output and the torque are linked by the following relation, where n denotes the rotational speed of the engine:

(3) $N = k_2 \cdot M_d \cdot n$ (where k_2 is another constant)

On substitution of formula (2) into formula (3) the following expression is obtained for the effective output:

(4) $N = K \cdot p_{mi} \cdot V_H \cdot n$ (where K is a constant)

This last formula signifies that the power output depends on the speed, the cubic capacity, the indicated mean effective pressure, and the constant K. The value of K depends on the type of engine. In the two-stroke engine the power stroke occurs once in every revolution of the crankshaft, whereas in the four-stroke engine it occurs only once in every two revolutions. For equal speed and cubic capacity, the two-stroke engine would thus theoretically attain twice the output of a four-stroke engine. In actual practice this is not so, since the two-stroke engine cannot—because of scavenging losses—be operated at as high a mean effective pressure as the four-stroke engine. When V_H is expressed in liters, p_{mi} in kg/cm^2, and n in rpm, the values of K are as follows: $K = 1/450$ for two-stroke engines, $K = 1/900$ for four-stroke engines.

The theoretical output determined on the basis of the cylinder-pressure diagram (Fig. 3) is not fully available at the output shaft. Some loss of power occurs in consequence of friction in the piston and bearings and also in driving pumps, fan, etc. The ratio of the effective output N_e to the theoretical output N_i is called the "mechanical efficiency" η_m; its numerical value is usually between 0.75 and 0.85:

(5) $\eta_m = N_e/N_i$

In combination with formula (4) the following expression is obtained for the effective output:

(6) $N_e = K \cdot p_{mi} \cdot \eta_m \cdot V_H \cdot n$ (in horsepower)

This formula can be simplified by introduction of the so-called "brake mean effective pressure" p_{me}, which is the indicated mean effective pressure p_{mi} multiplied by the mechanical efficiency; i.e.:

(7) $p_{me} = p_{mi} \cdot \eta_m$

Therefore:

(8) $N_e = K \cdot p_{me} \cdot V_H \cdot n$ (in horsepower)

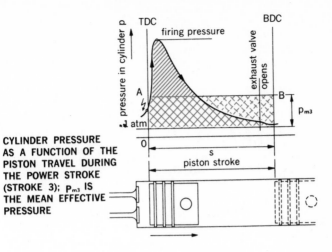

FIG. 2 CYLINDER PRESSURE AS A FUNCTION OF THE PISTON TRAVEL DURING THE POWER STROKE (STROKE 3); p_{m3} IS THE MEAN EFFECTIVE PRESSURE

FIG. 3 CYLINDER-PRESSURE DIAGRAM OF A FOUR-STROKE ENGINE

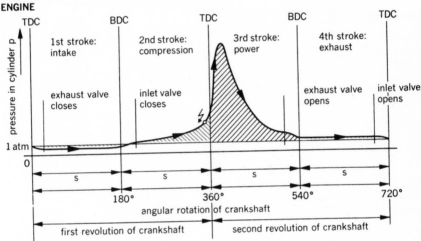

FIG. 4 CYLINDER-PRESSURE DIAGRAM (THE MORE USUAL FORM, DERIVED FROM FIG. 3)

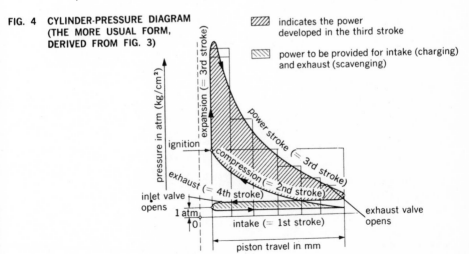

279

Increasing the cubic capacity—i.e., the piston-swept working volume of the cylinders—is the most obvious means of increasing the power output of an internal-combustion engine. According to formula (1) on page 278, the cubic capacity increases when the piston area F_k, the piston stroke s, and the number of cylinders i are increased. Any or all of these factors can be increased to obtain the desired effect. In an existing engine the cylinders can be bored out to a larger internal diameter so as to increase the piston area, though obviously there is a limit to what can be achieved in this way without unduly weakening the cylinder walls. See Fig. 2.

The piston stroke s is determined by the crank radius r, this being the distance from the center of the crankshaft to the center of the crankpin (to which the connecting rod is attached). When the radius is increased from r_1 to r_2 (Fig. 1), the piston stroke is correspondingly increased from s_1 to s_2. To make this modification it is of course necessary to fit a different crankshaft.

The measures indicated above are relatively inexpensive to apply and are a popular means of increasing the output of an engine. Thus a number of automobile manufacturers offer more powerful versions of standard engines, the improvement in performance having been achieved by an increase in the cubic capacity. For example, the German firm of Opel supplies 1700 and 1900 cc engines which are bored-out versions of the 1500 cc engine. Other firms have increased the capacity by using a crankshaft giving a larger piston stroke, as exemplified by the Volkswagen 1200 and 1300 cc engines.

Increasing the number of cylinders is of course more than a mere modification (Fig. 3). It involves the use of more parts, with additional cost of machining and assembly, so that the resulting bigger engine is of necessity also a significantly more expensive engine. European manufacturers produce four-cylinder cars with engine capacities up to about 2000 cc. For higher capacities, engines with six or eight cylinders are normally used.

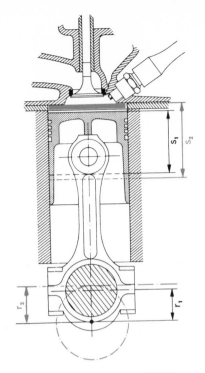

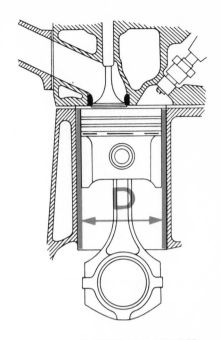

FIG. 2   INCREASING THE CYLINDER
DIAMETER (BORE)

FIG. 1   INCREASING THE STROKE

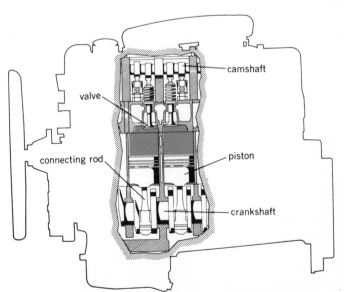

FIG. 3   INCREASING THE NUMBER OF CYLINDERS (TWO
EXTRA CYLINDERS ADDED TO A FOUR-CYLINDER
ENGINE)

INCREASING ENGINE EFFICIENCY: MEAN EFFECTIVE PRESSURE

The mean effective pressure is not constant, but varies with the rotational speed developed by the engine. With increasing speed, the mean effective pressure attains a maximum and then decreases (Fig. 1, curve A, representing more particularly the brake mean effective pressure p_{me}). According to formula (2) on page 278, the torque M_d is dependent on p_{mi} and therefore on p_{me}, while the two other factors in that formula are constant for an engine of given cubic capacity. Hence the curve that represents the torque as a function of engine speed (curve B) has the same general shape as curve A. Thus the torque and the brake mean effective pressure have their respective maximum values at the same engine speed (2500 rpm, for example, in Fig. 1). This is not, however, the speed at which the engine develops its maximum power output. The output is represented by curve C; its maximum at 5000 rpm (in this particular example) corresponds to 73 hp, associated with a brake mean effective pressure p_{me} of only 7.5 kg/cm^2 (as compared with the maximum value of 9 kg/cm^2 that p_{me} attains at 2500 rpm). In general, the value of p_{me} at which maximum power output is attained is between 7 and 8 kg/cm^2 for ordinary cars; for sports cars it is higher, up to about 10 kg/cm^2, while for racing cars it is between 12 and 13 kg/cm^2. The general object is to obtain the flattest possible shape for the p_{me} curve, so as to have a wide range of engine speeds within which the torque is nowhere very far below its maximum value. A relatively constant torque over a wide speed range ensures "flexibility" of the engine in the sense that there is no need for frequent gear changing.

Since p_{me} is the product of the indicated mean effective pressure p_{mi} and the mechanical efficiency η_m (formula 7 on page 278), it will be possible to increase p_{me} by increasing p_{mi} and also by increasing η_m, the latter result being achieved by reduction of the power losses due to friction and other causes.

One method of increasing p_{mi} is by increasing the *compression ratio*. At the beginning of the compression stroke the piston is at bottom dead center. As already explained, the gas then occupies the volume $V_Z + V_B$ (see page 276). When the piston moves to top dead center, the cylinder contents are compressed into the combustion chamber (volume V_B). The ratio between the total volume at the beginning and at the end of the compression stroke is termed the "compression ratio" (ε):

(9) $\quad \varepsilon = (V_Z + V_B)/V_B$

An increase in compression ratio results in an increase in effective pressure and therefore in engine power output. Also, the fuel is more efficiently utilized, so that the thermal efficiency of the engine is improved.

(more)

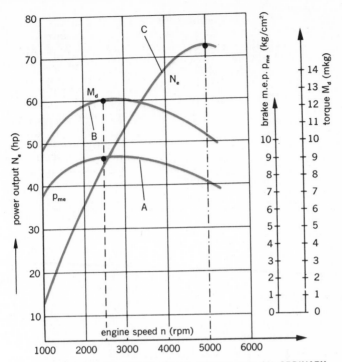

FIG. 1 ENGINE PERFORMANCE CURVES FOR AN ORDINARY
CAR ENGINE

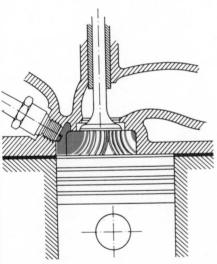

FIG. 2
DETONATION DUE TO EXCESSIVELY
HIGH COMPRESSION: THE CLASH
OF PRESSURE WAVES CAUSES KNOCKING

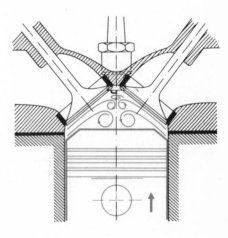

FIG. 3
HIGH-PERFORMANCE COMBUSTION CHAMBER
(AS USED FOR RACING ENGINES)

According to formula (9), the compression ratio can be increased by an increase in V_Z and a reduction in V_B. However, the ratio cannot be increased indefinitely If it were made too high, the powerful compression would cause excessive heating of the mixture, so that spontaneous combustion would occur, giving rise to the phenomenon known as "detonation"—or more specifically, "knocking" or "pinging" of the engine—caused by interference of the pressure waves set up by the self-ignited and the spark-ignited mixture (Fig. 2, page 283). This may damage the valves or the pistons, besides imposing severe sudden loads on the connecting-rod bearings and crankshaft bearings.

A badly designed combustion chamber is liable to cause detonation at relatively low compression. To achieve a high compression ratio without these adverse effects it is therefore necessary to use an antiknock gasoline (which has a high octane number), and the design of the combustion chamber should conform to certain principles, namely:

(a) The combustion chamber should be compact, presenting the smallest possible surface area for heat loss.

(b) Intensive turbulence of the mixture is essential, so that the ignition spreads rapidly throughout the chamber, leaving no pockets of unburned mixture.

(c) The spark plug should be as close as possible to the exhaust valve, this being the hottest spot in the chamber, and also in a central position so that the flame-travel path is of the same length (and as short as possible) in every direction.

(d) The combustion chamber should be located over the piston, and any recesses or cavities necessitated by practical reasons of construction should be as small as possible in order to minimize pockets of unburned gas.

Fig. 3 (page 283) illustrates a combustion chamber which comes closest to satisfying the above conditions. It is approximately hemispherical in shape and permits large valves to be installed. The central location of the spark plug in the compact hemispherical space ensures that the flame-travel distances are the same in every direction. These distances can be further reduced by the use of two spark plugs. To achieve high compression, the chamfered piston head penetrates into the combustion chamber. When the piston rises, it squeezes the mixture at high velocity out of the annular space at the circumference of its head, so that good turbulence is achieved and gas pockets liable to cause detonation are eliminated. In addition, very rapid combustion is ensured. With a premium-grade gasoline a 10:1 compression ratio is attainable. This type of combustion chamber is expensive to manufacture, however, and its use is therefore mainly confined to sports cars and racing cars.

Another favorably designed combustion chamber is illustrated in Fig. 4. Here the inclined valves are located off center in relation to the cylinder. The combustion chamber is in the shape of two intersecting hemispheres differing in size. Excellent turbulence is ensured, especially because the base of the chamber is smaller in area than the piston head, so that here again the gas is squeezed at high velocity out of a confined space into the interior of the chamber. Fig. 5 indicates the swirling motion imparted to the mixture entering the cylinder. During the compression stroke the mixture is still in swirling turbulence, so that good combustion is achieved, further enhanced by the above-mentioned squeezing effect.

(more)

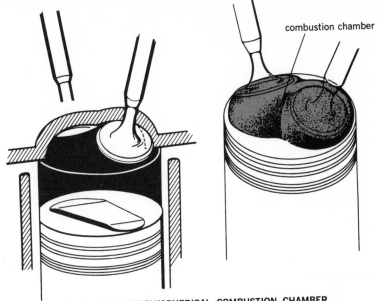

combustion chamber

FIG. 4   DOUBLE-HEMISPHERICAL COMBUSTION CHAMBER
USED IN BMW ENGINES

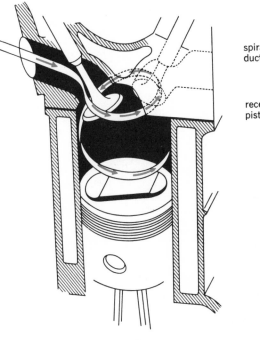

FIG. 5

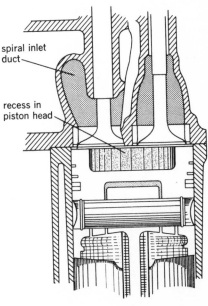

spiral inlet duct

recess in piston head

FIG. 6   COMBUSTION CHAMBER
OF AUDI ENGINE

285

The highest compression ratio ever obtained in an ordinary passenger car—a ratio of 11.2:1—has been achieved with the form of construction illustrated in Fig. 6 (page 285). In this design the inlet duct terminates in a spiral before the inlet valve, so that the mixture has a swirling motion on entering the combustion chamber (Fig. 7a). This is formed by a recess in the piston head, which causes acceleration of the swirling motion when the piston approaches top dead center (Fig. 7b). The rising piston moreover squeezes the swirling mixture into the chamber. In this way thorough mixing and turbulence are obtained, so that combustion is very rapid. There is a drawback, however. The shape of the inlet duct and the swirling motion it produces present a fairly high resistance to the flow of the mixture. Because of this, proper charging of the cylinder with the mixture cannot be achieved if the suction stroke is too rapid. This form of chamber is therefore not suitable for high-speed engines that have to develop high peak outputs.

With a combustion chamber as illustrated in Fig. 8 it is possible to fit large valves in a staggered arrangement. Only the exhaust valve (shown dotted in red) is located in the chamber. The spark plug is positioned directly beside the hottest part. The face of the inlet valve is flush with the cylinder top. Between this and the head of the piston at top dead center a narrow gap (clearance) remains from which the mixture is squeezed into the combustion chamber, where it is ignited by a spark. With this form of chamber it is possible to obtain a compression ratio of 9:1 for carburetor engines and 9.3:1 for engines with fuel injection.

Finally, the wedge-shaped combustion chamber in Fig. 9 calls for mention. It is comparatively cheap to manufacture and has been used in numerous variants. The valves are in a parallel disposition, one behind the other; they cannot be made as large as those in Fig. 8. Here again squeezing action and turbulence are achieved. This type of chamber can be used for compression ratios up to 9:1.

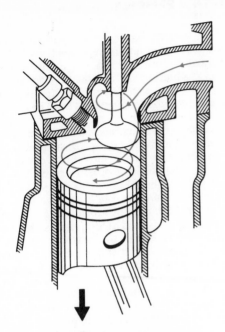

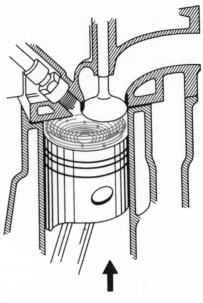

FIG. 7a MIXTURE IS SWIRLING
AS IT ENTERS THE CYLINDER

FIG. 7b THE SWIRLING MOTION
OF THE MIXTURE IS INTENSIFIED

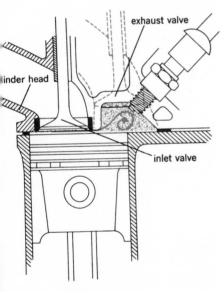

FIG. 8

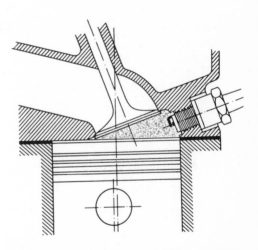

FIG. 9 WEDGE-SHAPED COMBUSTION CHAMBER

Another method of improving the engine performance by increasing the mean effective pressure consists in improving the so-called *volumetric efficiency*—i.e., the efficiency with which the cylinders are charged with the fuel-and-air mixture. The quantity of mixture drawn into the cylinder during the suction stroke determines the mean effective pressure and therefore the power output. This quantity should theoretically be equal to the working volume of the cylinder (= piston area × stroke). In reality the quantity of mixture drawn into the cylinder is less. The ratio of the actual to the theoretical quantity is known as the "volumetric efficiency." It depends on the size and shape of the inlet and exhaust ducts and ports, the shape of the combustion chamber, and the method whereby the fuel is introduced into the cylinder. The ducts should be so designed as to offer the least possible resistance to the gas flowing through them at high velocity. They should therefore be as straight as possible and with the fewest possible changes in diameter. Fig. 1 shows a section through a four-cylinder engine. The inlet pipe has been designed to ensure favorable gas-flow conditions. The water-heating jacket at the bend under the carburetor serves to prevent condensation of the vaporized gasoline in the mixture. The pipe functions as an "oscillation tube" (see page 290) and is, for this reason, relatively long. Within the cylinder head itself the duct is very short, to avoid excessive heating of the mixture drawn into the cylinder. The diameter adopted for the inlet and exhaust ducts depends on the cross-sectional areas of the valves associated with them. For a high-output engine the inlet valve should be as large as possible, to keep flow resistance low at high engine speeds (minimum throttling effect at the valve). In a well-designed normal engine operating at its maximum output, a gas velocity of about 300 ft./sec. (90 m/sec.) should occur in the opening between the valve head and its seat when the valve is fully open (Fig. 2). The exhaust valve may have a 15% lower discharge capacity than the inlet valve.

In many engines the inlet duct is made to taper toward the inlet valve. This helps to keep the flow velocity and therefore the resistance low in the carburetor and inlet manifold, while providing a suitably high velocity at the actual inlet valve. The exhaust duct also is given a divergent shape toward its outlet end for similar reasons (Fig. 3). Sudden changes in direction and cross section of the exhaust duct must likewise be avoided.

The combustion mixture is normally produced in the carburetor, which is connected to the inlet manifold that delivers this mixture to the inlet duct of each cylinder. Quite often the manifold is integral with the cylinder-head casting. The manifold and ducts system inevitably comprises bends which have an adverse effect on gas-flow conditions. Engines designed for very high outputs have an independent intake and mixture-producing system for each individual cylinder. Twin and multiple carburetors are used in such engines (Fig. 4).

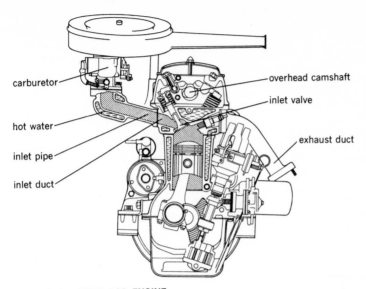

carburetor

hot water

inlet pipe

inlet duct

overhead camshaft

inlet valve

exhaust duct

FIG. 1 FOUR-CYLINDER GAS ENGINE

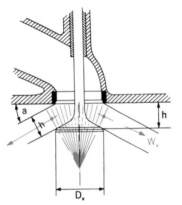

a = angle of valve seating

h_i = valve lift

W_v = gas velocity in valve-flow section

D_v = valve diameter

FIG. 2 CROSS SECTION THROUGH VALVE

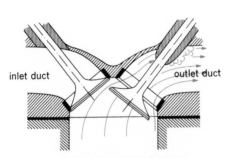

inlet duct

outlet duct

FIG. 3 INLET AND OUTLET DUCTS WITH FAVORABLE FLOW

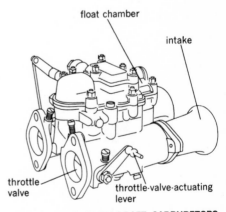

float chamber

intake

throttle valve

throttle-valve-actuating lever

FIG. 4 TWIN CROSS-DRAFT CARBURETORS

In addition to the measures described in the foregoing, an inlet-and-exhaust system of favorable design with regard to oscillation conditions of the gas does much to improve the intake and exhaust efficiency of the engine. The pulsating intake of the fuel-and-air mixture and discharge of the exhaust gases initiates oscillation in the system. At the end of the suction stroke the fuel-and-air mixture in the inlet duct flows at high velocity to the inlet valve, which is in the process of closing. This closure slows down the rush of the mixture, which impinges on the valve and causes a buildup of pressure in front of it. As a result, the fuel mixture continues to flow into the cylinder even after the piston has passed through bottom dead center and is rising again to start the compression stroke. But the inlet valve now closes completely and deflects the mixture back along the inlet duct. This is what initiates the oscillation in the duct. At the open end of the duct the fuel mixture is again deflected, and the cycle is repeated. If, at the instant when the inlet valve opens again, the pressure wave in the inlet duct is moving toward the valve, the mixture will immediately enter the cylinder. The system is now said to be in a state of *resonance*. As the inlet valve opens wider and the piston moves downwards, the pressure in the inlet duct drops, while the velocity rises to its maximum. Toward the end of the suction stroke the inlet valve begins to close again, so that the flow is again retarded, the pressure builds up, and the oscillation phenomena are repeated.

Optimum charging of the cylinder with the fuel mixture is achieved when the frequency of oscillation coincides with the opening and closing frequency of the valve so as to produce resonance, as envisaged above,—when the inrush of fuel mixture finds the valve just opening to let it into the cylinder. Evidently this will occur only at one particular engine speed. At other speeds the volumetric efficiency will be lower. Long inlet ducts provide good charging at high speeds, whereas short ones are better at relatively low speeds. The development of oscillation and resonance is counteracted by the flow resistance in the inlet duct, the constriction and turbulence at the throttle valve (in the carburetor), and the damping effect occurring at the open intake end of the duct. Figs. 1 and 2 show the oscillation system in a four-cylinder engine: the inlet pipes all emerge from a single connection at the carburetor, so that damping occurs there. The charging is therefore poorer than in the case of the inlet system of a fuel-injection spark-ignition engine as illustrated in Figs. 3 and 4 (further described on page 294).

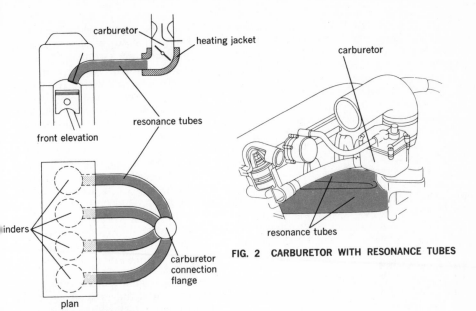

carburetor

heating jacket

carburetor

front elevation

resonance tubes

cylinders

plan

carburetor
connection
flange

resonance tubes

FIG. 2 CARBURETOR WITH RESONANCE TUBES

**FIG. 1   CARBURETOR ENGINE
WITH RESONANCE TUBES (SCHEMATIC)**

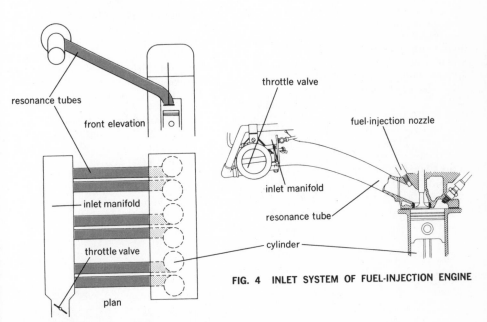

resonance tubes

front elevation

inlet manifold

throttle valve

plan

throttle valve

fuel-injection nozzle

inlet manifold

resonance tube

cylinder

FIG. 4   INLET SYSTEM OF FUEL-INJECTION ENGINE

**FIG. 3   FUEL-INJECTION ENGINE
WITH RESONANCE TUBES (SCHEMATIC)**

VALVE TIMING AND ENGINE EFFICIENCY

In connection with the resonance phenomena, it is necessary to consider the valve-opening times in relation to the rotation of the crankshaft—the so-called *valve timing*. Fig. 1 is the valve-timing diagram for a Porsche eight-cylinder Grand Prix racing engine. The long valve-opening periods are necessary in a high-speed engine to ensure efficient intake and exhaust of the cylinders. Also, at high engine speeds the acceleration and deceleration of the valve movements must not become inadmissibly high. Opening and closing must therefore be performed at a relatively slow rate: i.e., the valves must have a large travel, or lift. The exhaust valve opens at 81 degrees before bottom dead center, when the power stroke is still only little more than half completed and the combustion gases have not yet fully expanded. At low engine speeds this early opening of the exhaust valve would cause a lowering of the mean effective pressure and of the torque—an acknowledged drawback of the racing engine. The exhaust valve remains open until the crank has rotated to 51 degrees beyond top dead center. Although the piston on its way to bottom dead center has started the intake stroke, exhaust gas is nevertheless discharged from the cylinder in consequence of resonance phenomena in the exhaust duct. The inlet valve begins to open at 81 degrees before top dead center, while the piston is forcing the exhaust gas out of the cylinder. This likewise reduces the volumetric efficiency and the torque at low speeds; but at high speeds efficient charging is achieved on account of the oscillation and resonance phenomena established in the inlet system. Within the range shown hatched (in red) in Fig. 1, the inlet valve and the exhaust valve are open at the same time. Because of the suction in the exhaust system, this over-lapping of the valve-opening periods promotes the development of a low pressure (partial vacuum) in the cylinder and thus assists the intake of mixture and improves volumetric efficiency. The inlet valve closes at 71 degrees after bottom dead center, during the compression stroke. Thus the charging action due to the inertia of the flowing gas is utilized.

This kind of valve timing, while appropriate to a racing engine, is not suitable for an ordinary car engine because of the low torque at low and medium speeds, so that the engine would be deficient in flexibility of performance. The timing approximately suited for ordinary engines is also indicated in Fig. 1 (points 1 to 4): the valve-opening periods now overlap much less (points 3 and 1), the exhaust valve does not open so far in advance of bottom dead center (2), and the inlet valve does not close so late (4). Fig. 2 is a diagram showing the valve lift (or travel) plotted against the angular rotation of the crankshaft. It is seen that for equal valve timing it is nevertheless possible to have different amounts of lift and different cross-sectional flow areas through the opened valves (black and red curves respectively). The intake and exhaust can be improved by an increase in the valve lift. The valve movements are controlled by cams on the camshaft (Figs. 3 and 4), which rotates at half the speed of the crankshaft and is driven from the latter by a chain drive or gearing.

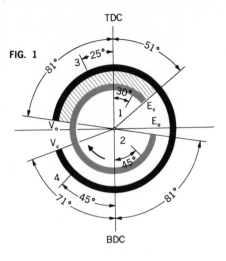

FIG. 1

TDC

BDC

Valve timing for a racing engine
V_o = inlet valve opens
V_c = inlet valve closes
E_o = exhaust valve opens
E_c = exhaust valve closes
TDC = top dead center
BDC = bottom dead center
The angles relate to the rotation of the crankshaft

**FIG. 2
GRAPH OF
VALUE PATH
PLOTTED
AGAINST
CRANKSHAFT
ROTATION**

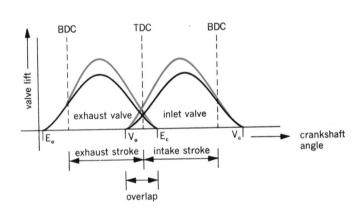

FIG. 3   CAMSHAFT

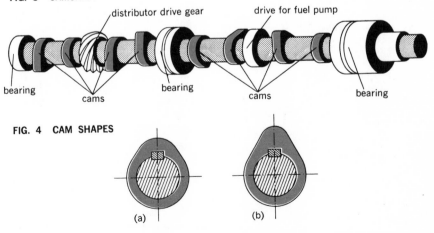

FIG. 4   CAM SHAPES

293

Instead of a carburetor, a *fuel-injection* system may be employed for introducing fuel (gasoline, petrol) into the cylinder. It is basically similar to the system employed in a diesel engine (see Vol. II, page 194), except that with gasoline as the fuel the ignition is initiated by an electric spark. A somewhat higher effective pressure and better output can be achieved by injection as compared with a carburetor system. Against this, the injection equipment is more expensive. In practice, this method of introducing the fuel is therefore confined to high-output or racing engines.

With injection, the inlet pipe for each cylinder can be designed to give optimum performance as an individual "oscillation tube." Since the fuel is injected straight into the cylinder, the need to heat the inlet pipe (to prevent condensation of gasoline vapor) is obviated. Consequently, cooler and therefore denser air is drawn into the cylinder, thus improving the volumetric efficiency. Injection of gasoline commences during the suction stroke. On entering the cylinder, the gasoline vaporizes, and the heat for evaporation is extracted from the air, so that this cools and decreases in volume, thus causing more air to be drawn in and thereby improving the volumetric efficiency.

Fig. 1 shows an arrangement in which the injection nozzle (colored red) is aimed at the hot exhaust valve, which is cooled by the gasoline. During the compression stroke the piston sweeps past the outlet of the nozzle and thus protects it from the high pressure that develops at the instant of combustion (initiated by spark ignition). A different arrangement is shown in Fig. 2, in which the injection nozzle is located outside the cylinder, protected from high pressure and temperature. It injects the fuel through the inlet port on to the opened inlet valve and thus into the cylinder.

The measures to improve volumetric efficiency that have been described in the foregoing relate to four-stroke internal-combustion engines which draw in the fuel-and-air mixture by the natural suction developed in the cylinder (self-aspirating, or suction-induced-charge, engine). A further means of increasing the power output is provided by *supercharging*. The supercharger is a compressor (axial-flow or centrifugal type) or blower which supplies air, or a combustion mixture of fuel and air, to the cylinders at a pressure greater than atmospheric. Because of this higher pressure, the air supplied to the cylinders has a higher density and absorbs more gasoline vapor. This increases the power output, but the gas consumption per horsepower is higher than in a suction-induced-charge engine, and wear and tear becomes more severe. Fig. 3 is a partial section through an American V8 engine equipped with a Roots supercharger with three-lobed rotors. The supercharger is usually driven from the crankshaft. Supercharging is not used for ordinary car engines; it is confined to aircraft or racing cars, and even for the latter the improvements achieved with suction induction in recent years have largely superseded the supercharger. Large diesel engines are often supercharged, the centrifugal compressor being driven by a small gas turbine motivated by the exhaust gases (exhaust-driven turbosupercharger).

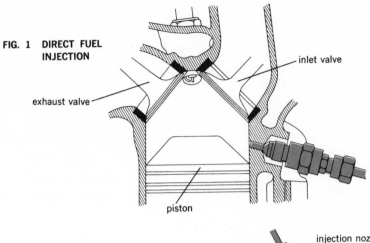

FIG. 1 DIRECT FUEL INJECTION

inlet valve

exhaust valve

piston

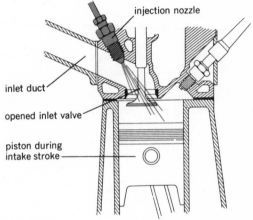

injection nozzle

FIG. 2 FUEL INJECTION INTO INLET PORT

inlet duct

opened inlet valve

piston during intake stroke

FIG. 3 V8 ENGINE WITH ROOTS SUPERCHARGER

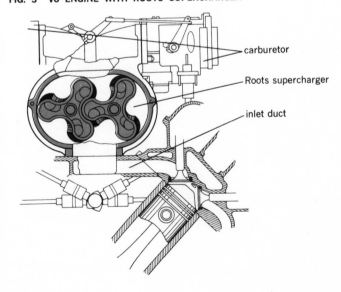

carburetor

Roots supercharger

inlet duct

295

IMPROVING THE ENGINE'S MECHANICAL EFFICIENCY

A significant part of the power developed by the expansion of the gas in the cylinders is used for overcoming friction (between piston and cylinder and in the bearings of the connecting rod and crankshaft) and for driving the water-circulation pump, oil pump, dynamo, camshaft and valves (Fig. 1). Hence only a certain proportion of the theoretical power output is available as effective output. This proportion is termed the "mechanical efficiency" of the engine. Depending on the type and design of the engine and on its state of maintenance, the mechanical efficiency is usually between 0.75 and 0.85.

More than half the loss of power is due to friction of the pistons and bearings. The piston friction depends on the pressure developed in the cylinder and on the piston speed, which is determined by the stroke and the speed of rotation. Generally speaking, the rotational speed should be as high as possible (cf. page 282). Therefore the only possible means of reducing the friction is to shorten the piston stroke. The friction developed at the piston rings depends on the number of rings per piston. To minimize the loss of gas, it is necessary always to have two compression rings; in addition, each piston has an oil-scraper ring (Fig. 2).

Friction in the crankshaft bearings can be reduced by the use of lighter connecting rods. This also reduces the lubricant requirement of the bearings, so that the oil-pump power input is lessened. A crankshaft rotating at high speed causes frictional losses due to turbulence and foaming of oil in the sump. For this reason high-speed engines have dry-sump lubrication (Fig. 3). In this system, oil entering the crankcase is immediately extracted by suction and is returned through a filter and a cooler to the oil tank. A second pump delivers the oil from the tank to the bearings.

A water-cooled engine is usually equipped with a fan. The fan is necessary only when the cooling-water temperature is high. For a substantial proportion of the engine's running time the fan is absorbing power without performing any useful function. For this reason fans have been developed that are switched on and off automatically, controlled by the temperature of the cooling water or air.

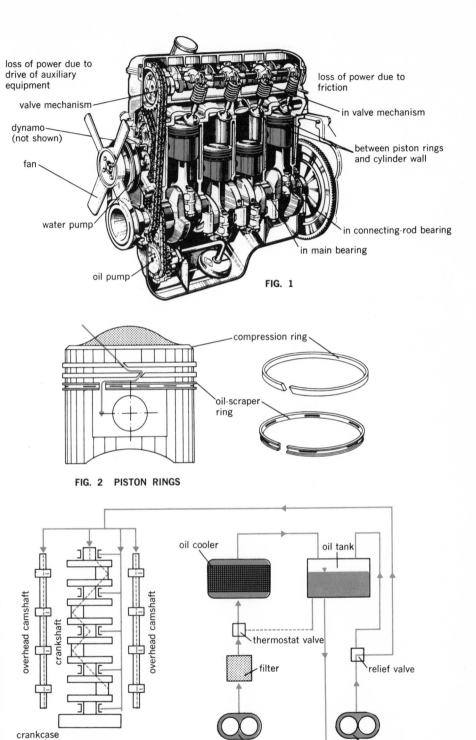

loss of power due to drive of auxiliary equipment

valve mechanism

dynamo (not shown)

fan

water pump

oil pump

loss of power due to friction

in valve mechanism

between piston rings and cylinder wall

in connecting-rod bearing

in main bearing

FIG. 1

compression ring

oil-scraper ring

FIG. 2   PISTON RINGS

overhead camshaft

crankshaft

overhead camshaft

crankcase

oil cooler

oil tank

thermostat valve

filter

relief valve

suction pump

force pump

FIG. 3   DRY-SUMP LUBRICATION

297

All measures for increasing the power output that have been described up to this point relate to the torque (see page 276). However, the formula for the output also contains the factor n, the rotational speed of the engine. The higher this speed, the higher will the output of an engine generally be. Unfortunately, this purely theoretical consideration cannot be fully translated into practical terms. With increasing engine speed, the piston speed increases and the frictional losses likewise become higher. At the same time, the mean effective pressure diminishes because of the higher resistance encountered in the inlet-and-exhaust system (throttling effect on the gas flow). This in turn reduces the volumetric efficiency. Besides, the inertia forces developed by the reciprocating parts of the crank and valve mechanisms are not allowed to exceed certain values, otherwise damage is liable to occur. When the cubic capacity for a new engine design has been determined, the influences of high speed that adversely affect power output and engine life can be largely obviated by a suitable choice of the number of cylinders, the stroke-bore ratio, and the piston speed. The engines used in ordinary present-day cars have rotational speeds of between 5000 and 6000 rpm—a range that only a few years ago was reserved for sports-car engines. Racing engines have meanwhile moved up into the 11,000–14,000 rpm range, though this result has been achieved only with considerable effort and cost.

The total cubic capacity (i.e., the total piston-swept working volume V_H) of an engine should be divided over the largest possible number of cylinders, to ensure that the reciprocating masses of the individual pistons and connecting rods will be small. The lighter these components are, the easier and less power-consuming will be their acceleration and deceleration at the ends of the piston stroke. For a given cubic capacity, the capacity of the individual cylinder is reduced, the bore and stroke are likewise reduced, and the piston speed is lower. However, an increase in the number of cylinders also has its drawbacks. For one thing, there are now more bearings in which friction occurs. In addition, the cost of manufacture goes up because of the more numerous components that have to be made, machined and assembled. For reasons of economy, the cubic capacity of a cylinder of an ordinary car engine is normally between 250 and 500 cc. A racing engine usually has many relatively small cylinders ranging from, for example, 62 cc (Honda) to about 200 cc.

(more)

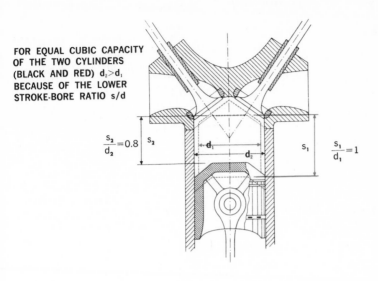

FOR EQUAL CUBIC CAPACITY
OF THE TWO CYLINDERS
(BLACK AND RED) $d_2 > d_1$,
BECAUSE OF THE LOWER
STROKE-BORE RATIO s/d

$$\frac{s_2}{d_2} = 0.8$$ s_2 d_1 d_2 s_1 $$\frac{s_1}{d_1} = 1$$

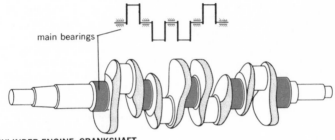

main bearings

2 FOUR-CYLINDER-ENGINE CRANKSHAFT
WITH FIVE MAIN BEARINGS

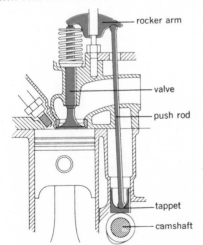

rocker arm

valve

push rod

tappet

camshaft

FIG. 3 ENGINE WITH LOW CAMSHAFT
AND PUSH ROD

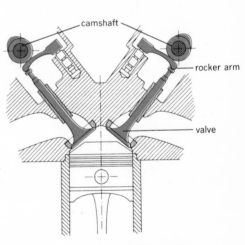

camshaft

rocker arm

valve

FIG. 4 ENGINE WITH INCLINED VALVES
AND TWO OVERHEAD CAMSHAFTS

In addition to dividing the total cubic capacity among a large number of cylinders each of relatively small capacity, other measures to reduce the reciprocating masses of the pistons and crank mechanism consist in the use of light-alloy pistons and connecting rods made from titanium, a metal not unlike steel, but lighter. When the capacity of the individual cylinder has been determined, the stroke s and the bore d can be determined from the stroke-bore ratio (s/d) that has been chosen. As a rule this ratio is somewhere between 0.7 and 1.0. It should be as low as possible for high-speed engines, so that the cylinder bore is larger than the stroke: i.e., the cylinder is relatively wide, making possible the use of large valves (see Fig. 1 on page 299). Besides, the piston speed is then also lower, so that the frictional and throttling losses during the suction stroke are less.

At high speeds the crankshaft functions under severe stress conditions because at each power stroke it is subjected to sudden impactlike torsional loading. The crankshaft must therefore be of very rigid construction; it must not deflect. Better resistance to deflection is obtained by closer positioning of the crankshaft bearings (usually called the main bearings). For this reason a high-speed crankshaft has a bearing on each side of each crankpin, as in Fig. 2 (page 299), which shows the crankshaft of a four-cylinder engine with five main bearings. (In a cheaper engine only three main bearings would be provided.) To achieve better balancing of the masses, the crankshaft has balanced webs.

Efficient design of the valve mechanism is of major importance in high-speed engines because accurate valve timing at all rotational speeds is essential. This calls for rigid and vibration-free construction. The valve is opened against the closing action of a spring; the force developed by the spring should be sufficiently powerful to ensure that at all speeds the valve motion accurately conforms to the shape of the cam (see page 293). At high speeds there is only very little time available in which closure of the valve can be effected, a mere fraction of a second. To keep the spring force needed for this within reasonable limits, the weight of the reciprocating valve parts in a high-speed engine should be reduced to a minimum. There are various methods of achieving this. Dividing the total cubic capacity among a large number of cylinders permits the use of correspondingly smaller and lighter valves. The high speeds of present-day engines have been attained partly as a result of using overhead camshafts, thereby eliminating transmission elements which make the valve mechanism slower and more cumbersome (compare Figs. 3 and 4, page 299). In the arrangements illustrated in Figs. 1a and 1b (page 301), the camshaft is located above the valve. Interposed between the cam and the valve is a rocker arm (Fig. 1a) or a cup-type hollow tappet (Fig. 1b); these intermediate elements protect the valve stem from friction forces exerted by the cam. For high-speed engines the arrangement in Fig. 1a is preferable to that in Fig. 1b because the moving masses in the former are smaller. Sports-car and racing-car engines have hemispherical combustion chambers, so that the valves have to be inclined. For this reason each row of valves is provided with its own camshaft (Fig. 4 on page 299). This solution is too expensive for the engines of ordinary cars. Alternatively, two rows of inclined valves can be actuated by one camshaft (Fig. 2), though in this arrangement the rockers constitute a larger moving mass. Fig. 3 shows a different overhead camshaft arrangement embodying a tappet.

(more)

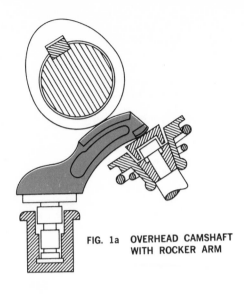

FIG. 1a OVERHEAD CAMSHAFT
WITH ROCKER ARM

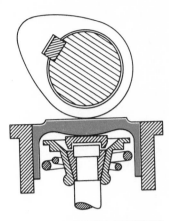

FIG. 1b OVERHEAD CAMSHAFT
WITH CUP TAPPET

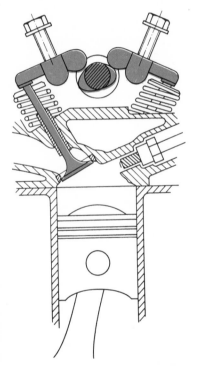

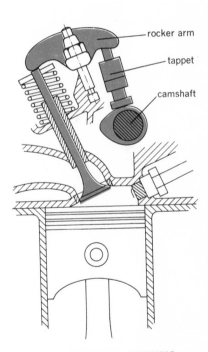

rocker arm

tappet

camshaft

FIG. 2 ENGINE WITH INCLINED VALVES
AND ONE OVERHEAD CAMSHAFT

FIG. 3 ENGINE WITH OVERHEAD
CAMSHAFT

301

In ordinary car engines, the overhead camshaft is usually driven by a chain from the crankshaft and at half the speed of the latter. To avoid objectionable noise arising from wear and thermal expansion, the chain is kept under uniform tension by a tensioning device. In some instances a silent valve drive in the form of a toothed plastic belt (reinforced with steel wire) is used instead of a metal chain. The camshaft drive systems illustrated in Figs. 1 and 2 are suitable for engine speeds up to 7000 rpm.

In racing engines, which operate at considerably higher speeds, the overhead camshafts are driven through the agency of gear systems or bevel-geared shafts (the latter are shown schematically in Fig. 3; actually these shafts are vertical). Such systems are preferable to chain drives because they are free of vibration and backlash effects. They are, of course, also more expensive.

Another means of reducing the weight of the valves consists in using valves with hollow stems. To improve the heat conduction and cooling of the exhaust valves, which become very hot, their stems are partly filled with sodium. At the high working temperatures the sodium is molten and its movements help to conduct heat from the valve head to the cooler parts of the stem, thus cooling the head (Fig. 4).

As an alternative to one large and heavy valve it is possible to employ two smaller, lighter valves. Thus the cylinders of some racing engines are each provided with two inlet valves and one exhaust valve. This is a very expensive form of construction and therefore unsuitable for ordinary engines. Various types of valve embodying "positive" actuation, as distinct from the spring-controlled reciprocating action of the usual poppet (or mushroom) valve envisaged here, have been devised, including more particularly the rotary valve, but have never achieved much practical significance.

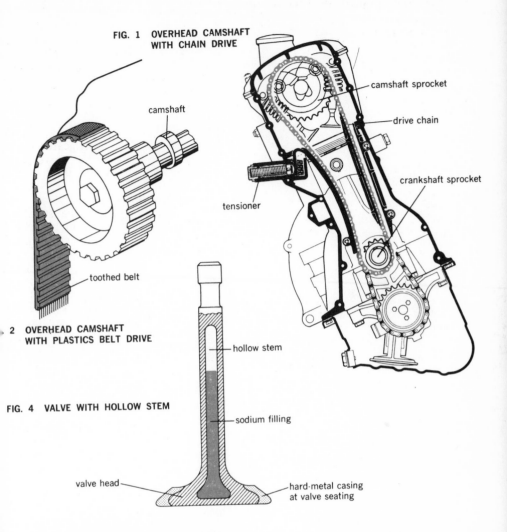

FIG. 1 OVERHEAD CAMSHAFT WITH CHAIN DRIVE

camshaft

toothed belt

2 OVERHEAD CAMSHAFT WITH PLASTICS BELT DRIVE

camshaft sprocket

drive chain

tensioner

crankshaft sprocket

hollow stem

FIG. 4 VALVE WITH HOLLOW STEM

sodium filling

valve head

hard-metal casing at valve seating

G. 3 DRIVE OF THE FOUR OVERHEAD CAMSHAFTS OF A PORSCHE OPPOSED CYLINDER ENGINE

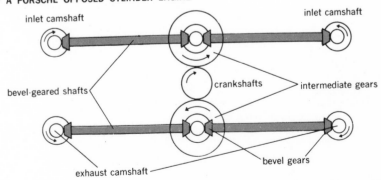

inlet camshaft

inlet camshaft

bevel-geared shafts

crankshafts

intermediate gears

exhaust camshaft

bevel gears

303

INDEX

306

This book is a production of
Edito-Service S.A., Geneva

Printed and Bound
U.S.A.